Glencoe Science
Features and Benefits

		Pages
Dynamic Instructional Strategies	... **present clear and comprehensive coverage of middle school science.**	
	■ Each engaging chapter opener includes a *Launch Lab* and *Foldables*™.	7, 35
	■ *National Geographic Visualizing* features illustrate important concepts in middle school science.	23, 51
A Strong Reading Strand	... **encourages active reading and learning for students of all reading levels. In the *Student Edition*:**	
	■ **as you read** gives students a preview of learning objectives and vocabulary for each section;	8, 36
	■ *Reading Checks* help students check their reading comprehension; and	9, 39
	■ *Caption questions* ask students to interpret visuals.	9, 39
	■ *Reading Essentials, An Interactive Student Textbook* is designed to help struggling readers comprehend core content. It is written at a reading level of about two to three grades below the *Student Edition*.	
Meeting the Needs of All Students	... **facilitates understanding of science concepts for students of all learning levels. In the *Teacher Wraparound Edition*:**	
	■ *Differentiated Instruction* strategies help meet the needs of students with learning disabilities and physical challenges, or create opportunities to enrich and extend students' learning;	9, 39
	■ *Daily Intervention* provides intervention strategies for struggling students; and	13, 41
	■ *Identifying Misconceptions* helps uncover and address common science misconceptions.	64F
	■ The *English/Spanish Glossary*, also in the *Student Edition*, helps English-language learners comprehend science terms.	222–227
Extensive Standardized Test Practice	... **gives students the opportunity to practice for state and national exams.**	
	■ Each chapter ends with a variety of standardized test practice questions, including *Multiple Choice, Short Response/Grid In*, and *Open Ended*.	62–63
A Variety of Labs	... **gets students excited about being involved in science. The *Student Edition* provides:**	
	■ *MiniLABs*, traditional labs, and *Design Your Own, Model and Invent*, and *Use the Internet* labs; and	11, 40
	■ *Extra Try at Home Labs* provide opportunities for students to practice their science skills at home with adult supervision using materials from the kitchen, junk drawer, or backyard.	196–198
	■ *Virtual Labs* CD-ROM contains an interactive virtual lab for each chapter.	11, 43
	■ *Video Labs* (VHS) reinforce lab techniques and safety skills, offer troubleshooting tips, and give expected outcomes.	25, 55
	■ The *Science Lab Manual, Probeware Lab Manual,* and *Science Inquiry Lab Manual* provide additional opportunities to practice laboratory techniques.	
Multi-Level Review	... **presents multiple opportunities for all students to review and master content.**	
	■ Each section ends with a review that contains a *Summary* of the section's major concepts and a *Self Check* that has questions to assess student learning and practice math or science skills.	13, 41
	■ The *Study Guide* at the end of each chapter can preview, review, summarize, and visualize the chapter's main ideas.	29, 59
	■ *Study Guide* and *Reinforcement* help students grasp core content.	
Teacher Resources	... **provide innovative strategies to help new and experienced teachers.**	
	■ *Chapter Resources Fast File* ™ contains important reproducible masters.	64B
	■ Section Focus, Assessment, and Teaching transparencies accompany each chapter.	34C
	■ *Performance Assessment in the Science Classroom* has assessment guidelines, strategies, sample rubrics, and more.	
Online Resources	... **enrich the learning experience with the click of a mouse.**	
	■ For prescreened Web links, standardized test practice, self-check quizzes, chapter tests, *Vocabulary PuzzleMaker*, extra math practice, science career information, current science news, and *WebQuest* interactive projects, visit **bookm.msscience.com**.	
	■ The complete interactive *Student Edition* is available at The McGraw-Hill Learning Network Web site, **mhln.com**.	
Technology	... **provides timesaving products to help teachers creatively engage their students.**	
	■ *MindJogger Videoquizzes* (VHS & DVD) provide a game-show style interactive quiz for each chapter.	
	■ Easy to edit *Interactive Chalkboard* Microsoft® PowerPoint® presentations include step-by-step lessons, an image bank, chapter and section review questions, standardized test practice, and transparencies.	
	■ *ExamView® Pro Testmaker* CD-ROM in English or Spanish allows you to customize assessments.	
	■ *TeacherWorks* CD-ROM is your all-in-one resource center that helps you plan and organize lessons.	
	■ *StudentWorks* CD-ROM solves the heavy backpack problem.	

SAFETY SYMBOLS

SAFETY SYMBOLS	HAZARD	EXAMPLES	PRECAUTION	REMEDY
DISPOSAL	Special disposal procedures need to be followed.	certain chemicals, living organisms	Do not dispose of these materials in the sink or trash can.	Dispose of wastes as directed by your teacher.
BIOLOGICAL	Organisms or other biological materials that might be harmful to humans	bacteria, fungi, blood, unpreserved tissues, plant materials	Avoid skin contact with these materials. Wear mask or gloves.	Notify your teacher if you suspect contact with material. Wash hands thoroughly.
EXTREME TEMPERATURE	Objects that can burn skin by being too cold or too hot	boiling liquids, hot plates, dry ice, liquid nitrogen	Use proper protection when handling.	Go to your teacher for first aid.
SHARP OBJECT	Use of tools or glassware that can easily puncture or slice skin	razor blades, pins, scalpels, pointed tools, dissecting probes, broken glass	Practice common-sense behavior and follow guidelines for use of the tool.	Go to your teacher for first aid.
FUME	Possible danger to respiratory tract from fumes	ammonia, acetone, nail polish remover, heated sulfur, moth balls	Make sure there is good ventilation. Never smell fumes directly. Wear a mask.	Leave foul area and notify your teacher immediately.
ELECTRICAL	Possible danger from electrical shock or burn	improper grounding, liquid spills, short circuits, exposed wires	Double-check setup with teacher. Check condition of wires and apparatus.	Do not attempt to fix electrical problems. Notify your teacher immediately.
IRRITANT	Substances that can irritate the skin or mucous membranes of the respiratory tract	pollen, moth balls, steel wool, fiberglass, potassium permanganate	Wear dust mask and gloves. Practice extra care when handling these materials.	Go to your teacher for first aid.
CHEMICAL	Chemicals can react with and destroy tissue and other materials	bleaches such as hydrogen peroxide; acids such as sulfuric acid, hydrochloric acid; bases such as ammonia, sodium hydroxide	Wear goggles, gloves, and an apron.	Immediately flush the affected area with water and notify your teacher.
TOXIC	Substance may be poisonous if touched, inhaled, or swallowed.	mercury, many metal compounds, iodine, poinsettia plant parts	Follow your teacher's instructions.	Always wash hands thoroughly after use. Go to your teacher for first aid.
FLAMMABLE	Flammable chemicals may be ignited by open flame, spark, or exposed heat.	alcohol, kerosene, potassium permanganate	Avoid open flames and heat when using flammable chemicals.	Notify your teacher immediately. Use fire safety equipment if applicable.
OPEN FLAME	Open flame in use, may cause fire.	hair, clothing, paper, synthetic materials	Tie back hair and loose clothing. Follow teacher's instruction on lighting and extinguishing flames.	Notify your teacher immediately. Use fire safety equipment if applicable.

 Eye Safety Proper eye protection should be worn at all times by anyone performing or observing science activities.

 Clothing Protection This symbol appears when substances could stain or burn clothing.

 Animal Safety This symbol appears when safety of animals and students must be ensured.

 Handwashing After the lab, wash hands with soap and water before removing goggles.

Teacher Wraparound Edition

Glencoe Science

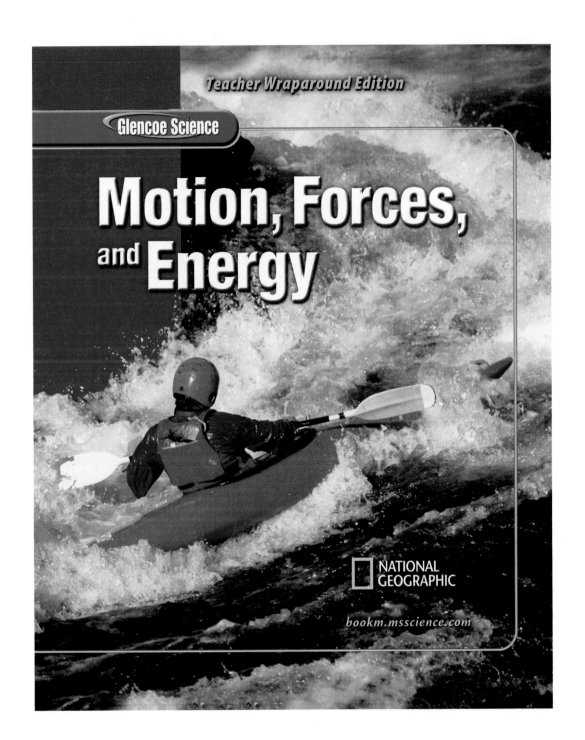

Motion, Forces, and Energy

NATIONAL GEOGRAPHIC

bookm.msscience.com

Mc Graw Hill **Glencoe**

New York, New York   Columbus, Ohio   Chicago, Illinois   Peoria, Illinois   Woodland Hills, California

Glencoe Science

Motion, Forces, and Energy

This kayaker battles the rapids on the Thompson River in British Columbia, Canada. A kayaker takes advantage of Newton's third law. The paddle exerts a force on the water and the water exerts an equal, but opposite, force on the kayaker.

 Glencoe

Send all inquiries to:
Glencoe/McGraw-Hill
8787 Orion Place
Columbus, OH 43240-4027

ISBN 0-07-861770-7 (Student Edition)
ISBN 0-07-861771-5 (Teacher Wraparound Edition)

Printed in the United States of America.

1 2 3 4 5 6 7 8 9 10 027/111 09 08 07 06 05 04

Authors

Education Division
Washington, D.C.

Thomas McCarthy, PhD
Science Department Chair
St. Edward's School
Vero Beach, FL

Dinah Zike
Educational Consultant
Dinah-Might Activities, Inc.
San Antonio, TX

Deborah Lillie
Math and Science Writer
Sudbury, MA

Margaret K. Zorn
Science Writer
Yorktown, VA

Series Consultants

CONTENT

Jack Cooper
Ennis High School
Ennis, TX

Sandra K. Enger, PhD
Associate Director, Associate
Professor
UAH Institute for Science Education
Huntsville, AL

Carl Zorn, PhD
Staff Scientist
Jefferson Laboratory
Newport News, VA

MATH

Michael Hopper, DEng
Manager of Aircraft Certification
L-3 Communications
Greenville, TX

Teri Willard, EdD
Mathematics Curriculum Writer
Belgrade, MT

READING

Barry Barto
Special Education Teacher
John F. Kennedy Elementary
Manistee, MI

SAFETY

Aileen Duc, PhD
Science 8 Teacher
Hendrick Middle School, Plano ISD
Plano, TX

Sandra West, PhD
Department of Biology
Texas State University-San Marcos
San Marcos, TX

ACTIVITY TESTERS

Nerma Coats Henderson
Pickerington Lakeview Jr. High
School
Pickerington, OH

Mary Helen Mariscal-Cholka
William D. Slider Middle School
El Paso, TX

**Science Kit and Boreal
Laboratories**
Tonawanda, NY

Series Reviewers

Sharla Adams
IPC Teacher
Allen High School
Allen, TX

John Barry
Seeger Jr-Sr. High School
West Lebanon, IN

Nora M. Prestinari Burchett
Saint Luke School
McLean, VA

Joanne Davis
Murphy High School
Murphy, NC

Sandra Everhart
Dauphin/Enterprise Jr. High Schools
Enterprise, AL

Lynne Huskey
Chase Middle School
Forest City, NC

Michelle Mazeika
Whiting Middle School
Whiting, IN

Mark Sailer
Pioneer Jr-Sr. High School
Royal Center, IN

Glencoe Science 15-Book Series

Teach science your way!

With the 15 Life, Earth, and Physical Science titles in our modular series, you can select the science topics you want to cover and customize your science curriculum in any way you choose.

K **The Nature of Matter**
1. Atoms, Elements, Compounds, and Mixtures
2. States of Matter
3. Properties and Changes of Matter
4. The Periodic Table

L **Chemistry**
1. Atomic Structure and Chemical Bonds
2. Chemical Reactions
3. Substances, Mixtures, and Solubility
4. Carbon Chemistry

M **Motion, Forces, and Energy**
1. Motion and Momentum
2. Force and Newton's Laws
3. Forces and Fluids
4. Work and Simple Machines
5. Energy and Energy Resources
6. Thermal Energy

N **Electricity and Magnetism**
1. Electricity
2. Magnetism
3. Electronics and Computers

O **Waves, Sound, and Light**
1. Waves
2. Sound
3. Electromagnetic Waves
4. Light, Mirrors, and Lenses

Multi-Level Review and Assessment

Each chapter provides five pages of review and testing to help you evaluate students' knowledge and ability to apply science concepts.

Section Review
- Summary pinpoints important concepts in the section.
- Skill-based questions promote critical thinking skills.

Study Guide
- Main idea summary of each section
- Concept mapping activity to help students visualize the main ideas

Chapter Review
- Using Vocabulary
- Checking Concepts
- Thinking Critically
- Performance Activities
- Applying Math

Standardized Test Practice
- Multiple Choice
- Short Response/ Grid In
- Open-Ended Questions

Dynamic Instruction

The consistent instructional strategies in each chapter strengthen students' learning—from the beginning of each chapter where students see "Chapter Preview," to the end where they have a chance to test the knowledge they have acquired and prepare for the next lesson.

Chapter Opener
- *Chapter Preview* introduces the main concepts.
- *Science Journal* promotes critical-thinking skills
- *Dinah Zike's Foldables*™ let students create interactive study guides.
- *Launch Labs* give students an opportunity to explore new ideas.

Section Opener
- *What You'll Learn* introduces main concepts.
- *Why It's Important* provides an answer to "Why do we have to learn this?"
- *Review Vocabulary* reviews a term that helps students better understand section content.
- *New Vocabulary* highlights new terms students will learn in the section.

Labs
- *Labs* allow students to design their own experiments or follow well-tested procedures, enabling them to learn and practice science processes.
- *MiniLABS* offer students quick and easy-to-do ways to clarify concepts and reinforce skills.

Assessment

Glencoe Science offers the Glencoe Assessment Advantage, a system designed to give you all the tools you need to prepare your students for success in any testing situation.

In the *Student Edition*

Section Review and **Applying Math** questions appear in every chapter.

Chapter Review questions help you evaluate students' knowledge and ability to apply science concepts.

Standardized Test Practice questions at the end of each chapter provide students with additional opportunities to practice their test-taking skills.

In the *Teacher Wraparound Edition*

Assessments located throughout the *Teacher Wraparound Edition* provide methods for assessing students' comprehension with Performance, Process, and Content exercises.

Teacher Classroom Resources

Performance Assessment in the Science Classroom
- Guidelines for assessing the performance of a task
- Reproducible activities for evaluating students
- Sample rubrics and checklists

***Fast File* Chapter Resources** provides six pages of assessment for every chapter including *Testing Concepts, Applying Concepts,* and *Writing Skills.*

Technology Support

MindJogger Videoquizzes are interactive video quizzes set in game show format. Each is designed for the full range of student learning styles.

Exam*View*® Pro Testmaker CD-ROM for Windows® and Macintosh® provides an easy way to create, edit, and customize your tests. Select your own test items by objective from two different levels of difficulty, or write and edit your own. Translate tests from English to Spanish and vice versa.

Rubrics

The following rubrics are sample scoring devices for short response and open-ended questions.

Short Response

Points	Description
2	The student demonstrates a thorough understanding of the science of the task. The response may contain minor flaws that do not detract from the demonstration of a thorough understanding.
1	The student has provided a response that is only partially correct.
0	The student has provided a completely incorrect solution or no response at all.

Open Ended

Points	Description
4	The student demonstrates a thorough understanding of the science of the task. The response may contain minor flaws that do not detract from the demonstration of a thorough understanding.
3	The student demonstrates an understanding of the science of the task. The response is essentially correct and demonstrates an essential but less than thorough understanding of the science.
2	The student demonstrates only a partial understanding of the science of the task. Although the student may have used the correct approach to a solution or may have provided a correct solution, the work lacks an essential understanding of the underlying science concepts.
1	The student demonstrates a very limited understanding of the science of the task. The response is incomplete and exhibits many flaws.
0	The student provides a completely incorrect solution or no response at all.

Time-Saving Teacher Resources

Glencoe Science provides an extensive array of support materials and resources designed to help you create and customize your science course quickly and easily.

FAST FILE Chapter Resources

For each chapter, Chapter Resources contain key reproducible masters along with additional teaching strategies, teacher support, and answer keys.

Teacher Wraparound Edition

The *Teacher Wraparound Edition* is your key to the teaching resources available. In addition to teaching strategies and suggestions, the *Teacher Wraparound Edition* provides a guide for all print and software materials available for each lesson.

Transparencies

Color Transparencies provides three types of transparencies for use while teaching each chapter. The *Section Focus Transparencies* are designed to generate interest and focus students' attention on the topic being presented in the section. The *Teaching Transparency* for each chapter addresses a major concept that will benefit from an extra visual learning aid. The *Assessment Transparency* for each chapter is set up to resemble standardized tests.

Exam*View*® Pro Testmaker CD-ROM

This CD-ROM will help you create, edit, and customize tests. In addition, it will help you create multiple versions of tests, translate tests from English to Spanish and vice versa, and build tests aligned with state standards.

Video Labs

These VHS cassettes contain step-by-step procedures for selected *Student Edition* labs. They also contain lab safety skills, teacher support, and troubleshooting advice.

Teacher Works™

This CD-ROM is your all-in-one teacher resource center. Personalize a lesson plan, access resources from the *Teacher Wraparound Edition*, connect to the Internet, or make a to-do list. These are only a few of the many features that can assist you in the planning and organizing of your lessons.

Student Works™

This CD-ROM is a valuable resource for students to access content online and use online resources to continue learning chapter concepts.

This CD-ROM brings Microsoft® PowerPoint® presentations right to your door. With the large number of graphics provided, students can use a visual approach to learning chapter content.

Virtual Labs CD-ROM Program

The Virtual Labs CD-ROM contains a collection of labs that allow students to complete labs that are too expensive, take too long to complete, or might be too dangerous in a classroom laboratory.

This website is a portal to hundreds of pre-screened Internet sites (Web links) that correlate to content in the text. Visit this link to find interactive activities that review chapter concepts and to access the *Student Edition* online.

mhln.com is an online teaching and learning space for teachers, students, and parents.

Differentiated Instruction

Teaching Strategies

Following each suggested assessment and activity, ability levels are supplied to accommodate all students. For a key to the Teaching Strategies designations, see the C page before each chapter.

Identifying Misconceptions

These short, diagnostic, and perscriptive lessons target common science misconceptions.

Multiple Learning Styles

Look for these italicized designations under various activities to help you target your lessons to each student's preferred learning style.

- *Kinesthetic* learners learn through touch, movement, and manipulating objects.
- *Visual-Spatial* learners think in terms of images, illustrations, and models.
- *Interpersonal* learners understand and work well with other people.
- *Intrapersonal* learners can analyze their own strengths and weaknesses and may prefer to work on their own.
- *Linguistic* learners write clearly and easily understand the written word.
- *Logical-Mathematical* learners understand numbers easily and have highly-developed reasoning skills.

Daily Interventions

Found at the end of each chapter section, this feature is designed to intercept students who are struggling and prescribe a system to help them get back on track. *Reteach* provides reinforcement of the section's concepts through visual activities.

Differentiated Instruction

These activities present various teaching strategies designed to help you meet the special needs of students with learning disabilities, physical challenges, visual impairment, and hearing impairment. *Challenge* activities provide opportunities for students who excel to engage in activities and research projects that extend the chapter's concepts. English-language learners in the classroom will also find exercises that bridge the gap between language barriers and the chapter content.

Cultural Diversity

These readings provide insights into the unique ways in which people of different ethnicities and cultural heritage have approached science. The intent of these features is to build awareness and appreciation for the global community in which we live.

Inquiry-Based Science

The call for more inquiry-based science by the *National Science Education Standards* has been met by Glencoe Science.

Glencoe Science recognizes the importance of conducting inquiry-based science activities in the classroom. The process of doing inquiry models actual science practice, encouraging problem-solving strategies and developing critical thinking skills. Inquiry gets students actively involved in the learning process by allowing them to determine materials, procedures, or the topics and questions they want to investigate.

Inquiry can range from a very structured activity for those students who need more guidance to a more open-ended approach where students lead the investigations. Glencoe Science recognizes that the inquiry activities suggested will not look the same in every classroom. We encourage teachers to modify the suggested activities in a manner that best supports your students.

Glencoe also provides teachers with *Alternative Inquiry Labs,* teaching strategies or suggestions for making existing labs more inquiry-based.

Research-Based Learning Strategies

Glencoe Science incorporates the most current and applicable educational research on science learning and follows recommendations from the American Association for the Advancement of Science and the National Science Teachers Association. The following research-based strategies can be found throughout the text.

Learning Strategies

The following research-based strategies can be found throughout the text:

- **Using Prior Knowledge** Glencoe Science encourages students to use their prior knowledge to learn information because this adds relevance to the material. Students are referred back to other parts of the text or to their own real-life experiences.

- **Practicing Important Tasks** By offering students an opportunity to practice important tasks using a variety of labs and activities in the *Student Edition, Teacher Wraparound Edition,* ancillaries and technology, Glencoe Science makes learning fun and relevant for students.

- **Using Visuals to Communicate, Organize, and Reinforce Learning** High-quality art and photos throughout the text communicate concepts more efficiently and reinforce learning, while allowing students to organize information.

White Paper

The Glencoe Science White Paper outlines the educational strategies on which this program was based. This document provides specific examples from the *Student Edition, Teacher Wraparound Edition,* ancillary program, and technology resources, highlighting extensive use of educationally sound strategies that help students learn science.

- **Motivating Students to Achieve** Active strategies and real-world experiences motivate students to achieve. Throughout Glencoe's programs, students are encouraged to apply their knowledge in ways that will motivate them to learn.

- **Developing Decoding and Reading Comprehension Strategies** Throughout the text, students are supplied with caption questions, reading checks, and other strategies to aid in comprehension.

- **Using Study Strategies** Through the use of highlighting, outlining, note-taking, summarizing, and other such strategies, students can monitor their own progress and organize information more effectively, thereby increasing their scientific literacy. These strategies are found throughout the text and ancillaries.

The use of these strategies within Glencoe Science will help teachers to achieve the goals set forth by the *National Science Education Standards.*

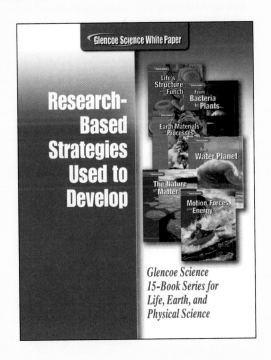

Glencoe Science White Paper

Research-Based Strategies Used to Develop

Life's Structure and Function

From Bacteria to Plants

Earth Materials and Processes

The Water Planet

The Nature of Matter

Motion, Forces, and Energy

Glencoe Science 15-Book Series for Life, Earth, and Physical Science

Field Research and Testing

Feedback from students, teachers, curriculum supervisors, department chairpersons, parents, learning specialists, and science content experts was invaluable in the development of this program. The following pre-publication and post-publication research was conducted.

Prior to Publication

- Detailed classroom teacher and curriculum supervisor **surveys** were conducted by independently contracted researchers.

- A **nationwide panel** of science teachers, curriculum supervisors, and department chairpersons provided countless hours of feedback and assistance throughout program development.

- A wide range of **educator and content reviewers** provided in-depth reviews of and suggestions for manuscripts and pre-publication versions of the program.

- **Face-to-face interviews** with science teachers provided insight into teachers' day-to-day challenges.

After Publication

- Field tests were conducted in which students and teachers used a pre-publication manuscript in the classroom.

- Follow-up interviews, observations, and surveys of Glencoe Science users provide ongoing opportunities for program development and verification of program success.

Field-Test Results

- Field-test research indicates that test scores increased among students using Glencoe Science programs.

- Nine out of ten students earned higher scores after using Glencoe programs.

- Scores improved among both male and female students.

- Scores improved among both minority and non-minority students.

- Overall, the gap between the average pre-test score and a perfect score closed by 33 percent. Stated differently, on average, **scores increased 77 percent after students used the Glencoe program.**

KS Studios

National Education Standards

Correlation of *Glencoe Science* to the National Science Education Standards.

Content Standard	Chapter and Section
(UCP) Unifying Concepts and Processes	
1. Systems, order, and organization	K1-1, K1-2, K1-3, K2-1, K2-2, K2-3, K3-1, K3-2, K4-1, K4-2, K4-3, L1-1, L1-2, L2-1, L2-2, L3-1, L3-2, L3-3, L4-1, L4-2, L4-3, M2-1, M2-2, M2-3, M5-1, M5-2, M5-3, M6-1, M6-2, M6-3, N1-1, N1-2, N1-3, N2-1, N2-2, N3-1, N3-2, O1-1, O1-2, O1-3, O2-1, O2-2, O3-1, O3-2, O3-3
2. Evidence, models, and explanation	K1-1, K1-2, K1-3, K2-1, K2-2, K2-3, K3-1, K3-2, K4-1, K4-2, K4-3, L1-1, L1-2, L2-1, L2-2, L3-1, L3-2, L3-3, L4-1, L4-2, L4-3, M1-1, M1-2, M1-3, M2-1, M2-2, M2-3, M3-1, M3-2, M3-3, M4-1, M4-2, M4-3, M5-1, M5-2, M5-3, M6-1, M6-2, M6-3, N1-1, N1-2, N1-3, N2-1, N2-2, N3-1, N3-2, O1-1, O1-2, O1-3, O2-1, O2-2, O3-1, O3-2, O3-3, O4-1, O4-2, O4-3, O4-4
3. Change, constancy, and measurement	K1-1, K1-2, K1-3, K2-1, K2-2, K2-3, K3-1, K3-2, K4-1, K4-2, K4-3, L1-1, L1-2, L2-1, L2-2, L3-1, L3-2, L3-3, L4-1, L4-2, L4-3, M1-1, M1-2, M1-3, M2-1, M2-2, M2-3, M3-1, M3-2, M3-3, M4-1, M4-2, M4-3, M5-1, M5-2, M5-3, M6-1, M6-2, M6-3, N1-1, N1-2, N1-3, N2-1, N2-2, N3-1, N3-2, O1-1, O1-2, O1-3, O2-1, O2-2, O3-1, O3-2, O3-3, O4-1, O4-2, O4-3, O4-4
4. Evolution and equilibrium	L3-1, L3-2, L3-3, M4-1, M4-2, M4-3
5. Form and function	K1-1, K1-2, K1-3, K2-1, K2-2, K2-3, K3-1, K3-2, K4-1, K4-2, K4-3, L1-1, L1-2, L2-1, L2-2, L3-1, L3-2, L3-3, L4-1, L4-2, L4-3, M1-1, M1-2, M1-3, M2-1, M2-2, M2-3, M3-1, M3-2, M3-3, M5-1, M5-2, M5-3, M6-1, M6-2, M6-3, N1-1, N1-2, N1-3, N2-1, N2-2, N3-1, N3-2, O1-1, O1-2, O1-3, O2-1, O2-2, O3-1, O3-2, O3-3, O4-1, O4-2, O4-3, O4-4
(A) Science as Inquiry	
1. Abilities necessary to do scientific inquiry	K1-1, K1-2, K1-3, K2-1, K2-2, K2-3, K3-1, K3-2, K4-1, K4-2, K4-3, L1-1, L1-2, L2-1, L2-2, L3-1, L3-2, L3-3, L4-1, L4-2, L4-3, M1-1, M1-2, M1-3, M2-1, M2-2, M2-3, M3-1, M3-2, M3-3, M4-1, M4-2, M4-3, M5-1, M5-2, M5-3, M6-1, M6-2, M6-3, N1-1, N1-2, N1-3, N2-1, N2-2, N3-1, N3-2, O1-1, O1-2, O1-3, O2-1, O2-2, O3-1, O3-2, O3-3, O4-1, O4-2, O4-3, O4-4
2. Understandings about scientific theory	K1-1, K1-2, K1-3, K2-1, K2-2, K2-3, K3-1, K3-2, K4-1, K4-2, K4-3, L1-1, L1-2, L2-1, L2-2, L3-1, L3-2, L3-3, L4-1, L4-2, L4-3, M1-1, M1-2, M1-3, M2-1, M2-2, M3-1, M3-2, M3-3, M4-1, M4-2, M4-3, M5-1, M5-2, M5-3, M6-1, M6-2, M6-3, N1-1, N1-2, N1-3, N2-1, N2-2, N3-1, N3-2, O1-1, O1-2, O1-3, O2-1, O2-2, O3-1, O3-2, O3-3, O4-1, O4-2, O4-3, O4-4
(B) Physical Science	
1. Properties and changes of properties in matter	K1-1, K1-2, K1-3, K2-1, K2-2, K2-3, K3-1, K3-2, K4-1, K4-2, K4-3, L1-1, L1-2, L2-1, L2-2, L3-1, L3-2, L3-3, L4-1, L4-2, L4-3, M1-1, M1-2, M1-3, M2-1, M2-2, M2-3, M3-1, M3-2, M3-3, M5-1, M5-2, M6-1, M6-2, N1-1, N1-2, N1-3, N2-1, N2-2, O2-1, O2-2, O3-1, O3-2, O3-3, O4-1
2. Motions and forces	K1-1, K2-1, K2-2, K2-1, L1-1, L1-2, L2-2, L3-2, M1-1, M1-2, M1-3, M2-2, M2-3, M3-1, M3-2, M3-3, M4-1, M4-2, M4-3, M5-1, M5-2, M6-2, M6-3, N1-1, N1-2, N1-3, N2-1, N2-2, O1-2, O1-3, O2-1, O2-2, O3-1, O3-2, O3-3, O4-1, O4-2, O4-3, O4-4
3. Transfer of energy	K2-1, K2-2, K3-2, K4-2, K4-3, L2-1, L2-2, L3-2, M2-2, M2-3, M4-1, M4-2, M4-3, M5-1, M5-2, M5-3, M6-1, M6-2, M6-3, N1-1, N1-2, N1-3, O1-2, O1-3, O2-1, O2-2, O3-1, O3-2, O3-3
(C) Life Science	
1. Structure and function in living systems	L4-1, L4-2, L4-3
(D) Earth and Space Science	
1. Structure of the Earth system	M3-1, O1-1, O1-2, O1-3
2. Earth's history	N2-1, N2-2
3. Earth and the solar system	O2-1, O3-2
(E) Science and Technology	
1. Abilities of technological design	K2-3
2. Understandings about science and technology	K2-3, N3-1, N3-2
(F) Science in Personal and Social Perspectives	
1. Personal health	K4-3
2. Populations, resources, and environments	M5-3, O2-2
3. Natural hazards	K3-2, M3-3, N1-3
4. Risks and benefits	M5-3
5. Science and technology in society	M2-3, N3-1, N3-2

Content Standard	Chapter and Section
(G) History and Nature of Science	
1. Science as a human endeavor	K1-1, K1-2, K1-3, K4-1, K4-3
2. Nature of science	M2-1, M3-2, M5-1
3. History of science	K1-1, K1-3, K2-3, K3-2, K4-1, M2-1, M5-1, N1-3, N3-2, O2-2, O4-4

How Glencoe Science Aligns with the National Science Education Standards

The correlations at the left and above show the close alignment between Glencoe Science and the grade-appropriate standards. Glencoe Science allows students to discover concepts within each of the content standards and gives students opportunities to make connections among the science disciplines. Hands-on activities and inquiry-based lessons reinforce the science processes emphasized in the standards.

How Glencoe Science Aligns with the NCTM Standards for Grades 6–8

Throughout Glencoe Science, each Applying Math activity provides students with the opportunity to practice and apply some of the mathematical concepts and applications described in the NCTM Standards. These activities serve to reinforce mathematical skills in real-life situations, thus preparing students to meet their needs in an ever-changing world.

Correlation of *Glencoe Science* to NCTM Standards

Math Standard	Page
1. Number and Operations	K-59, K-84, K-93, K-123, L-31, L-42, L-59, L-91, L-121, M-16, M-20, M-31, M-45, M-61, M-67, M-93, M-100, M-101, M-105, M-107, M-121, M-142, M-153, M-179, N-21, N-24, N-33, N-61, N-89, O-31, O-61, O-83, O-91, O-123
2. Algebra	K-84, K-93, K-123, L-42, L-59, L-121, M-16, M-20, M-31, M-45, M-61, M-67, M-93, M-100, M-101, M-105, M-107, M-121, M-142, M-153, M-160, M-179, N-21, N-24, N-33, N-89, O-31, O-83, O-91
3. Geometry	K-93, M-93
4. Measurement	K-84, K-93, L-91, M-160, M-179
5. Data Analysis and Probability	K-35, K-67, K-93, K-123, L-31, L-59, L-91, L-121, M-31, M-93, M-121, M-142, N-33, N-61, O-123
6. Problem Solving	K-59, L-31, M-142, O-123
7. Reasoning and Proof	K-59
8. Communication	M-142
9. Connections	K-84, K-93, K-123, L-31, L-42, L-59, L-91, L-121, M-16, M-20, M-31, M-45, M-61, M-67, M-93, M-100, M-101, M-105, M-107, M-121, M-142, M-153, M-160, M-179, N-21, N-24, N-33, N-89, O-31, O-61, O-83, O-91, O-123
10. Representation	K-67, L-42, L-59, M-142

Foldables™

Foldables™ are easy-to-make, three-dimensional, interactive graphic organizers that students create out of simple sheets of paper. These unique hands-on tools for studying and reviewing were created exclusively for Glencoe by education specialist Dinah Zike.

Research Behind Foldables™

According to research (Bransford, 1979; Corno, 1994), study strategies help students understand, organize, remember and apply new information presented in science textbooks. Some study strategies include concept mapping, highlighting, outlining, note taking, summarizing, and underlining (Peverly, Brobst, Graham & Shaw, 2003). Glencoe Science offers Dinah Zike's Foldables™ Study Organizers as an organizational tool and study guide for students.

Foldables™

- Build prereading skills
- Encourage active reading and writing
- Summarize content for review

FOLDABLES™ Study Organizer

Primary and Secondary Succession Make the following Foldable to help you illustrate the main ideas about succession.

STEP 1 Fold a vertical sheet of paper in half from top to bottom.

For more ideas on how to incorporate Foldables™ into your lessons consult **Dinah Zike's *Teaching Science with Foldables*™**

Educational Partnerships

NATIONAL GEOGRAPHIC

Some topics in the chapter either require or benefit from a larger, more detailed visual explanation. The National Geographic Society has created *Visualizing* features that call out an important concept from the chapter and illustrate it in a way that will inform, excite, and motivate your students.

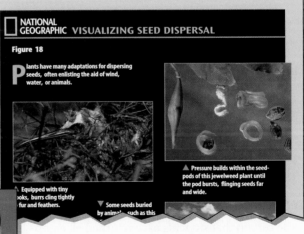

NATIONAL GEOGRAPHIC VISUALIZING SEED DISPERSAL

Figure 18

Plants have many adaptations for dispersing seeds, often enlisting the aid of wind, water, or animals.

▲ Pressure builds within the seed-pods of this jewelweed plant until the pod bursts, flinging seeds far and wide.

▲ Equipped with tiny hooks, burrs cling tightly to fur and feathers.

▼ Some seeds buried by animals such as this

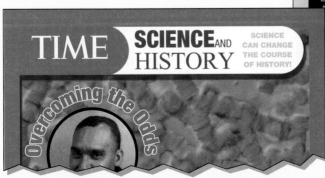

TIME SCIENCE AND HISTORY SCIENCE CAN CHANGE THE COURSE OF HISTORY!

Overcoming the Odds

TIME

TIME magazine brings science topics and history together to further explain the chapter's main ideas and show how science relates to real life.

Safety in the Laboratory

All activities are designed to minimize dangers in the laboratory. Careful laboratory planning and management by both the instructor and the student are essential to a safe laboratory experience. **Local, state, and federal laboratory safety laws and regulations must be strictly followed.** The information provided here is one of the many resources to which you can refer for information about laboratory safety.

Classroom and Laboratory Preparation

1. Store equipment properly and securely and other thing.
   a. Clean and dry all equipment before storing.
   b. Protect electronic equipment and microscopes from dust, humidity, and extreme temperatures.
   c. Number, catalog, and organize equipment.
2. Ensure adequate work space for each student.
3. Ensure adequate classroom and storeroom ventilation.
4. Explain and post safety and evacuation guidelines along with expectations of conduct.
5. Ensure that all safety equipment is functioning properly and is clearly visible.
6. Provide hot plates as a heat source whenever possible. If gas burners are used, know where the central gas supply shutoff valve is located.
7. Ensure that each workstation has a GFCI-protected electrical source.
8. Provide safety goggles consistent with ANSI Standard Z87.1 for each student, including students who wear corrective lenses.

Before Each MiniLAB or Lab

1. Arrange the lab in such a way that equipment and supplies are clearly labeled and easily accessible.
2. Have available only equipment and supplies needed to complete the assigned investigation.
3. Review the procedure with students, emphasizing any caution statements or safety symbols that appear.
4. Be sure all students know the proper procedures to follow if an accident should occur.

After the MiniLAB or Lab

1. Be certain that students have returned all equipment and disposed of broken glassware and chemicals properly.
2. Be sure that all hot plates and electrical connections are off.

Storage of Chemicals

Be sure to store all chemicals properly. The following are guidelines commonly used. Your school, city, county, or state may have additional requirements for handling chemicals. It is the responsibility of each teacher to become informed of the rules or guidelines in effect in his or her area.

1. Separate chemicals by reaction type. Strong acids should be stored together. Likewise, strong bases should be stored together and should be separated from acids. Oxidants should be stored away from easily oxidized materials, and so on.
2. Be sure all chemicals are stored in labeled containers indicating contents, concentration, source, date purchased (or prepared), any precautions for handling and storage, and expiration date.
3. Hazardous chemicals require special storage containers and conditions. Be sure to know which chemicals those are and the accepted practices for your area. Some substances must be stored outside the building.

Disposal of Chemicals

Local, state, and federal laws regulate the proper disposal of chemicals. These laws should be consulted before chemical disposal is attempted. Although many substances encountered in the science classroom can be flushed down the drain with plenty of water, it is not safe to assume that this is always true.

DISCLAIMER

Glencoe Publishing Company makes no claims to the completeness of this discussion of laboratory safety and chemical storage. The material presented is not all-inclusive, nor does it address all of the hazards associated with handling, storing, and disposing of chemicals, or with laboratory management.

Preparation of Solutions

It is important to use safe laboratory techniques when handling all chemicals. Always check the MSDS (Material Safety Data Sheet) for each chemical before using it in the classroom. Many substances might appear harmless, but might be toxic, corrosive, or very reactive. Chemicals should never be ingested. Use proper techniques to smell any chemical, wear safety goggles and an apron in the laboratory, and observe the following precautions.

1. **Dilution of Acids and Bases** When diluting acids with water, always add the acids to the water. Never add water to acids. When sulfuric acid and sodium hydroxide are added to water, a large amount of thermal energy is released. Use extra care when handling these substances.

2. **Poisonous and Corrosive Liquids or Vapors** Use a fume hood if possible. Examples include hydrochloric acid, acetic acid, nitric acid, and ammonium hydroxide.

3. **Poisonous and Corrosive to Eyes, Lungs, and Skin** Examples include acids, bases, silver nitrate, iodine, and potassium permanganate.

Bromthymol blue: Add 0.5 g bromthymol blue powder to 500 mL distilled water to make a BTB stock solution. Dilute 40 mL BTB stock solution to 2 L with distilled water. Solution should be bright blue. If not, add one drop of NaOH at a time, swirling to mix. Check color.

Hydrochloric acid (HCL) solution: To make a 5% solution, add 13.6 mL concentrated HCl to 73 mL water while stirring. To make a $0.1M$ solution, add 1 mL concentrated hydrochloric acid to 100 mL water while stirring.

Iodine solution/Iodine stain: Dilute 1 part Lugol's solution with 15 parts water.

Lugol's solution: Dissolve 10 g potassium iodide in 100 mL distilled water. Then add and dissolve 5 g iodine. Store in dark bottle. Keeps indefinitely.

Phenolphthalein indicator: From a drug store, buy a package of any laxative that contains phenolphthalein. To make 1% solution, mash 4 tablets and pour the powder into 10 mL of rubbing alcohol. Let mixture soak for 15 minutes. Pour liquid into and store in a dropper bottle.

Potassium permanganate: For a $0.01M$ solution of potassium permanganate, dissolve 0.15 g $KMnO_4$ in 100 mL water.

Red cabbage concentrate: Put 5 leaves of red cabbage in a pot. Add 1 L of water, bring to a boil, and simmer until water turns a deep purple. Pour liquid through a strainer or piece of cheesecloth into a storage bottle. Keep refrigerated.

Salt solution: For a 3.5% salt (NaCl) solution that simulates the concentration of ocean water, dissolve 35 g of salt (NaCl) in 965 mL of water. For a 1% solution (weak), dissolve 1 g of salt (NaCl) in 99 mL of water. For a 6% solution, dissolve 6 g of salt (NaCl) in 94 mL of water.

Silver nitrate solution: To make a 10% solution, put 5 g of silver nitrate in 50 mL of distilled water.

Sugar solution: Add 1 tablespoon of sugar to 1 cup of warm water in a deep jar or flask. Stir to dissolve.

Sodium hydroxide (dilute): To make a 1% solution, dissolve 1 g NaOH in 99 mL of water.

Equipment and Materials List

Refer to the Chapter Organizer in front of each chapter for a list of equipment and materials used for each laboratory activity in the chapter.

Material	Launch Lab (Chapter)	MiniLAB (Chapter-Section)	Lab (Chapter-Section)
Consumables			
balloons			2-3
clay, soft		5-2	
clear-plastic wrap		5-3	
cups, insulated foam			1-3
dirt, sand, or snow		3-1	
eraser, flat		2-1	
food coloring		6-2	
meat trays, insulated foam			1-3
plastic, black		5-3	
soap, bar		2-1	
spoon, plastic		3-1	
straw	3		1-3, 2-3
string		3-3	2-3
Nonconsumables			
aluminum pan			3-2
balance			4-3
beaker		6-2	3-2, 6-2, 6-3
beverage containers			6-3
block(s), wooden			4-1
book	2, 4, 5		4-1
bricks			4-3
broomstick		4-3	
coffee cup		6-2	
computer probe		5-3	
electrical motor, small			5-2
funnel			3-2
glass		6-2	
golf ball		5-2	2-3
graduated cylinder			3-2, 6-3
headphone jack			5-2
hot plate		6-2	2, 3
key(s)		2-1	
lid, plastic			2-3
marble(s)	2, 5	5-2	1-3
metal object			
notebook		2-1	4-1
pans	6		
pins, straight			1-3
pot, large		5-3	
pulley systems			4-3
radio or CD player			5-2
ramp		4-1	
rope		4-3	4-3
scale		4-1	
spring scale			2-3, 3-2, 4-1, 4-3
steel bar			4-3
tennis ball(s)	1		
thermal gloves or mitts			6-3
thermometer, Celsius		5-3	6-2, 6-3
tongs		6-2	6-3
weights			4-3

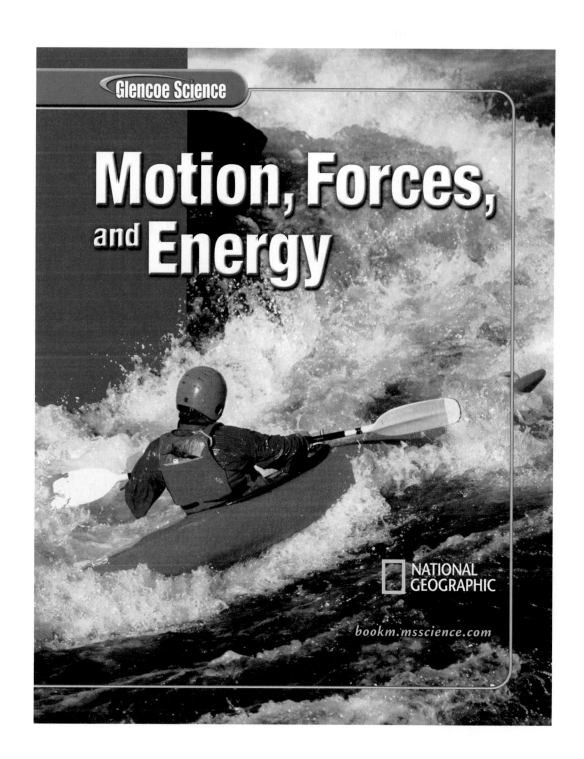

Glencoe Science

Motion, Forces, and Energy

NATIONAL GEOGRAPHIC

bookm.msscience.com

Glencoe

New York, New York   Columbus, Ohio   Chicago, Illinois   Peoria, Illinois   Woodland Hills, California

HOW TO...

Use Your Science Book

Before You Read

- **Chapter Opener** Science is occurring all around you, and the opening photo of each chapter will preview the science you will be learning about. The **Chapter Preview** will give you an idea of what you will be learning about, and you can try the **Launch Lab** to help get your brain headed in the right direction. The **Foldables** exercise is a fun way to keep you organized.

- **Section Opener** Chapters are divided into two to four sections. The **As You Read** in the margin of the first page of each section will let you know what is most important in the section. It is divided into four parts. **What You'll Learn** will tell you the major topics you will be covering. **Why It's Important** will remind you why you are studying this in the first place! The **Review Vocabulary** word is a word you already know, either from your science studies or your prior knowledge. The **New Vocabulary** words are words that you need to learn to understand this section. These words will be in **boldfaced** print and highlighted in the section. Make a note to yourself to recognize these words as you are reading the section.

Glencoe Science

Motion, Forces, and Energy

NATIONAL GEOGRAPHIC

As You Read

- **Headings** Each section has a title in large red letters, and is further divided into blue titles and small red titles at the beginnings of some paragraphs. To help you study, make an outline of the headings and subheadings.

- **Margins** In the margins of your text, you will find many helpful resources. The **Science Online** exercises and **Integrate** activities help you explore the topics you are studying. **MiniLabs** reinforce the science concepts you have learned.

- **Building Skills** You also will find an **Applying Math** or **Applying Science** activity in each chapter. This gives you extra practice using your new knowledge, and helps prepare you for standardized tests.

- **Student Resources** At the end of the book you will find **Student Resources** to help you throughout your studies. These include **Science, Technology,** and **Math Skill Handbooks,** an **English/Spanish Glossary,** and an **Index.** Also, use your **Foldables** as a resource. It will help you organize information, and review before a test.

- **In Class** Remember, you can always ask your teacher to explain anything you don't understand.

FOLDABLES™
Study Organizer

Science Vocabulary Make the following Foldable to help you understand the vocabulary terms in this chapter.

STEP 1 **Fold** a vertical sheet of notebook paper from side to side.

STEP 2 **Cut** along every third line of only the top layer to form tabs.

STEP 3 **Label** each tab with a vocabulary word from the chapter.

Build Vocabulary As you read the chapter, list the vocabulary words on the tabs. As you learn the definitions, write them under the tab for each vocabulary word.

Look For...

FOLDABLES™

At the beginning of every section.

In Lab

Working in the laboratory is one of the best ways to understand the concepts you are studying. Your book will be your guide through your laboratory experiences, and help you begin to think like a scientist. In it, you not only will find the steps necessary to follow the investigations, but you also will find helpful tips to make the most of your time.

- Each lab provides you with a **Real-World Question** to remind you that science is something you use every day, not just in class. This may lead to many more questions about how things happen in your world.

- Remember, experiments do not always produce the result you expect. Scientists have made many discoveries based on investigations with unexpected results. You can try the experiment again to make sure your results were accurate, or perhaps form a new hypothesis to test.

- Keeping a **Science Journal** is how scientists keep accurate records of observations and data. In your journal, you also can write any questions that may arise during your investigation. This is a great method of reminding yourself to find the answers later.

Look For...
- **Launch Labs** start every chapter.
- **MiniLabs** in the margin of each chapter.
- **Two Full-Period Labs** in every chapter.
- **EXTRA Try at Home Labs** at the end of your book.
- the **Web site** with laboratory demonstrations.

Before a Test

Admit it! You don't like to take tests! However, there *are* ways to review that make them less painful. Your book will help you be more successful taking tests if you use the resources provided to you.

- Review all of the **New Vocabulary** words and be sure you understand their definitions.

- Review the notes you've taken on your **Foldables,** in class, and in lab. Write down any question that you still need answered.

- Review the **Summaries** and **Self Check questions** at the end of each section.

- Study the concepts presented in the chapter by reading the **Study Guide** and answering the questions in the **Chapter Review.**

Look For...

- **Reading Checks** and **caption questions** throughout the text.
- the **Summaries** and **Self Check questions** at the end of each section.
- the **Study Guide** and **Review** at the end of each chapter.
- the **Standardized Test Practice** after each chapter.

a or b?
?
T or F?

Let's Get Started

To help you find the information you need quickly, use the Scavenger Hunt below to learn where things are located in Chapter 1.

1 What is the title of this chapter?

2 What will you learn in Section 1?

3 Sometimes you may ask, "Why am I learning this?" State a reason why the concepts from Section 2 are important.

4 What is the main topic presented in Section 2?

5 How many reading checks are in Section 1?

6 What is the Web address where you can find extra information?

7 What is the main heading above the sixth paragraph in Section 2?

8 There is an integration with another subject mentioned in one of the margins of the chapter. What subject is it?

9 List the new vocabulary words presented in Section 2.

10 List the safety symbols presented in the first Lab.

11 Where would you find a Self Check to be sure you understand the section?

12 Suppose you're doing the Self Check and you have a question about concept mapping. Where could you find help?

13 On what pages are the Chapter Study Guide and Chapter Review?

14 Look in the Table of Contents to find out on which page Section 2 of the chapter begins.

15 You complete the Chapter Review to study for your chapter test. Where could you find another quiz for more practice?

Teacher Advisory Board

The Teacher Advisory Board gave the authors, editorial staff, and design team feedback on the content and design of the Student Edition. They provided valuable input in the development of the 2005 edition of *Glencoe Science.*

John Gonzales
Challenger Middle School
Tucson, AZ

Rachel Shively
Aptakisic Jr. High School
Buffalo Grove, IL

Roger Pratt
Manistique High School
Manistique, MI

Kirtina Hile
Northmor Jr. High/High School
Galion, OH

Marie Renner
Diley Middle School
Pickerington, OH

Nelson Farrier
Hamlin Middle School
Springfield, OR

Jeff Remington
Palmyra Middle School
Palmyra, PA

Erin Peters
Williamsburg Middle School
Arlington, VA

Rubidel Peoples
Meacham Middle School
Fort Worth, TX

Kristi Ramsey
Navasota Jr. High School
Navasota, TX

Student Advisory Board

The Student Advisory Board gave the authors, editorial staff, and design team feedback on the design of the Student Edition. We thank these students for their hard work and creative suggestions in making the 2005 edition of *Glencoe Science* student friendly.

Jack Andrews
Reynoldsburg Jr. High School
Reynoldsburg, OH

Peter Arnold
Hastings Middle School
Upper Arlington, OH

Emily Barbe
Perry Middle School
Worthington, OH

Kirsty Bateman
Hilliard Heritage Middle School
Hilliard, OH

Andre Brown
Spanish Emersion Academy
Columbus, OH

Chris Dundon
Heritage Middle School
Westerville, OH

Ryan Manafee
Monroe Middle School
Columbus, OH

Addison Owen
Davis Middle School
Dublin, OH

Teriana Patrick
Eastmoor Middle School
Columbus, OH

Ashley Ruz
Karrer Middle School
Dublin, OH

The Glencoe middle school science Student Advisory Board taking a timeout at COSI, a science museum in Columbus, Ohio.

Contents

In each chapter, look for these opportunities for review and assessment:
- Reading Checks
- Caption Questions
- Section Review
- Chapter Study Guide
- Chapter Review
- Standardized Test Practice
- Online practice at **bookm.msscience.com**

Student Resources

Cross-Curricular Readings/Labs

available as a video lab

Content Details

INTEGRATE

Science Online

Standardized Test Practice

Content Details

Science in Motion

Introduction

This feature introduces students to scientific inquiry by guiding them through the steps scientists have used to determine how objects move. Scientists who have studied motion have used scientific methods by:

1. Asking a question such as "How fast do things fall?"
2. Gathering and using information to form hypotheses;
3. Testing hypotheses by performing experiments or making observations;
4. Analyzing data they have collected and looking for patterns in the data; and
5. Drawing conclusions about their data.

1 Motivate

Record responses as students describe examples of motion they have observed in different sports. **What causes each of the motions in the list?** Possible answers: hitting a baseball or golf ball, kicking a football or soccer ball, throwing a football or basketball, pushing with your legs when running or jumping, gravity causing a diver or gymnast to fall toward the ground **What general statement can you make about the cause of motion?** Some students may infer that a force is needed to cause motion.

Science in Motion

Figure 1 Motion, like on this busy road, is all around you.

Figure 2 At his school in ancient Athens, Greece, Aristotle taught philosophy and science.

How do scientists learn more about the world? Scientists usually follow an organized set of procedures to solve problems. These procedures are called scientific methods. Although the steps in these methods can vary depending on the type of problem a scientist is solving, they all are an organized way of asking a question, forming a possible answer, investigating the answer, and drawing conclusions about the answer. Humans have investigated questions about motion for thousands of years, asking questions such as: "What causes motion? How fast do things fall? How does a pendulum work?" However, scientific methods were not always used to learn the answers to these questions.

Early Scientists

The ancient Greeks believed in supernatural beings—gods and goddesses—whose powers made the world work. In the 500s B.C., a group of Greek philosophers in the city of Miletus proposed that natural events should only be explained by what humans can learn with their senses—sight, hearing, smell, touch, and taste. 200 years later, Aristotle, a Greek philosopher and teacher, developed a system of logic for distinguishing truth from falsehood. He also studied plants and animals and recorded detailed observations of them. Because of these practices, he is considered one of the first scientists as they are defined today.

Fun Fact

Peregrine falcons are the fastest moving animals. When diving toward the ground, they can reach speeds of more than 300 km/h.

Aristotle also investigated how objects move and why they continue moving. He believed that the speed of a falling object depends on its weight. Unfortunately, Aristotle did not have a scientific method to test his ideas. Therefore, Aristotle's untested theory was not proven wrong for hundreds of years. In the late 1500s, Italian scientist Galileo Galilei conducted experiments to test Aristotle's ideas. He rolled balls down inclined planes and swung pendulums, measuring how far and how fast they moved. According to legend, Galileo climbed to the top of the Tower of Pisa and dropped two objects of different weights. They hit the ground at the same time, finally proving that the speed of a falling object doesn't depend on its weight.

Figure 3 Galileo made observations of the motion of pendulums in order to learn about motion.

Developing Scientific Methods

Galileo and others that came after him gradually developed new ideas about how to learn about the universe. These new methods of scientific investigation were different from the methods used by earlier philosophers in an important way. A scientific explanation makes predictions that can be tested by observations of the world or by doing experiments. If the predictions are not supported by the observations or experiments, the scientific explanation cannot be true and has to be changed or discarded.

Figure 4 A scientific explanation of motion would explain the motion of this roller coaster.

Content Background

Gravitational force causes objects to fall toward Earth. When an object is falling through air, it collides with air molecules that also exert a force. The force of air molecules striking an object is called air resistance. Air resistance depends on the size and shape of the object, the density of the air, and the speed of the motion. A dropped table-tennis ball accelerates downward. As its velocity increases, so does the air resistance on it. If it falls long enough, at some time the air resistance force will equal the force of gravity, and the velocity of the ball becomes constant. This constant velocity is called terminal velocity. A table-tennis ball has a terminal velocity of 9 m/s, while a baseball can reach 42 m/s.

Discussion

Write Newton's first two laws of motion on the board. **How does Newton's first law explain why people riding in cars should wear safety belts?** People in a car tend to stay in motion, even if the car suddenly stops moving. **If you use identical engines to exert the same force in different cars, how does Newton's second law explain which car will accelerate more?** Because force equals mass times acceleration, the car with the smaller mass will accelerate more.

Differentiated Instruction

Learning Disabled Allow students to drop marbles or metal balls with different masses from the same height onto a mound of clay. Direct them to observe which ones make the deepest indentations in the clay. Ask students to determine how the mass of the marble or ball affects the force with which the marble hits the clay. The more massive the marble, the greater the force with which it hits the clay.

Quick Demo

Show students a small book, a sheet of paper, and a second sheet of paper that has been crumpled into a ball. **What will happen if I knock each object off my desk?** All will fall to the floor. Hold the book and sheet of paper above the floor at the same height. Drop both at the same time as students observe. **Which hit the floor first?** the book Repeat the demonstration with the book and the crumpled paper as students observe. **Which hit the floor first?** Both hit the floor at the same time. **How might your hypothesis about falling objects differ if you only observed one pair of falling objects?** From viewing only the first pair, one might hypothesize that heavier objects fall faster. From viewing only the second pair, one might hypothesize that all objects fall equally fast.

Activity

Give each group of students a table-tennis ball to which you have securely taped a piece of string. Use strong tape, such as duct tape. Demonstrate how to swing the ball in a circular motion a few inches above the floor. Tell students they are to answer the question: How does a circling object move when you release the string. Ask each group to form a hypothesis, test their hypothesis, analyze their results, and draw a conclusion.

The NATURE OF SCIENCE

Scientific Methods

1. **Identify a question.**
   Determine a question to be answered.
2. **Form a hypothesis.**
   Gather information and propose an answer to the question.
3. **Test the hypothesis.**
   Perform experiments or make observations to see if the hypothesis is supported.
4. **Analyze results.**
   Look for patterns in the data that have been collected.
5. **Draw a conclusion.**
   Decide what the test results mean. Communicate your results.

Scientists use scientific methods to answer questions about motion.

Physical Science

The study of motion, forces, and energy is part of physical science. Physical scientists also learn about elements, atoms, electricity, sound, and more.

Like all scientists, they use experimentation and careful observation to answer questions about how the world works. Other scientists learn about these experiments and try to repeat them. In this way, scientists eliminate the flaws in their work and participate in the search for answers.

Scientific Methods

The understanding of motion was undertaken by philosophers such as Descartes and scientists such as Galileo. Their efforts led to the creation of procedures, called scientific methods, which scientists use to investigate the world. Scientific methods generally include several steps.

Identifying a Question

The first step in a scientific method is to identify a question to be answered. For example, Aristotle wanted to know what causes motion. The answer to one question often leads to others. Aristotle wondered how an object's weight affects the speed at which it falls. After Galileo showed that an object's weight does not affect its falling speed, Newton wanted to know how fast objects fall, regardless of their weight.

Forming a Hypothesis

The next step is to form a hypothesis. A hypothesis is a possible answer to the question that is consistent with available information. A hypothesis can result from analyzing data or from observations. For example, data show that lung cancer occurs more frequently in smokers than in nonsmokers. A hypothesis might be that smoking causes lung cancer. Observations of falling objects might lead to the hypothesis that heavier objects fall faster than lighter ones.

Curriculum Connection

History Have interested students research and make a multimedia presentation on the development of clocks and other timing devices. Their presentations should also include how these developments influenced the progress of scientific research.

Science Journal

Using Scientific Methods Ask students to identify some questions that deal with aspects of physical science. List these questions on the board. Have each student select one question from the list. In their Science Journals, have students write a description how scientific methods could be used to answer the question. Remind students to refer to the chart of scientific methods as they write.

Testing a Hypothesis

A hypothesis must be testable to see if it is correct. This is done by performing experiments and measuring the results. Galileo tested Aristotle's hypothesis by rolling balls of differing weight down an inclined plane to see which, if either, rolled faster. Since a well-designed experiment is crucial, Galileo made sure the inclined plane was smooth and the balls were released in the same way.

Analyzing Results

Scientists collect information, called data, which must be analyzed. In order to organize, study, and detect patterns in data, scientists use graphs and other methods.

Collecting data requires careful measurements. Many experiments of the past were flawed because the measuring devices were inaccurate. Because Galileo needed precise timing, he used a water clock to measure the time for a ball to roll down the inclined plane. If his clock had been inaccurate, Galileo's results would have been less useful.

Drawing a Conclusion

The last step in a scientific experiment is to draw a conclusion based on results and observations. Sometimes the data does not support the original hypothesis and scientists must start the process again, beginning with a new hypothesis. Other times, though, the data supports the original hypothesis. If a hypothesis is supported by repeated experiments, it can become a theory—an idea that has withstood repeated testing and is used to explain observations. Scientists, however, know that nothing is certain. A new idea, a new hypothesis, and a new experiment can alter what is believed to be true about the world.

Figure 5 These students are conducting an experiment to learn how objects move.

You Do It

A ball may fall, but will it bounce back? What determines how high and how fast it will bounce? Make a list of possible factors that affect the way a ball bounces. Choose one of these and form a hypothesis about it. Think of experiments you could do to test your hypothesis.

Section/Objectives	Standards		Labs/Features
Chapter Opener	**National**	**State/Local**	**Launch Lab:** Motion After a Collision, p. 7 **Foldables,** p. 7
	See pp. 9T–10T for a Key to Standards.		
Section 1 What is motion? 🕐 2 sessions 📦 1 block 1. **Define** distance, speed, and velocity. 2. **Graph** motion.	National Content Standards: UCP.2, UCP.3, UCP.5, A.1, A.2, B.1, B.2		**Integrate Life Science,** p. 10 **Applying Math:** Speed of a Swimmer, p. 10 **MiniLAB:** Measuring Average Speed, p. 11 **Science Online,** p. 12
Section 2 Acceleration 🕐 3 sessions 📦 1.5 blocks 3. **Define** acceleration. 4. **Predict** what effect acceleration will have on motion.	National Content Standards: UCP.2, UCP.3, UCP.5, A.1, A.2, B.1, B.2		**Applying Math:** Acceleration of a Bus, p. 16 **MiniLAB:** Modeling Acceleration, p. 17
Section 3 Momentum 🕐 4 sessions 📦 2 blocks 5. **Explain** the relationship between mass and inertia. 6. **Define** momentum. 7. **Predict** motion using the law of conservation of momentum.	National Content Standards: UCP.2, UCP.3, UCP.5, A.1, A.2, B.1, B.2		**Integrate Social Studies,** p. 20 **Applying Math:** Momentum of a Bicycle, p. 20 **Science Online,** p. 22 **Visualizing Conservation of Momentum,** p. 23 **Lab:** Collisions, p. 25 **Lab:** Care Safety Testing, pp. 26–27 **Oops! Accidents in Science:** What Goes Around Comes Around, p. 28

Glencoe Exclusive!
TeacherWorks
All-In-One Planner and Resource Center

Lab Materials	Reproducible Resources	Section Assessment	Technology
Launch Lab: 2 baseballs, 2 tennis balls	**Chapter FAST FILE Resources** Foldables Worksheet, p. 17 Directed Reading Overview, p. 19 Note-taking Worksheets, pp. 33–34	GLENCOE'S ASSESSMENT ADVANTAGE	TeacherWorks includes: • Interactive Teacher Edition • Lesson Planner with calendar • Access to all program blacklines • Correlations to standards • Web links
MiniLAB: masking tape, meterstick, stopwatch *Need materials?* Contact Science Kit at 1-800-828-7777 or www.sciencekit.com on the Internet.	**Chapter FAST FILE Resources** Transparency Activity, p. 44 MiniLAB, p. 3 Enrichment, p. 30 Reinforcement, p. 27 Directed Reading, p. 20 Lab Activity, pp. 9–11 Transparency Activity, pp. 47–48 **Physical Science Critical Thinking/Problem Solving,** pp. 2, 21	Portfolio Active Reading, p. 9 Performance Applying Math, p. 10 MiniLAB, p. 11 Applying Math, p. 13 Content Section Review, p. 13	Section Focus Transparency Teaching Transparency Virtual Labs CD-ROM Guided Reading Audio Program Interactive Chalkboard CD-ROM
MiniLAB: masking tape, meterstick	**Chapter FAST FILE Resources** Transparency Activity, p. 45 MiniLAB, p. 4 Enrichment, p. 31 Reinforcement, p. 28 Directed Reading, p. 20 Transparency Activity, pp. 47–48 Lab Activity, pp. 13–15	Portfolio Assessment, p. 18 Performance Applying Math, p. 16 MiniLAB, p. 17 Applying Math, p. 18 Content Section Review, p. 18	Section Focus Transparency Guided Reading Audio Program Interactive Chalkboard CD-ROM
Lab: 5 small marbles, 2 large marbles, 2 metersticks, tape **Lab:** insulated foam meat trays or fast-food trays, insulated foam cups, straws, straight pins, tape, plastic eggs	**Chapter FAST FILE Resources** Transparency Activity, p. 46 Enrichment, p. 32 Reinforcement, p. 29 Directed Reading, pp. 21, 22 Lab Worksheets, pp. 5–6, 7–8 **Home and Community Involvement,** p. 48	Portfolio Currculum Connection, p. 20 Performance Applying Math, p. 20 Applying Math, p. 24 Content Section Review, p. 24	Section Focus Transparency Guided Reading Audio Program Interactive Chalkboard CD-ROM Video Lab

End of Chapter Assessment

GLENCOE'S ASSESSMENT ADVANTAGE

Blackline Masters	Technology	Professional Series
Chapter Fast File Resources Chapter Review, pp. 37–38 Chapter Tests, pp. 39–42 **Standardized Test Practice,** pp. 7–10	MindJogger Videoquiz Virtual Labs CD-ROM ExamView® Pro Testmaker TeacherWorks CD-ROM Interactive Chalkboard CD-ROM	**Performance Assessment in the Science Classroom (PASC)**

Transparencies

Section Focus

SECTION 1 | Section Focus Transparency | **Air Canvas**

This is a photo of the artist Pablo Picasso. While he often worked with paints, here he is creating an image with a flashlight. The photograph recorded the path of the flashlight as he moved it through the air.

1. What creature did Picasso draw with his flashlight?
2. Can you see where the light started? Estimate the distance between the starting point and the end point.
3. Is the distance between the starting point and the end point greater than, equal to, or less than the overall distance traveled by the light?

L2

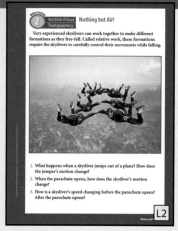

SECTION 2 | Section Focus Transparency | **Nothing but Air!**

Very experienced skydivers can work together to make different formations as they free-dive. Called relative work, these formations require the skydivers to carefully control their movements while falling.

1. What happens when a skydiver jumps out of a plane? How does the jumper's motion change?
2. When the parachute opens, how does the skydiver's motion change?
3. How is a skydiver's speed changing before the parachute opens? After the parachute opens?

L2

SECTION 3 | Section Focus Transparency | **Massive and Moving**

A fast-moving, heavily loaded train is difficult to stop. Increasing its velocity or mass will make it even harder to slow down. The greater the velocity and amount of matter in an object, the harder it is to bring it to rest.

1. Compare stopping a train that is moving 40 kilometers per hour with stopping a car that is moving 40 kilometers per hour.
2. How would halving the number of cars pulled by the train affect the train's ability to stop?
3. Which could speed up more quickly: an empty coal train, or the same train fully loaded?

L2

This is a representation of key blackline masters available in the Teacher Classroom Resources. See Resource Manager boxes within the chapter for additional information.

Assessment

Assessment Transparency | **Motion and Momentum**

Directions: Carefully review the table and answer the following questions.

Subject	Speed (m/s)
Aortic blood	0.3
Sound	331
Cheetah	28
Light	300,000,000

1. A girl is playing outside when she notices a storm is approaching. If all other factors are equal, the girl would most likely ___.
   A hear thunder first, then see lightning
   B see lightning first, then hear thunder
   C hear thunder and see lightning at the same time
   D see lightning and thunder twenty minutes apart
2. The fastest human is recorded as having a running speed of about 11 m/s. According to this information, which of the following is slower than the runner?
   F Aortic blood
   G Sound
   H Cheetah
   J Light
3. Which factor would have the LEAST effect on measuring these speeds?
   A The distance measured
   B The time measured
   C The time of day
   D The speed formula used

L2

Teaching

SECTION 2 | Teaching Transparency | **Distance-Time Graph Speed-Time Graph**

Distance vs. Time
Student A
Student B

Speed vs. Time

L2

Key to Teaching Strategies

The following designations will help you decide which activities are appropriate for your students.

L1 Level 1 activities should be appropriate for students with learning difficulties.

L2 Level 2 activities should be within the ability range of all students.

L3 Level 3 activities are designed for above-average students.

ELL ELL activities should be within the ability range of English Language Learners.

COOP LEARN Cooperative Learning activities are designed for small group work.

LS Multiple Learning Styles logos, as described on page 6T, are used throughout to indicate strategies that address different learning styles.

P These strategies represent student products that can be placed into a best-work portfolio.

PBL Problem-Based Learning activities apply real-world situations to learning.

Hands-on Activities

Student Text Lab Worksheet

Activity **Collisions**

Lab Preview
Directions: Answer these questions before you begin the Activity.
1. How many large marbles do you need for this activity? How many small marbles?
2. How will you limit the marble's range of motion to a straight line?

A collision occurs when a baseball bat hits a baseball, or a tennis racket hits a tennis ball. What would happen if you hit a baseball with a table-tennis paddle, or a table-tennis ball with a baseball bat? How do the masses of colliding objects change the results of collisions?

What You'll Investigate
How does changing the size and number of marbles in a collision affect the collision?

Materials
small marbles (5)
large marbles (2)
metersticks (2)
tape

Goals
■ Compare and contrast different collisions.
■ Determine how the speeds after a collision depend on the masses of the colliding objects

Safety Precautions

Procedure
1. Tape the metersticks next to each other, slightly farther apart than the width of the large marbles. This limits the motion of the marbles to nearly a straight line. Record your observations in the table in the Data and Observations section.
2. Place a large marble in the center of the track formed by the metersticks. Place a small marble at one end of the track.

Shoot this marble toward the target marble by flicking it with your finger. Describe the collision.
3. Repeat step 2, replacing the two small marbles with the two large marbles.
4. Repeat step 2, replacing the small shooter marble with a large marble.
5. Repeat step 2, replacing the small target marble with a large marble.
6. Repeat step 2, replacing the small target marble with four small marbles that are touching.
7. Place two small marbles at opposite ends of the metersticks. Shoot the marbles toward each other and describe the collision.
8. Place two large marbles at opposite ends of the metersticks. Shoot the marbles toward each other and describe the collision.
9. Place a small marble and a large marble at opposite ends of the metersticks. Shoot the marbles toward each other and describe the collision.

L2

Laboratory Activities

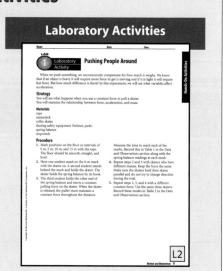

LAB 1 | Laboratory Activity | **Pushing People Around**

When we push something, we unconsciously compensate for how much it weighs. We know that if an object is heavy it will require more force to get it moving and if it is light it will require less force. But how much difference is there? In this experiment, we will see what variables affect acceleration.

Strategy
You will see what happens when you use a constant force to pull a skater.
You will examine the relationship between force, acceleration, and mass.

Materials
tape
meterstick
roller skates
skating safety equipment (helmet, pads)
spring balance
stopwatch

Procedure
1. Mark positions on the floor at intervals of 0 m, 5 m, 10 m, and 15 m with the tape. The floor should be smooth, straight, and level.
2. Have one student stand on the 0-m mark with the skates on. A second student stands behind the mark and holds the skater. The skater holds the spring balance by its hook.
3. The third student holds the other end of the spring balance and exerts a constant pulling force on the skater. When the skater is released, the puller must maintain a constant force throughout the distance.

Measure the time to reach each of the marks. Record this in Table 1 in the Data and Observations section along with the spring balance readings at each mark.
4. Repeat steps 2 and 3 with skaters who have different masses. Keep the force the same. Make sure the skaters hold their skates parallel and do not try to change direction during the trial.
5. Repeat steps 2, 3, and 4 with a different constant force. Use the same three skaters. Record these results in Table 2 in the Data and Observations section.

L2

Meeting Different Ability Levels

Content Outline

Reinforcement

Enrichment

Directed Reading (English/Spanish)

Study Guide

Reading Essentials

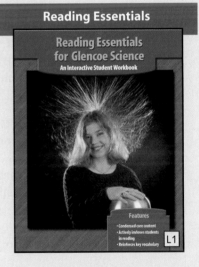

Assessment

Test Practice Workbook

Chapter Review

Chapter Tests

Science Content Background

 ## What is motion?
Changing Position

Distance is a scalar quantity. This means that it has only a magnitude, such as 6 km. Displacement is a vector quantity; it has both magnitude and direction, such as 8 km south. A car or bike odometer displays distance, not displacement.

Speed

Speed, unlike displacement and velocity, is a scalar quantity. Speedometers display speed, not velocity, because they do not indicate direction. Speedometers indicate instantaneous speed, which is the speed at a given instant of time. In planning a trip, however, average speed is more useful for determining the time required to travel.

Graphing Motion

Because distance is how far an object has traveled, a distance-time graph can never have a line that slopes downward in the positive-time direction (has a negative slope). This is because it is impossible to travel a negative distance. However, a displacement-time graph can have a negative slope, which means the object is moving closer to its point of reference.

 ## Acceleration
Acceleration and Motion

Acceleration is the rate of change of an object's velocity. If velocity is expressed as meters/second and time is given in seconds, then acceleration is expressed in units of meters per second per second, m/s/s or (m/s $\times$ 1/s) or m/s^2.

If the direction of motion is defined as the positive direction, then when an object's velocity increases, the object experiences positive acceleration. When its velocity decreases, the object experiences negative acceleration. Acceleration also occurs when an object changes direction. For example, as Earth orbits the Sun, it is accelerating. Although Earth travels at a nearly constant speed, its direction is constantly changing.

 ## Momentum
Mass and Inertia

Students may attribute inertia to an object's weight instead of mass, so that a weightless object would have no inertia. However, even in deep space where there is almost no gravitational force on an object, its inertia is unchanged.

Momentum

Momentum and force are related. The time rate of change of an object's momentum is equal to the force exerted on the object or exerted by the object. In collisions, momentum is conserved only if there are no external forces, such as friction, acting on the colliding objects.

chapter content resources

Internet Resources
For additional content background, visit
bookm.msscience.com to:

- access your book online
- find references to related articles in popular science magazines
- access Web links with related content background
- access current events with science journal topics

Print Resources
Eyewitness: Force & Motion, by Peter Lafferty, Dorling Kindersley Publishing, 2000
Hands-On Physics Activities with Real-Life Applications : Easy-to-Use Labs and Demonstrations for Grades 8–12, by James Cunningham & Norman Herr, Jossey-Bass, 1994

IDENTIFYING ▷ **Misconceptions**

Find Out What Students Think

Students may think that . . .

distance and displacement are the same, and

speed and velocity are the same.

One difficulty with the terms velocity and displacement is that they are both vector quantities, and students are much more familiar with scalar quantities. To confuse matters more, the term velocity is sometimes used in everyday language in a non-scientific way. Finally, the terms displacement and distance sound similar, and this may make it easier to confuse them.

Demonstration

After initially teaching the difference between distance and displacement, ask students whether the phrase "as the crow flies," when estimating how far something is, is more like distance or more like displacement.

Promote Understanding

Activity

• Draw Figures 1 and 2 on the board. Explain that the distance-time graph and the displacement-time graph both show Samantha's walking motion after she left her house.

• Ask students to supply a possible story to describe her motion. Ask them what she might be doing when the lines of the two graphs are horizontal.

• Students should see that the distance-time graph and displacement-time graph for the same motion look very different. In this case, the distance traveled is how far Samantha actually walked. Her displacement shows how far she is from her house.

Figure 1:
Distance-time graph

Figure 2:
Displacement-time graph

• A plausible story for both graphs has Samantha walking at constant speed directly away from her house, then resting a bit, and then walking at constant speed directly back to her house.

Assess

After completing the chapter, see *Identifying Misconceptions* in the Study Guide at the end of a chapter.

Chapter Vocabulary

speed, p. 10
average speed, p. 11
instantaneous speed, p. 11
velocity, p. 13
acceleration, p. 14
mass, p. 19
inertia, p. 19
momentum, p. 20
law of conservation of
momentum, p. 21

Science Journal Student responses will vary.

PowerPoint® Presentations

This CD-ROM is an editable Microsoft® PowerPoint® presentation that includes:
- a pre-made presentation for every chapter
- interactive graphics
- animations
- audio clips
- image bank
- all new section and chapter questions
- Standardized Test Practice
- transparencies
- pre-lab questions for all labs
- Foldables directions
- links to bookm.msscience.com

Motion and Momentum

chapter preview

sections

1 What is motion?

2 Acceleration

3 Momentum
  Lab Collisions
  Lab Car Safety Testing
  Virtual Lab How does horizontal motion affect vertical motion?

A Vanishing Act

You hear the crack of the bat and an instant later the ball disappears into a diving infielder's glove. Think of how the motion of the ball changed—it moved toward the batter, changed direction when it collided with the bat, and then stopped when it collided with the infielder's glove.

Science Journal Describe how your motion changed as you moved from your school's entrance to your classroom.

Theme Connection

Stability and Change An object can be in motion or at rest. If in motion, the motion can be constant or accelerated. If accelerated, the acceleration can be constant or changing.

About the Photo

Home-Run Hitting Many baseball fans love the excitement of seeing long balls hit far into the outfield. The distance the ball travels depends, in part, on the momentum of the bat and ball when they collide. Every year, it seems like hitters send the ball flying further, so some people think the ball must be being changed somehow. However, the mass and size of the baseball has remained the same since 1872.

Start-Up Activities

Motion After a Collision

How is it possible for a 70-kg football player to knock down a 110-kg football player? The smaller player usually must be running faster. Mass makes a difference when two objects collide, but the speed of the objects also matters. Explore the behavior of colliding objects during this lab.

1. Space yourself about 2 m away from a partner. Slowly roll a baseball on the floor toward your partner, and have your partner roll a baseball quickly into your ball.

2. Have your partner slowly roll a baseball as you quickly roll a tennis ball into the baseball.

3. Roll two tennis balls toward each other at the same speed.

4. **Think Critically** In your Science Journal, describe how the motion of the balls changed after the collisions, including the effects of speed and type of ball.

 Preview this chapter's content and activities at bookm.msscience.com

 Motion and Momentum
Make the following Foldable to help you understand the vocabulary terms in this chapter.

STEP 1 Fold a vertical sheet of notebook paper from side to side.

STEP 2 Cut along every third line of only the top layer to form tabs.

STEP 3 Label each tab.

Build Vocabulary As you read the chapter, list the vocabulary words about motion and momentum on the tabs. As you learn the definitions, write them under the tab for each vocabulary word.

Purpose Use the Launch Lab to introduce students to the way the speeds and masses of the objects in a collision affect the collision. L2 IS **Kinesthetic**

Preparation Ask students to bring in balls, or arrange to borrow them at your school.

Materials two baseballs, two tennis balls

Alternate Materials Different types of balls can be used as long as the balls in each pair have identical masses.

Teaching Strategy Remind students of what they have observed in other collisions. For example, which ball is harder to catch?

Think Critically

In the first case, the slower ball reversed direction and increased speed after the collision. The faster ball reversed direction, and its speed decreased. In the second case, both balls reversed direction. The baseball slightly increased in speed, and the tennis ball decreased in speed. In the third case, the balls reversed direction when they collided, but moved off at about the same speed as before.

Assessment

Process Ask students to predict what would happen if a small child, running fast, ran into an adult who wasn't moving. In the collision, the child would slow down, and the adult would move. Both would stumble in the direction the child was first moving, but at a slower speed. Use **Performance Assessment in the Science Classroom,** p. 89.

 Dinah Zike Study Fold

Student preparation materials for this Foldable are available in the **Chapter FAST FILE Resources.**

What is motion?

Tie to Prior Knowledge

Races Ask students to describe races they have watched or in which they have participated. Possibilities include running, swimming, bicycling, car racing, and horse racing, among others. Discuss what is being measured in each type of race.

as you read

What You'll Learn
- **Define** distance, speed, and velocity.
- **Graph** motion.

Why It's Important
The different motions of objects you see every day can be described in the same way.

⊘ **Review Vocabulary**
meter: SI unit of distance, abbreviated m; equal to approximately 39.37 in

New Vocabulary
- speed
- average speed
- instantaneous speed
- velocity

Matter and Motion

All matter in the universe is constantly in motion, from the revolution of Earth around the Sun to electrons moving around the nucleus of an atom. Leaves rustle in the wind. Lava flows from a volcano. Bees move from flower to flower as they gather pollen. Blood circulates through your body. These are all examples of matter in motion. How can the motion of these different objects be described?

Changing Position

To describe an object in motion, you must first recognize that the object is in motion. Something is in motion if it is changing position. It could be a fast-moving airplane, a leaf swirling in the wind, or water trickling from a hose. Even your school is moving through space attached to Earth. When an object moves from one location to another, it is changing position. The runners shown in **Figure 1** sprint from the start line to the finish line. Their positions change, so they are in motion.

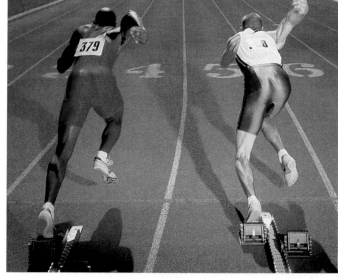

Figure 1 When running a race, you are in motion because your position changes.

Relative Motion Determining whether something changes position requires a point of reference. An object changes position if it moves relative to a reference point. To visualize this, picture yourself competing in a 100-m dash. You begin just behind the start line. When you pass the finish line, you are 100 m from the start line. If the start line is your reference point, then your position has changed by 100 m relative to the start line, and motion has occurred. Look at **Figure 2.** How can you determine that the dog has been in motion?

✔ **Reading Check** *How do you know if an object has changed position?*

Distance and Displacement Suppose you are to meet your friends at the park in five minutes. Can you get there on time by walking, or should you ride your bike? To help you decide, you need to know the distance you will travel to get to the park. This distance is the length of the route you will travel from your house to the park.

Suppose the distance you traveled from your house to the park was 200 m. When you get to the park, how would you describe your location? You could say that your location was 200 m from your house. However, your final position depends on both the distance you travel and the direction. Did you go 200 m east or west? To describe your final position exactly, you also would have to tell the direction from your starting point. To do this, you would specify your displacement. Displacement includes the distance between the starting and ending points and the direction in which you travel. **Figure 3** shows the difference between distance and displacement.

Figure 2 Motion occurs when something changes position relative to a reference point.
Explain *whether the dog's position would depend on the reference point chosen.*

Figure 3 Distance is how far you have walked. Displacement is the direction and difference in position between your starting and ending points.

Distance: 40 m
Displacement: 40 m east

Distance: 70 m
Displacement: 50 m northeast

Distance: 140 m
Displacement: 0 m

INTEGRATE Life Science

Animal Speeds Answers will vary. Some characteristics might be a streamlined body shape to help swim, long legs to help run, and low body mass to help fly.

Activity

Converting Speed In the United States, students are more likely to encounter speeds in miles per hour or feet per second. Give students practice problems to help them get accustomed to converting between these units. Have them convert 60 miles per hour to kilometers per hour; 97 km/h 35 miles per hour to kilometers per hour; 56 km/h 80 km per hour to miles per hour; 50 mi/h and 66 feet per second to meters per second. 20 m/s [L2] [LS]
Logical-Mathematical

IDENTIFYING Misconceptions

Word Differences Students may think that distance and displacement are the same and that speed and velocity are the same. See page F at the beginning of the chapter for teaching tips related to this misconception.

Applying Math

National Math Standards
Correlation to Mathematics Objectives
1, 2, 9

Answers to Practice Problems

1. In the first race, the runner's speed was (400 m)/(43.9 s) = 9.1 m/s. In the second race, the runner's speed was (100 m)/(10.4 s) = 9.6 m/s. His speed was faster in the second race.
2. 350 km/3.5 h = 100 km/h

INTEGRATE Life Science

Animal Speeds Different animals can move at different top speeds. What are some of the fastest animals? Research the characteristics that help animals run, swim, or fly at high speed.

Speed

To describe motion, you usually want to describe how fast something is moving. The faster something is moving, the less time it takes to travel a certain distance. **Speed** is the distance traveled divided by the time taken to travel the distance. Speed can be calculated from this equation:

Speed Equation

$$\text{speed (in meters/second)} = \frac{\text{distance (in meters)}}{\text{time (in seconds)}}$$

$$s = \frac{d}{t}$$

Because speed equals distance divided by time, the unit of speed is the unit of distance divided by the unit of time. In SI units, distance is measured in m and time is measured in s. As a result, the SI unit of speed is the m/s—the SI distance unit divided by the SI time unit.

Applying Math — **Solve a Simple Equation**

SPEED OF A SWIMMER Calculate the speed of a swimmer who swims 100 m in 56 s.

Solution

1 *This is what you know:*
- distance: $d = 100$ m
- time: $t = 56$ s

2 *This is what you need to know:*
speed: $s = ?$ m/s

3 *This is the procedure you need to use:*
Substitute the known values for distance and time into the speed equation and calculate the speed:
$$s = \frac{d}{t} = \frac{100 \text{ m}}{56 \text{ s}} = \frac{100}{56} \frac{\text{m}}{\text{s}} = 1.8 \text{ m/s}$$

4 *Check your answer:*
Multiply your answer by the time. You should get the distance that was given.

Practice Problems

1. A runner completes a 400-m race in 43.9 s. In a 100-m race, he finishes in 10.4 s. In which race was his speed faster?

2. A passenger train travels from Boston to New York, a distance of 350 km, in 3.5 h. What is the train's speed?

 For more practice, visit bookm.msscience.com/math_practice

Curriculum Connection

Music Ask students to identify the units used to measure speed in music and to demonstrate how speed is used in music. Beats per minute are the units used. A rapid beat or slow beat affects the mood of a piece.
[L3] [ELL] [LS] **Auditory-Musical**

Teacher **FYI**

Pulse Rate Before people had accurate timekeeping devices, they used their pulse rate to measure time. Early musicians based the tempo of music on their pulse rate, and Galileo analyzed the movement of a pendulum using his pulse.

Average Speed If a sprinter ran the 100-m dash in 10 s, she probably couldn't have run the entire race with a speed of 10 m/s. Consider that when the race started, the sprinter wasn't moving. Then, as she started running, she moved faster and faster, which increased her speed. During the entire race, the sprinter's speed could have been different from instant to instant. However, the sprinter's motion for the entire race can be described by her average speed, which is 10 m/s. **Average speed** is found by dividing the total distance traveled by the time taken.

✓ Reading Check *How is average speed calculated?*

An object in motion can change speeds many times as it speeds up or slows down. The speed of an object at one instant of time is the object's **instantaneous speed.** To understand the difference between average and instantaneous speeds, think about walking to the library. If it takes you 0.5 h to walk 2 km to the library, your average speed would be as follows:

$$s = \frac{d}{t}$$
$$= \frac{2 \text{ km}}{0.5 \text{ h}} = 4 \text{ km/h}$$

However, you might not have been moving at the same speed throughout the trip. At a crosswalk, your instantaneous speed might have been 0 km/h. If you raced across the street, your speed might have been 7 km/h. If you were able to walk at a steady rate of 4 km/h during the entire trip, you would have moved at a constant speed. Average speed, instantaneous speed, and constant speed are illustrated in **Figure 4.**

Figure 4 The average speed of each ball is the same from 0 s to 4 s.

The top ball is moving at a constant speed. In each second, the ball moves the same distance.

The bottom ball has a varying speed. Its instantaneous speed is fast between 0 s and 1 s, slower between 2 s and 3 s, and even slower between 3 s and 4 s.

Graphing Motion

You can represent the motion of an object with a distance-time graph. For this type of graph, time is plotted on the horizontal axis, and distance is plotted on the vertical axis. **Figure 5** shows the motion of two students who walked across a classroom, plotted on a distance-time graph.

Distance-Time Graphs and Speed The distance-time graph can be used to compare the speeds of objects. Look at the graph shown in **Figure 5.** According to the graph, after 1 s student A traveled 1 m. Her average speed during the first second is as follows:

$$\text{speed} = \frac{\text{distance}}{\text{time}} = \frac{1 \text{ m}}{1 \text{ s}} = 1 \text{ m/s}$$

Student B, however, traveled only 0.5 m in the first second. His average speed is

$$\text{speed} = \frac{\text{distance}}{\text{time}} = \frac{0.5 \text{ m}}{1 \text{ s}} = 0.5 \text{ m/s}$$

So student A traveled faster than student B. Now compare the steepness of the lines on the graph in **Figure 5.** The line representing the motion of student A is steeper than the line for student B. A steeper line on the distance-time graph represents a greater speed. A horizontal line on the distance-time graph means that no change in position occurs. In that case, the speed, represented by the line on the graph is zero.

Figure 5 The motion of two students walking across a classroom is plotted on this distance-time graph.

Use the graph to determine which student had the faster average speed.

Distance v. Time

(graph showing Distance (m) vs Time (s), with Student A and Student B lines)

Curriculum Connection

Math The horizontal axis of a graph represents the independent variable; that is, the variable in which a change causes a change in the other variable. In distance-time graphs the independent variable is time. The vertical axis shows the dependent variable, in this case distance.

Differentiated Instruction

Challenge The motion of groups of objects can be modeled using graph paper. Have students divide a sheet of graph paper into six regions to represent one-second intervals from 0 to 5 s. Have students use the graph paper to illustrate what happens to four objects moving at different speeds and directions at t = 0, 1, 2, 3, 4, and 5 s. Then ask them to predict when and if various pairs of objects meet. [L3] [IS] **Visual-Spatial**

Velocity

If you are hiking in the woods, it is important to know in which direction you should walk in order to get back to camp. You want to know not only your speed, but also the direction in which you are moving. The **velocity** of an object is the speed of the object and direction of its motion. This is why a compass and a map, like the one shown in **Figure 6,** are useful to hikers. The map and the compass help the hikers to determine what their velocity must be. Velocity has the same units as speed, but it also includes the direction of motion.

The velocity of an object can change if the object's speed changes, its direction of motion changes, or they both change. For example, suppose a car is traveling at a speed of 40 km/h north and then turns left at an intersection and continues on with a speed of 60 km/h. The speed of the car is constant at 40 km/h, but the velocity changes from 40 km/h north to 40 km/h west. Why can you say the velocity of a car changes as it comes to a stop at an intersection?

1.5 m/s west

1.5 m/s south

△START/FINISH

N

Figure 6 A map helps determine the direction in which you need to travel. Together with your speed, this gives your velocity.

section 1 review

Summary

Changing Position
- An object is in motion if it changes position relative to a reference point.
- Motion can be described by distance, speed, displacement, and velocity, where displacement and velocity also include direction.

Speed and Velocity
- The speed of an object can be calculated by dividing the distance traveled by the time needed to travel the distance.
- For an object traveling at constant speed, its average speed is the same as its instantaneous speed.
- The velocity of an object is the speed of the object and its direction of motion.

Graphing Motion
- A line on a distance-time graph becomes steeper as an object's speed increases.

Self Check

1. **Identify** the two pieces of information you need to know the velocity of an object.
2. **Make and Use Graphs** You walk forward at 1.5 m/s for 8 s. Your friend decides to walk faster and starts out at 2.0 m/s for the first 4 s. Then she slows down and walks forward at 1.0 m/s for the next 4 s. Make a distance-time graph of your motion and your friend's motion. Who walked farther?
3. **Think Critically** A bee flies 25 m north of the hive, then 10 m east, 5 m west, and 10 m south. How far north and east of the hive is it now? Explain how you calculated your answer.

Applying Math

4. **Calculate** the average velocity of a dancer who moves 5 m toward the left of the stage over the course of 15 s.
5. **Travel Time** An airplane flew a distance of 650 km at an average speed of 300 km/h. How much time did the flight take?

Science Online bookm.msscience.com/self_check_quiz

SECTION 1 What is motion? **M** ◆ **13**

section 1 review

1. speed and direction
2. The horizontal axis should be marked from 0 s to 8 s, and the vertical axis should be marked from 0 m to 12 m. The graph of your motion is a diagonal line from (0,0) to (8,12). The graph of your friend's motion is a 2-part line extending from (0,0) to (4,8) and from (4,8) to (8,12). You and your friend walked the same distance, 12 m.
3. 15 m north (25 − 10) and 5 m east (10 − 5)
4. 5 m left ÷ 15 s = 0.33 m/s left
5. 650 km ÷ 300 km/h = 2.17 h

Acceleration

INTERACTIVE
CHALKBOARD
PowerPoint® Presentations

Bellringer

Section Focus Transparencies
also are available on the
Interactive Chalkboard CD-ROM.

L2 ELL

SECTION
2 Section Focus
Transparency **Nothing but Air!**

Very experienced skydivers can work together to make different
formations as they free-fall. Called relative work, these formations
require the skydivers to carefully control their movements while falling.

1. What happens when a skydiver jumps out of a plane? How does
   the jumper's motion change?

2. When the parachute opens, how does the skydiver's motion
   change?

3. How is a skydiver's speed changing before the parachute opens?
   After the parachute opens?

L2

Motion and Momentum

Tie to Prior Knowledge

Car Acceleration Bring to class a
car advertising statement like
"goes from 0 to 60 in 8.3 s." Ask
students to describe acceleration
using this example. What would
it mean if the car reached a faster
speed in 8.3 s? higher acceleration
What would it mean if it took
12 s to reach 60 mi/h? lower acceleration What do people mean
when they say a car has "no
acceleration"? that it won't increase
its speed very rapidly

as you read

What **You'll Learn**

■ **Define** acceleration.
■ **Predict** what effect acceleration
   will have on motion.

Why **It's Important**

Whenever the motion of an object
changes, it is accelerating.

⊙ **Review Vocabulary**
kilogram: SI unit of mass, abbreviated kg; equal to approximately
2.2 lbs

New Vocabulary
● acceleration

Figure 7 The toy car is accelerating to the right. Its speed is
increasing.

Acceleration and Motion

When you watch the first few seconds of a liftoff, a rocket
barely seems to move. With each passing second, however, you
can see it move faster until it reaches an enormous speed. How
could you describe the change in the rocket's motion? When an
object changes its motion, it is accelerating. **Acceleration** is the
change in velocity divided by the time it takes for the change to
occur.

Like velocity, acceleration has a direction. If an object speeds
up, the acceleration is in the direction that the object is moving.
If an object slows down, the acceleration is opposite
to the direction that the object is moving. What if the direction
of the acceleration is at an angle to the direction of motion?
Then the direction of motion will turn toward the direction of
the acceleration.

Speeding Up You get on a bicycle and begin to pedal. The
bike moves slowly at first, and then accelerates because its speed
increases. When an object that is already in motion speeds up, it
also is accelerating. Imagine that you are biking along a level
path and you start pedaling harder. Your speed increases. When
the speed of an object increases, it is accelerating.

Suppose a toy car is speeding up, as shown in **Figure 7.** Each
second, the car moves at a greater speed and travels a greater distance than it did in the previous second. When the car stops
accelerating, it will move in a straight line at the speed it had
when the acceleration stopped.

| 0 cm | 10 cm | 20 cm | 30 cm | 40 cm | 50 cm | 60 cm | 70 cm |

0 s   1 s   2 s   3 s

Section 2 Resource Manager

Chapter *FAST FILE* Resources
Transparency Activity, p. 45
Directed Reading for Content Mastery, p. 20
MiniLAB, p.4

Enrichment, p. 31
Reinforcement, p. 28
Lab Activity, pp. 13–15

0 cm   10 cm   20 cm   30 cm   40 cm   50 cm   60 cm   70 cm

0 s   1 s   2 s   3 s

Slowing Down Now suppose you are biking at a speed of 4 m/s and you apply the brakes. This causes you to slow down. It might sound odd, but because your speed is changing, you are accelerating. Acceleration occurs when an object slows down, as well as when it speeds up. The car in **Figure 8** is slowing down. During each time interval, the car travels a smaller distance, so its speed is decreasing.

In both of these examples, speed is changing, so acceleration is occurring. Because speed is decreasing in the second example, the direction of the acceleration is opposite to the direction of motion. Any time an object slows down, its acceleration is in the direction opposite to the direction of its motion.

Changing Direction Motion is not always along a straight line. If the acceleration is at an angle to the direction of motion, the object will turn. At the same time, it might speed up, slow down, or not change speed at all.

Again imagine yourself riding a bicycle. When you lean to one side and turn the handlebars, the bike turns. Because the direction of the bike's motion has changed, the bike has accelerated. The acceleration is in the direction that the bicycle turned.

Figure 9 shows another example of an object that is accelerating. The ball starts moving upward, but its direction of motion changes as its path turns downward. Here the acceleration is downward. The longer the ball accelerates, the more its path turns toward the direction of acceleration.

Reading Check What are three ways to accelerate?

Figure 9 The ball starts out by moving forward and upward, but the acceleration is downward, so the ball's path turns in that direction.

Figure 8 The car is moving to the right but accelerating to the left. In each time interval, it covers less distance and moves more slowly.
Determine *how the car's velocity is changing.*

Caption Answer
Figure 8 slowing down

Use Science Words

Word Origins Ask students to look up the origin of the word *accelerate* and explain how it relates to the scientific use of the word. Accelerate comes from the Latin prefix *ac-*, meaning "toward," the Latin root word *celer*, meaning "swift," and the Latin suffix *-ate*, meaning "cause to become." These together mean "cause to become swift toward." This covers one meaning, to move faster, of the scientific use of the word accelerate. It does not cover slowing down or turning. L3 IS **Linguistic**

Visual Learning

Figures 7, 8, 9 Review with students the accelerations shown in **Figures 7, 8,** and **9.** Ask students how else the car might accelerate. by changing direction

Quick Demo
Circular Motion
Materials spool, length of string (about 1 m)
Estimated Time 15 minutes
Procedure Tie a small spool to the end of a piece of string and whirl it around your head. **WARNING:** *Make sure that the spool is fastened tightly to the string and that you have enough space so the spool won't hit anyone.* Discuss with students the motion of the spool and the fact that the string pulls on the spool, accelerating it, to keep it moving in a circle. L2 ELL IS **Visual-Spatial**

Reading Check
Answer speeding up, slowing down, and changing direction

Science Journal

Accelerating to School Have students note each time they accelerate on their way to school and write their observations in their Science Journals. Make sure they include each time they stop, start, and turn on their journeys. L2 ELL IS **Linguistic**

Fun Fact
The velocity any object needs to reach to escape Earth's gravity and get into space is about 11 km/s. That's equivalent to almost 40,000 km/h (about 25,000 miles per hour)!

Squared Seconds Have students look at the equations on this page. Why is acceleration measured in meters divided by seconds *squared*? Velocity is measured in meters per second. To find acceleration, you divide velocity by time, which has units of seconds. Therefore, the final answer has units of distance divided by time (velocity) divided by time = m/s². L2 **Logical-Mathematical**

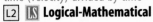

National Math Standards

Correlation to Mathematics Objectives

1, 2, 9

Answers to Practice Problems

1. $a = (17 \text{ m/s} - 7 \text{ m/s}) \div 120 \text{ s} = 0.083 \text{ m/s}^2$

2. $a = (6 \text{ m/s} - 0 \text{ m/s}) \div 2 \text{ s} = 3 \text{ m/s}^2$

Differentiated Instruction

Learning Disabled Provide extra practice problems for students who have difficulty understanding the mathematics discussed on these pages. Make sure students understand the basic principles used both to set up and solve the problems.

Calculating Acceleration

If an object is moving in a straight line, its acceleration can be calculated using this equation.

Acceleration Equation

acceleration (in m/s²) =
$$\frac{(\textbf{final speed (in m/s)} - \textbf{initial speed (in m/s)})}{\textbf{time (in s)}}$$

$$a = \frac{(s_f - s_i)}{t}$$

In this equation, time is the length of time over which the motion changes. In SI units, acceleration has units of meters per second squared (m/s²).

Applying Math — Solve a Simple Equation

ACCELERATION OF A BUS Calculate the acceleration of a bus whose speed changes from 6 m/s to 12 m/s over a period of 3 s.

Solution

1 *This is what you know:*
- initial speed: $s_i = 6$ m/s
- final speed: $s_f = 12$ m/s
- time: $t = 3$ s

2 *This is what you need to know:*

acceleration: $a = ?$ m/s²

3 *This is the procedure you need to use:*

Substitute the known values of initial speed, final speed and time in the acceleration equation and calculate the acceleration:

$$a = \frac{(s_f - s_i)}{t} = \frac{(12 \text{ m/s} - 6 \text{ m/s})}{3 \text{ s}} = 6 \frac{\text{m}}{\text{s}} \times \frac{1}{3 \text{ s}} = 2 \text{ m/s}^2$$

4 *Check your answer:*

Multiply the calculated acceleration by the known time. Then add the known initial speed. You should get the final speed that was given.

Practice Problems

1. Find the acceleration of a train whose speed increases from 7 m/s to 17 m/s in 120 s.

2. A bicycle accelerates from rest to 6 m/s in 2 s. What is the bicycle's acceleration?

 For more practice, visit bookm.msscience.com/math_practice

Differentiated Instruction

Challenge When doing calculations, students may be helped by doing unit analysis. In doing unit analysis, you write the initial problem with units included and cancel appropriately to see what units the answer will have. If the answer does not have the right units, the problem is set up incorrectly. Have students do a unit analysis of the problem of finding the time needed to accelerate from 3 m/s to 8 m/s at 2 m/s². The units should cancel leaving the unit of time, seconds. The change in velocity is 5 m/s. Rearrange the equation for acceleration to: time = change in velocity ÷ acceleration. Substituting units in this equation gives

time = (m/s − m/s) ÷ m/s² = m/s × s²/m = s

$t = (5 \text{ m/s}) \div (2 \text{ m/s}^2) = 2.5 \text{ s}$ L3

Logical-Mathematical

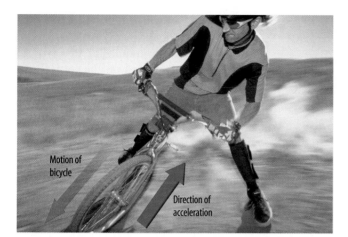

Direction of acceleration

Figure 10 When skidding to a stop, you are slowing down. This means you have a negative acceleration.

Positive and Negative Acceleration

An object is accelerating when it speeds up, and the acceleration is in the same direction as the motion. An object also is accelerating when it slows down, but the acceleration is in the direction opposite to the motion, such as the bicycle in **Figure 10.** How else is acceleration different when an object is speeding up and slowing down?

Suppose you were riding your bicycle in a straight line and increased your speed from 4 m/s to 6 m/s in 5 s. You could calculate your acceleration from the equation on the previous page.

$$a = \frac{(s_f - s_i)}{t}$$
$$= \frac{(6 \text{ m/s} - 4 \text{ m/s})}{5 \text{ s}} = \frac{+2 \text{ m/s}}{5 \text{ s}}$$
$$= +0.4 \text{ m/s}^2$$

When you speed up, your final speed always will be greater than your initial speed. So subtracting your initial speed from your final speed gives a positive number. As a result, your acceleration is positive when you are speeding up.

Suppose you slow down from a speed of 4 m/s to 2 m/s in 5 s. Now the final speed is less than the initial speed. You could calculate your acceleration as follows:

$$a = \frac{(s_f - s_i)}{t}$$
$$= \frac{(2 \text{ m/s} - 4 \text{ m/s})}{5 \text{ s}} = \frac{-2 \text{ m/s}}{5 \text{ s}}$$
$$= -0.4 \text{ m/s}^2$$

Because your final speed is less than your initial speed, your acceleration is negative when you slow down.

Modeling Acceleration

Procedure
1. Use **masking tape** to lay a course on the floor. Mark a starting point and place marks along a straight path at 10 cm, 40 cm, 90 cm, 160 cm, and 250 cm from the start.
2. Clap a steady beat. On the first beat, the person walking the course should be at the starting point. On the second beat, the walker should be on the first mark, and so on.

Analysis
1. Describe what happens to your speed as you move along the course. Infer what would happen if the course were extended farther.
2. Repeat step 2, starting at the other end. Are you still accelerating? Explain.

SECTION 2 Acceleration **M** ◆ **17**

Purpose Students observe constant acceleration. L2 LS **Kinesthetic**

Materials meterstick or other measuring device, masking tape

Teaching Strategy Explain to students that the actual time interval used doesn't matter, as long as it is constant—it could be 1 s–1 s–1 s, or 3 s–3 s–3 s, or any other regular time interval. Clapping steadily is easier than trying to watch the clock and the course at the same time.

Safety Precaution Suggest that students leave space at the fast end of the course to come to a stop.

Analysis
1. I speed up. I would go faster and faster with each clap, because I would be covering a greater distance in the same amount of time.
2. Yes, because my speed is changing. In this case, I am slowing down.

Assessment

Process Ask students to repeat the experiment using different steady beats—very slow or very fast. How does this affect the acceleration they experience? The faster the beat, the greater the acceleration, because the time between beats decreases. Use **Performance Assessment in the Science Classroom,** p. 97.

Activity

Final Speed Have students calculate the final speed of a bicyclist who accelerates at 0.3 m/s² for 10 s from an initial speed of 4 m/s.

Curriculum Connection

History An early problem in the study of motion was to measure the acceleration of an object due to gravity. Does the acceleration of an object depend on its mass? Have students do research to find Galileo's contributions to understanding the answers to these problems. He showed that gravity causes all falling objects to have the same constant acceleration. L3 LS **Linguistic**

Teacher FYI

Negative Velocity A negative number multiplied by a positive number results in a negative number. Because time is always positive, a negative acceleration multiplied by a positive time will always give a negative change in velocity.

SECTION 2 Acceleration **M** ◆ **17**

Figure 11 A speed-time graph can be used to find acceleration. When the line rises, the object is speeding up. When the line falls, the object is slowing down.
Infer *what acceleration a horizontal line represents.*

Graphing Accelerated Motion The motion of an object that is accelerating can be shown with a graph. For this type of graph, speed is plotted on the vertical axis and time on the horizontal axis. Take a look at **Figure 11.** On section A of the graph, the speed increases from 0 m/s to 10 m/s during the first 2 s, so the acceleration is +5 m/s². The line in section A slopes upward to the right. An object that is speeding up will have a line on a speed-time graph that slopes upward.

Now look at section C. Between 4 s and 6 s, the object slows down from 10 m/s to 4 m/s. The acceleration is −3 m/s². On the speed-time graph, the line in section C is sloping downward to the right. An object that is slowing down will have a line on a speed-time graph that slopes downward.

On section B, where the line is horizontal, the change in speed is zero. So a horizontal line on the speed-time graph represents an acceleration of zero or constant speed.

section ② review

Summary

Acceleration and Motion

- Acceleration is the change in velocity divided by the time it takes to make the change. Acceleration has direction.

- Acceleration occurs whenever an object speeds up, slows down, or changes direction.

Calculating Acceleration

- For motion in a straight line, acceleration can be calculated from this equation:

$$a = \frac{s_f - s_i}{t}$$

- If an object is speeding up, its acceleration is positive; if an object is slowing down, its acceleration is negative.

- On a speed-time graph, a line sloping up represents positive acceleration, a line sloping down represents negative acceleration, and a horizontal line represents zero acceleration or constant speed.

Self Check

1. **Compare and contrast** speed, velocity, and acceleration.

2. **Infer** the motion of a car whose speed-time graph shows a horizontal line, followed by a straight line that slopes downward to the bottom of the graph.

3. **Think Critically** You start to roll backward down a hill on your bike, so you use the brakes to stop your motion. In what direction did you accelerate?

Applying Math

4. **Calculate** the acceleration of a runner who accelerates from 0 m/s to 3 m/s in 12 s.

5. **Calculate Speed** An object falls with an acceleration of 9.8 m/s². What is its speed after 2 s?

6. **Make and Use a Graph** A sprinter had the following speeds at different times during a race: 0 m/s at 0 s, 4 m/s at 2 s, 7 m/s at 4 s, 10 m/s at 6 s, 12 m/s at 8 s, and 10 m/s at 10 s. Plot these data on a speed-time graph. During what time intervals is the acceleration positive? Negative? Is the acceleration ever zero?

 Science Online bookm.msscience.com/self_check_quiz

section ② review

1. Speed and velocity both include rate of change in position. Acceleration measures rate of change in velocity. Both velocity and acceleration include direction; speed does not.

2. The car first travels at constant speed (horizontal line) and then slows down (sloping line) and comes to a stop (bottom of the graph).

3. Against the motion; I accelerated uphill.

4. $a = (3 \text{ m/s} - 0 \text{ m/s}) \div 12 \text{ s} = 0.25 \text{ m/s}^2$

5. $s_f = 0 \text{ m/s} + 9.8 \text{ m/s}^2 \times 2 \text{ s} = 19.6 \text{ m/s}$

6. Check students' graphs; positive from 0 s to 8 s; negative from 8 s to 10 s. The acceleration must become zero for some short time as it changes from positive to negative between 8 and 10 s.

Mass and Inertia

The world you live in is filled with objects in motion. How can you describe these objects? Objects have many properties such as color, size, and composition. One important property of an object is its mass. The **mass** of an object is the amount of matter in the object. In SI units, the unit for mass is the kilogram.

The weight of an object is related to the object's mass. Objects with more mass weigh more than objects with less mass. A bowling ball has more mass than a pillow, so it weighs more than a pillow. However, the size of an object is not the same as the mass of the object. For example, a pillow is larger than a bowling ball, but the bowling ball has more mass.

Objects with different masses are different in an important way. Think about what happens when you try to stop someone who is rushing toward you. A small child is easy to stop. A large adult is hard to stop. The more mass an object has, the harder it is to start it moving, slow it down, speed it up, or turn it. This tendency of an object to resist a change in its motion is called **inertia**. Objects with more mass have more inertia, as shown in **Figure 12**. The more mass an object has, the harder it is to change its motion.

 Reading Check *What is inertia?*

Figure 12 The more mass an object has, the greater its inertia is. A table-tennis ball responds to a gentle hit that would move a tennis ball only slightly.

as you read

 What You'll Learn
- **Explain** the relationship between mass and inertia.
- **Define** momentum.
- **Predict** motion using the law of conservation of momentum.

Why It's Important

Objects in motion have momentum. The motion of objects after they collide depends on their momentum.

Review Vocabulary
triple-beam balance: scientific instrument used to measure mass precisely by comparing the mass of a sample to known masses

New Vocabulary
- mass
- inertia
- momentum
- law of conservation of momentum

INTEGRATE
Social Studies

Forensics and Momentum
Forensic investigations of accidents and crimes often involve determining the momentum of an object. For example, the law of conservation of momentum sometimes is used to reconstruct the motion of vehicles involved in a collision. Research other ways momentum is used in forensic investigations.

Momentum

You know that the faster a bicycle moves, the harder it is to stop. Just as increasing the mass of an object makes it harder to stop, so does increasing the speed or velocity of the object. The **momentum** of an object is a measure of how hard it is to stop the object, and it depends on the object's mass and velocity. Momentum is usually symbolized by p.

Momentum Equation

momentum (in kg · m/s) = **mass** (in kg) $\times$ **velocity** (in m/s)

$$p = mv$$

Mass is measured in kilograms and velocity has units of meters per second, so momentum has units of kilograms multiplied by meters per second (kg · m/s). Also, because velocity includes a direction, momentum has a direction that is the same as the direction of the velocity.

Reading Check *Explain how an object's momentum changes as its velocity changes.*

Applying Math   Solve a Simple Equation

MOMENTUM OF A BICYCLE Calculate the momentum of a 14-kg bicycle traveling north at 2 m/s.

Solution

1 *This is what you know:*
- mass: $m = 14$ kg
- velocity: $v = 2$ m/s north

2 *This is what you need to find:*
momentum: $p = ?$ kg · m/s

3 *This is the procedure you need to use:*
Substitute the known values of mass and velocity into the momentum equation and calculate the momentum:
$p = mv = (14$ kg$) (2$ m/s north$) = 28$ kg · m/s north

4 *Check your answer:*
Divide the calculated momentum by the mass of the bicycle. You should get the velocity that was given.

Practice Problems

1. A 10,000-kg train is traveling east at 15 m/s. Calculate the momentum of the train.

2. What is the momentum of a car with a mass of 900 kg traveling north at 27 m/s?

 Science Online
For more practice, visit
bookm.msscience.com/
math_practice

Curriculum Connection

Physical Education Momentum and inertia are part of all sports. Ask each student to choose a sport and prepare a poster illustrating how momentum and inertia are important in that sport. Possibilities include the inertia of a runner racing around an oval track, the momentum of a soccer ball going past a goalie, and the inertia of a wrestler. [L2] [IS] **Visual-Spatial** [P]

Fun Fact

When an object falls toward Earth, its momentum downward is balanced by Earth's momentum upward — but Earth is so massive that its velocity is too tiny to be felt!

Conservation of Momentum

If you've ever played billiards, you know that when the cue ball hits another ball, the motions of both balls change. The cue ball slows down and may change direction, so its momentum decreases. Meanwhile, the other ball starts moving, so its momentum increases. It seems as if momentum is transferred from the cue ball to the other ball.

In fact, during the collision, the momentum lost by the cue ball was gained by the other ball. This means that the total momentum of the two balls was the same just before and just after the collision. This is true for any collision, as long as no outside forces such as friction act on the objects and change their speeds after the collision. According to the **law of conservation of momentum,** the total momentum of objects that collide is the same before and after the collision. This is true for the collisions of the billiard balls shown in **Figure 13,** as well as for collisions of atoms, cars, football players, or any other matter.

Using Momentum Conservation

Outside forces, such as gravity and friction, are almost always acting on objects that are colliding. However, sometimes, the effects of these forces are small enough that they can be ignored. Then the law of conservation of momentum enables you to predict how the motions of objects will change after a collision.

There are many ways that collisions can occur. Two examples are shown in **Figure 14.** Sometimes, the objects that collide will bounce off of each other, like the bowling ball and bowling pins. In other collisions, objects will stick to each other after the collision, like the two football players. In both of these types of collisions, the law of conservation of momentum enables the speeds of the objects after the collision to be calculated.

Figure 13 When the cue ball hits the other billiard balls, it slows down because it transfers some of its momentum to the other billiard balls.
Predict *what would happen to the speed of the cue ball if all of its momentum were transferred to the other billiard balls.*

Figure 14 In these collisions, the total momentum before the collision equals the total momentum after the collision.

When one player tackles the other, they both change speeds, but momentum is conserved.

When the bowling ball hits the pins, some of its momentum is transferred to the pins. The ball slows down, and the pins speed up.

Use an Analogy

Using Momentum People sometimes use the word momentum to say things such as "The push for reform is gaining momentum." How is this analogous to the use of the word momentum in physical science? Both suggest motion and that as momentum increases, something becomes harder to stop. L2 **IS** **Linguistic**

Teacher FYI

Collisions There are two types of collisions. In an elastic collision, both momentum and mechanical energy are conserved. In an inelastic collision, momentum is conserved, but kinetic energy is not. In most inelastic collisions, the final kinetic energy is less than the initial kinetic energy. Some of this energy is converted to heat energy in the collision.

Make a Model

Marble Collisions Have students model collisions by putting marbles in a pie pan and shaking the pie pan. As more marbles are added or the marbles move faster, they collide more frequently. If students shake the pie pan at a steady rate, the speeds of the marbles even out over time as faster marbles transfer momentum to slower marbles in collisions. L2 **ELL** **IS** **Kinesthetic**

Differentiated Instruction

Learning Disabled Help these students follow conservation of momentum using physical models. Use sliding cups, each containing a number of pennies or other identical small units. When the cups collide, the pennies can be traded between cups, but they cannot be lost from the system or added from the outside. L1 **IS** **Kinesthetic**

Visual Learning

Figure 14 Ask students to use the pictures as a guide and think of other examples of collisions in which objects rebound or stick together. rebound: ice cubes in a glass, billiard balls colliding, particles colliding; stick together: catching a ball, jumping on a skateboard L2 **IS** **Visual-Spatial**

Discussion

Ball Motion Suppose two balls approach each other at 1 m/s from opposite directions. Their total momentum is zero. After the collision, they both zoom off at 1 m/s in opposite directions. What is their momentum? It is still zero. What do you know about the masses of the two balls? If the total momentum is zero and the two balls have the same speed in opposite directions, the balls must have the same mass. L2 IS **Logical-Mathematical**

Quick Demo

Momentum Conservation

Materials ball, rolling cart or roller skates

Estimated Time 15 minutes

Procedure While sitting on a rolling cart or standing on roller skates, use both hands to throw a ball forcefully forward. Explain that, because you and the ball were initially at rest, the total initial momentum was zero. When you threw the ball, you gave it positive momentum in the forward direction. As a result, you started to roll backward (negative momentum) so that the total momentum would still be zero.

Before the student on skates and the backpack collide, she is not moving.

After the collision, the student and the backpack move together at a slower speed than the backpack had before the collision.

Figure 15 Momentum is conserved in the collision of the backpack and the student.

Science Online

Topic: Collisions

Visit bookm.msscience.com for Web links to information about collisions between objects with different masses.

Activity Draw diagrams showing the results of collisions between a bowling ball and a tennis ball if they are moving in the same direction and if they are in opposite directions.

Sticking Together Imagine being on skates when someone throws a backpack to you, as in **Figure 15.** When you catch the backpack, you and the backpack continue to move in the same direction as the backpack was moving before the collision.

The law of conservation of momentum can be used to find your velocity after you catch the backpack. Suppose a 2-kg backpack is tossed at a speed of 5 m/s. Your mass is 48 kg, and initially you are at rest. Then the total initial momentum is

$$\text{total momentum} = \text{momentum of backpack} + \text{your momentum}$$
$$= 2 \text{ kg} \times 5 \text{ m/s} + 48 \text{ kg} \times 0 \text{ m/s}$$
$$= 10 \text{ kg} \cdot \text{m/s}$$

After the collision, the total momentum remains the same, and only one object is moving. Its mass is the sum of your mass and the mass of the backpack. You can use the equation for momentum to find the final velocity.

$$\text{total momentum} = (\text{mass of backpack} + \text{your mass}) \times \text{velocity}$$
$$10 \text{ kg} \cdot \text{m/s} = (2 \text{ kg} + 48 \text{ kg}) \times \text{velocity}$$
$$10 \text{ kg} \cdot \text{m/s} = (50 \text{ kg}) \times \text{velocity}$$
$$0.2 \text{ m/s} = \text{velocity}$$

This is your velocity right after you catch the backpack. As you continue to move on your skates, the force of friction between the ground and the skates slows you down. Because of friction, the momentum of you and the backpack together continually decreases until you come to a stop. **Figure 16** shows the results of some collisions between two objects with various masses and velocities.

 LAB DEMONSTRATION

Purpose to observe and measure momentum during an inelastic collision

Materials 2 toy cars, 2 metersticks, balance, timer

Preparation Set up a straight course bounded by two metersticks set end to end.

Procedure Measure and record the mass of each toy car. Place one car at the zero mark of the second meterstick. Push the other car so that it starts rolling at the zero mark of the first meterstick and hits the first car. Measure the time it takes the rolling car to reach the standing car, and measure the time and distance the two cars roll after the collision. Calculate the momentum before and after the collision.

Assessment

Was momentum conserved in this collision? Answers will depend on experimental results. If not, why not? Friction caused the toy cars to slow down, so their total momentum decreased.

Figure 16

The law of conservation of momentum can be used to predict the results of collisions between different objects, whether they are subatomic particles smashing into each other at enormous speeds, or the collisions of marbles, as shown on this page. What happens when one marble hits another marble initially at rest? The results of the collisions depend on the masses of the marbles.

A Here, a less massive marble strikes a more massive marble that is at rest. After the collision, the smaller marble bounces off in the opposite direction. The larger marble moves in the same direction that the small marble was initially moving.

B Here, the large marble strikes the small marble that is at rest. After the collision, both marbles move in the same direction. The less massive marble always moves faster than the more massive one.

C If two objects of the same mass moving at the same speed collide head-on, they will rebound and move with the same speed in the opposite direction. The total momentum is zero before and after the collision.

SECTION 3 Momentum **M ◆ 23**

NATIONAL GEOGRAPHIC

Visualizing Conservation of Momentum

Have students examine the pictures and read the captions. Then ask the following questions.

If a small car is stopped at a traffic light and is hit from behind by a truck, what will happen? Both vehicles will move forward, with the car moving faster than the truck.

What will happen if two marbles of the same mass, traveling toward each other, collide? The marbles will collide and reverse directions, moving away from each other at the same speed as before the collision.

Activity

Marble Tracks Have small groups of students tape two metersticks to a flat surface. The space between them should be wide enough to allow marbles to travel in the space. Have students form a ramp by placing one end of a grooved ruler on two or three books and the other end at one end of the track. They should place three marbles in the track and roll one marble down the ruler into the track and observe what happens. Ask students to repeat the procedure rolling two and three marbles down the ramp together. Ask them to explain their observations in terms of conservation of momentum. L2 IS **Kinesthetic**

Differentiated Instruction

Challenge Have students research collision tests that are used to rate cars. Ask them to present oral reports on the tests and how the conservation of momentum applies. L3 IS **Linguistic**

Figure 17 When bumper cars collide, they bounce off each other, and momentum is transferred.

Colliding and Bouncing Off In some collisions, the objects involved, like the bumper cars in **Figure 17,** bounce off each other. The law of conservation of momentum can be used to determine how these objects move after they collide.

For example, suppose two identical objects moving with the same speed collide head on and bounce off. Before the collision, the momentum of each object is the same, but in opposite directions. So the total momentum before the collision is zero. If momentum is conserved, the total momentum after the collision must be zero also. This means that the two objects must move in opposite directions with the same speed after the collision. Then the total momentum once again is zero.

section 3 review

Summary

Mass, Inertia, and Momentum

- Mass is the amount of matter in an object.
- Inertia is the tendency of an object to resist a change in motion. Inertia increases as the mass of an object increases.
- The momentum of an object in motion is related to how hard it is to stop the object, and can be calculated from the following equation:

$$p = mv$$

- Because velocity has a direction, momentum also has a direction.

The Law of Conservation of Momentum

- The law of conservation of momentum states that in a collision, the total momentum of the objects that collide is the same before and after the collision.

Self Check

1. **Explain** how momentum is transferred when a golfer hits a ball with a golf club.

2. **Determine** if the momentum of an object moving in a circular path at constant speed is constant.

3. **Explain** why the momentum of a billiard ball rolling on a billiard table changes.

4. **Think Critically** Two identical balls move directly toward each other with equal speeds. How will the balls move if they collide and stick together?

Applying Math

5. **Momentum** What is the momentum of a 0.1-kg mass moving with a speed of 5 m/s?

6. **Momentum Conservation** A 1-kg ball moving at 3 m/s strikes a 2-kg ball and stops. If the 2-kg ball was initially at rest, find its speed after the collision.

24 ◆ M CHAPTER 1 Motion and Momentum bookm.msscience.com/self_check_quiz

Collisions

A collision occurs when a baseball bat hits a baseball or a tennis racket hits a tennis ball. What would happen if you hit a baseball with a table-tennis paddle or a table-tennis ball with a baseball bat? How do the masses of colliding objects change the results of collisions?

▶ Real-World Question

How does changing the size and number of objects in a collision affect the collision?

Goals
- **Compare and contrast** different collisions.
- **Determine** how the speeds after a collision depend on the masses of the colliding objects.

Materials
small marbles (5)   metersticks (2)
large marbles (2)   tape

Safety Precautions

▶ Procedure

1. Tape the metersticks next to each other, slightly farther apart than the width of the large marbles. This limits the motion of the marbles to nearly a straight line.

2. Place a small target marble in the center of the track formed by the metersticks. Place another small marble at one end of the track. Flick the small marble toward the target marble. Describe the collision.

3. Repeat step 2, replacing the two small marbles with the two large marbles.

4. Repeat step 2, replacing the small shooter marble with a large marble.

5. Repeat step 2, replacing the small target marble with a large marble.

6. Repeat step 2, replacing the small target marble with four small marbles that are touching.

7. Place two small marbles at opposite ends of the metersticks. Shoot the marbles toward each other and describe the collision.

8. Place two large marbles at opposite ends of the metersticks. Shoot the marbles toward each other and describe the collision.

9. Place a small marble and a large marble at opposite ends of the metersticks. Shoot the marbles toward each other and describe the collision.

▶ Conclude and Apply

1. **Describe** In which collisions did the shooter marble change direction? How did the mass of the target marble compare with the mass of the shooter marble in these collisions?

2. **Explain** how momentum was conserved in these collisions.

𝒞ommunicating
Your Data

Make a chart showing your results. You might want to make before-and-after sketches, with short arrows to show slow movement and long arrows to show fast movement.

▶ Real-World Question

Purpose Students observe the changes in momentum occurring in different collisions. L2 **IS** **Kinesthetic**

Process Skills identify and manipulate variables, observe and infer, interpret data, draw conclusions

Time Required 50 minutes

▶ Procedure

Safety Precautions Make sure no loose marbles remain on the classroom floor when the experiment is done.

Teaching Strategy Caution students not to shoot the marbles so hard that they bounce or make the other marbles jump when they hit them.

▶ Conclude and Apply

1. The shooter marble changed direction when it hit a target marble with more mass than itself.
2. by being transferred from the shooter marble to the target marble, slowing down or stopping the shooter marble and setting the target marble in motion

---

✓ Assessment

Process Predict what will happen when a small shooter marble hits a line of five large target marbles. The shooter marble will stop, and the last target marble in line will be set in motion, with a velocity smaller than that of the shooter marble. Use **Performance Assessment in the Science Classroom,** p. 89.

𝒞ommunicating
Your Data

Students can work together on a large chart to be displayed as a class poster.

BENCH TESTED

LAB

Design Your Own

C🚗r Safety Testing

▶ **Real-World**
Question

Purpose Students will construct a car that will protect an egg from a rapid deceleration.

Time Required approximately 70 minutes

Alternate Materials The list for materials that can be used to create the car is nearly endless. Don't use items that are sharp or breakable.

Safety Precautions Because the cars are intended to crash, students should wear safety goggles.

▶ **Form a**
Hypothesis

Possible Hypothesis The egg will be most likely to survive in a car that gradually brings the egg to a stop, thus cushioning it.

▶ **Test Your**
Hypothesis

Possible Procedures The car must roll freely to be fast. The egg must be protected or slowed gradually to a stop by some sort of layers or barriers or restraints.

Teaching Strategy Students will often have elaborate and complex ideas that may be too difficult to be practical. Try to steer them clear of such ideas without stifling their creativity

---

Goals
■ **Construct** a fast car.
■ **Design** a safe car that will protect a plastic egg from the effects of inertia when the car crashes.

Possible Materials
insulated foam meat trays or fast food trays
insulated foam cups
straws, narrow and wide
straight pins
tape
plastic eggs

Safety Precautions

WARNING: *Protect your eyes from possible flying objects.*

▶ **Real-World Question**

Imagine that you are a car designer. How can you create an attractive, fast car that is safe? When a car crashes, the passengers have inertia that can keep them moving. How can you protect the passengers from stops caused by sudden, head-on impacts?

▶ **Form a Hypothesis**

Develop a hypothesis about how to design a car to deliver a plastic egg quickly and safely through a race course and a crash at the end.

▶ **Test Your Hypothesis**

Make a Plan

1. Be sure your group has agreed on the hypothesis statement.

2. **Sketch** the design for your car. List the materials you will need. Remember that to make the car move smoothly, narrow straws will have to fit into the wider straws.

Differentiated Instruction

Learning Disabled Students who have learning challenges are sometimes good at manipulating or building things. Perhaps one student in a group could design an idea and another could physically create it.

Alternative Inquiry Lab

Car Materials To make this Lab an Inquiry Lab, allow students to propose and use alternative materials in the construction of their cars.

3. As a group, make a detailed list of the steps you will take to test your hypothesis.

4. Gather the materials you will need to carry out your experiment.

Follow Your Plan

1. Make sure your teacher approves your plan before you start. Include any changes suggested by your teacher in your plans.

2. Carry out the experiment as planned.

3. **Record** any observations that you made while doing your experiment. Include suggestions for improving your design.

◯ *Analyze Your Data*

1. **Compare** your car design to the designs of the other groups. What made the fastest car fast? What slowed the slowest car?

2. **Compare** your car's safety features to those of the other cars. What protected the eggs the best? How could you improve the unsuccessful designs?

3. **Predict** What effect would decreasing the speed of your car have on the safety of the egg?

◯ *Conclude and Apply*

1. **Summarize** How did the best designs protect the egg?

2. **Apply** If you were designing cars, what could you do to better protect passengers from sudden stops?

*C*ommunicating
Your Data

Write a descriptive paragraph about ways a car could be designed to protect its passengers effectively. Include a sketch of your ideas.

Expected Outcome Cars that cushioned their eggs will be most successful. Students should try to discover why some were successful and others weren't.

◯ *Analyze Your Data*

Answers to Questions

1. Reducing friction and air resistance makes the cars go faster.

2. Eggs with layers of protection to gradually slow them to a stop work best. Such protections have the same effects as car seat belts and air bags.

3. Decreasing the speed would give the egg a better chance for survival because the egg would experience a smaller deceleration during a crash.

Error Analysis Ask students to name features that allowed eggs to survive.

◯ *Conclude and Apply*

1. The best designs protected the egg in the same way seat belts and airbags protect people.

2. Provide devices to restrain people from being thrown as the car stops.

☑ Assessment

Content Divide the class into groups and ask each group to develop and perform a short skit comparing the cart with the egg to a real car carrying people. Use **Performance Assessment in the Science Classroom**, p. 147.

☑ Active Reading

Synthesis Journal In this strategy, students reflect on a project, paper, or performance in light of their own experiences and plan to apply it personally. Ask students to write a Synthesis Journal entry for this activity. Have each student divide a sheet of paper into three sections. For this activity, have them record *What I did*, *What I learned*, and *How I can use it*.

*C*ommunicating
Your Data

To complete their writing, students could also briefly research how the automobile industry tests vehicle safety. Students may also find photos or videos of industry tests to incorporate into their writing.

Oops! Accidents in SCIENCE

Content Background

Not all boomerangs return to their throwers. A true boomerang is nothing more than a curved stick that is thrown. The early boomerangs used for hunting by peoples of many ancient cultures (including many tribes in the western United States) were much longer, straighter, and heavier than the more familiar returning types. Returning boomerangs are too light and thin to do much damage to any living thing. Returning boomerangs became popular primarily as playthings for Aborigines in Australia. Some hunters there used them to imitate hawks in flight and so to serve as a decoy to drive other game birds into nets strung from trees. Otherwise, they don't have any real practical uses because they are difficult to throw very accurately. They also probably wouldn't have enough momentum to return to the thrower after hitting something.

Activity

Varying Throw Angle Take students outside and have volunteers throw boomerangs first from a horizontal starting position and then from varying angles. Ask students what is different about the paths of the boomerangs. A boomerang thrown from a horizontal position flies off until it stops spinning and then falls. Boomerangs thrown at different angles curve. Explain to students that when a boomerang is thrown from an angle slightly different from the horizontal, the motions of its wings and its speed through the air cause it to experience a force that makes it circle back to the thrower. L2 LS **Kinesthetic**

What Goes Around Comes Around

The Story of Boomerangs

Imagine a group gathered on a flat, yellow plain on the Australian Outback. One youth steps forward and, with the flick of an arm, sends a long, flat, angled stick soaring and spinning into the sky. The stick's path curves until it returns right back into the thrower's hand. Thrower after thrower steps forward, and the contest goes on all afternoon.

This contest involved throwing boomerangs—elegantly curved sticks. Because of how boomerangs are shaped, they always return to the thrower's hand

This amazing design is over 15,000 years old. Scientists believe that boomerangs developed from simple clubs thrown to stun and kill animals for food. Differently shaped clubs flew in different ways. As the shape of the club was refined, people probably started throwing them for fun too. In fact, today, using boomerangs for fun is still a popular sport, as world-class throwers compete in contests of strength and skill.

Boomerangs come in several forms, but all of them have several things in common. First a boomerang is shaped like an airplane's wing: flat on one side and curved on the other. Second, boomerangs are angled, which makes them spin as they fly. These two features determine the aerodynamics that give the boomerang its unique flight path.

From its beginning as a hunting tool to its use in today's World Boomerang Championships, the boomerang has remained a source of fascination for thousands of years.

Design Boomerangs are made from various materials. Research to find instructions for making boomerangs. After you and your friends build some boomerangs, have a competition of your own.

Science Online
For more information, visit bookm.msscience.com/oops

Design Possible competitions might include the best catch, longest flight time, and greatest curvature in flight. Students might also construct targets to hit or paper barriers to curve through. Caution students that, although boomerangs are very light, they can hit hard when moving fast, so students should be careful when throwing them and wear protective goggles and gloves.

Resources for Teachers and Students

Boomerang: Behind an Australian Icon, by Philip Jones, Ten Speed Press, 1997

Many Happy Returns, Quarterly Newsletter of the United States Boomerang Association

Reviewing Main Ideas

Section 1 **What is motion?**

1. The position of an object depends on the reference point that is chosen.

2. An object is in motion if the position of the object is changing.

3. The speed of an object equals the distance traveled divided by the time:
$$s = \frac{d}{t}$$

4. The velocity of an object includes the speed and the direction of motion.

5. The motion of an object can be represented on a speed-time graph.

Section 2 **Acceleration**

1. Acceleration is a measure of how quickly velocity changes. It includes a direction.

2. An object is accelerating when it speeds up, slows down, or turns.

3. When an object moves in a straight line, its acceleration can be calculated by
$$a = \frac{(s_f - s_i)}{t}$$

Section 3 **Momentum**

1. Momentum equals the mass of an object times its velocity:
$$p = mv$$

2. Momentum is transferred from one object to another in a collision.

3. According to the law of conservation of momentum, the total amount of momentum of a group of objects doesn't change unless outside forces act on the objects.

Reviewing Main Ideas

Summary statements can be used by students to review the major concepts of the chapter.

Visualizing Main Ideas

See student page.

Science online

Visit bookm.msscience.com
/self_check_quiz
/interactive_tutor
/vocabulary_puzzlemaker
/chapter_review
/standardized_test

Visualizing Main Ideas

Copy and complete the following table on motion.

Describing Motion

Quantity	Definition	Direction
Distance	length of path traveled	no
Displacement	direction and change in position	yes
Speed	rate of change in position	no
Velocity	rate of change in position and direction	yes
Acceleration	rate of change in velocity	yes
Momentum	mass times velocity	yes

 bookm.msscience.com/interactive_tutor **CHAPTER STUDY GUIDE** M ◆ **29**

Identifying Misconceptions

Use the assessment as follow-up to page 6F after students have completed the chapter.

Materials protractor, paper, ruler, string

Procedure Have each student use the protractor to draw a large circle and label four

points 90 degrees apart A, B, C and D. Have them place an object at point A, and tell them the object will travel around the circle. Their mission is to find the object's distance trav-

Assess

eled and displacement at points B, C, and D. Tell them the top of the paper is north.

Expected Outcome Ways to find the distance traveled include using the string to measure the circle or using the formula for a perimeter of a circle.

Using Vocabulary

1. Both measure rate of change in position, but velocity includes a direction.

2. Both are rates of change in motion. Velocity is the rate of change in position, and acceleration is the rate of change in velocity.

3. Momentum is mass multiplied by velocity. The higher the velocity, the higher the momentum.

4. The law of conservation of momentum states that the total momentum of a group of objects is the same before and after they collide unless some outside force acts on the objects.

5. Momentum is mass multiplied by velocity. The higher the mass, the higher the momentum.

6. Mass is a measure of inertia.

7. An object always has inertia. It only has momentum when it is in motion. Both indicate how hard it is to change the object's motion.

8. Both measure rate of change in position. Instantaneous speed gives the speed at a moment in time; average speed gives the average of instantaneous speeds over a given time or distance interval.

Checking Concepts

9. D
10. A
11. C
12. C
13. D
14. B
15. C
16. D
17. C
18. C

Using Vocabulary

acceleration p. 14
average speed p. 11
inertia p. 19
instantaneous speed p. 11
law of conservation
   of momentum p. 21
mass p. 19
momentum p. 20
speed p. 10
velocity p. 13

Explain the relationship between each pair of words.

1. speed—velocity

2. velocity—acceleration

3. velocity—momentum

4. momentum—law of conservation of momentum

5. mass—momentum

6. mass—inertia

7. momentum—inertia

8. average speed—instantaneous speed

Checking Concepts

Choose the word or phrase that best answers the question.

9. What measures the quantity of matter?
   A) speed
   B) weight
   C) acceleration
   D) mass

10. Which of the following objects is NOT accelerating?
    A) a jogger moving at a constant speed
    B) a car that is slowing down
    C) Earth orbiting the Sun
    D) a car that is speeding up

11. Which of the following equals speed?
    A) acceleration/time
    B) (change in velocity)/time
    C) distance/time
    D) displacement/time

12. A parked car is hit by a moving car, and the two cars stick together. How does the speed of the combined cars compare to the speed of the car before the collision?
    A) Combined speed is the same.
    B) Combined speed is greater.
    C) Combined speed is smaller.
    D) Any of these could be true.

13. What is a measure of inertia?
    A) weight
    B) gravity
    C) momentum
    D) mass

14. What is 18 cm/h north an example of?
    A) speed
    B) velocity
    C) acceleration
    D) momentum

15. Ball A bumps into ball B. Which is the same before and after the collision?
    A) the momentum of ball A
    B) the momentum of ball B
    C) the sum of the momentums
    D) the difference in the momentums

16. Which of the following equals the change in velocity divided by the time?
    A) speed
    B) displacement
    C) momentum
    D) acceleration

17. You travel to a city 200 km away in 2.5 hours. What is your average speed in km/h?
    A) 180 km/h
    B) 12.5 km/h
    C) 80 km/h
    D) 500 km/h

18. Two objects collide and stick together. How does the total momentum change?
    A) Total momentum increases.
    B) Total momentum decreases.
    C) The total momentum doesn't change.
    D) The total momentum is zero.

Science Online bookm.msscience.com/vocabulary_puzzlemaker

Use the Exam*View*® Pro Testmaker CD-ROM to:
- create multiple versions of tests
- create modified tests with one mouse click for inclusion students
- edit existing questions and add your own questions
- build tests aligned with state standards using built-in State Curriculum Tags
- change English tests to Spanish with one mouse click and vice versa

Thinking Critically

19. Explain You run 100 m in 25 s. If you later run the same distance in less time, explain if your average speed increase or decrease.

Use the graph below to answer questions 20 and 21.

Speed Versus Time

20. Compare For the motion of the object plotted on the speed-time graph above, how does the acceleration between 0 s and 3 s compare to the acceleration between 3 s and 5 s?

21. Calculate the acceleration of the object over the time interval from 0 s to 3 s.

22. Infer The molecules in a gas are often modeled as small balls. If the molecules all have the same mass, infer what happens if two molecules traveling at the same speed collide head on.

23. Calculate What is your displacement if you walk 100 m north, 20 m east, 30 m south, 50 m west, and then 70 m south?

24. Infer You are standing on ice skates and throw a basketball forward. Infer how your motion after you throw the basketball compares with the motion of the basketball.

25. Determine You throw a ball upward and then it falls back down. How does the velocity of the ball change as it rises and falls?

Use the graph below to answer question 26.

26. Make and Use Graphs The motion of a car is plotted on the speed-time graph above. Over which section of the graph is the acceleration of the car zero?

Performance Activities

27. Demonstrate Design a racetrack and make rules that specify the types of motion allowed. Demonstrate how to measure distance, measure time, and calculate speed accurately.

Applying Math

28. Speed of a Ball Calculate the speed of a 2-kg ball that has a momentum of 10 kg · m/s.

29. Distance Traveled A car travels for a half hour at a speed of 40 km/h. How far does the car travel?

Use the graph below to answer question 30.

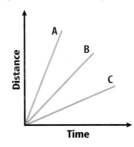

30. Speed From the graph determine which object is moving the fastest and which is moving the slowest.

Thinking Critically

19. It increases; when you divide the same distance by a smaller time, the speed increases.

20. The acceleration between 0 s and 3 s is greater because the slope of this part of the line is steeper.

21. 1 m/s²

22. The molecules reverse direction and travel at the same speed away from each other.

23. 30 m west

24. The basketball and I experience the same force in opposite directions, so we are accelerated in opposite directions. The basketball's acceleration is greater than my acceleration because its mass is lower.

25. The ball slows down as it moves upward, comes to a stop at the top of the throw, and speeds up as it falls back down

26. the horizontal section

Performance Activities

27. Check students' work. Use **Performance Assessment in the Science Classroom,** p. 145.

Applying Math

National Math Standards
1, 2, 5, 9

28. 10 kg·m/s ÷ 2 kg = 5 m/s

29. 40 km/h × 0.5 h = 20 km

30. Object A is moving fastest; object C is moving slowest.

✔ Assessment — Resources

Reproducible Masters

Chapter *Fast File* Resources
Chapter Review, pp. 37–38
Chapter Tests, pp. 39–42
Assessment Transparency Activity, p. 49

Glencoe Science Web site
Chapter Review Test
Standardized Test Practice

Glencoe Technology

Assessment Transparency
Exam*View®* Pro Testmaker
MindJogger Videoquiz
Interactive Chalkboard

Answer Sheet A practice answer sheet can be found at bookm.msscience.com/answer_sheet.

Part 1 Multiple Choice

1. C	7. B
2. B	8. B
3. A	9. B
4. A	10. D
5. D	11. C
6. D	

Part 2 Short Response

12. No; because inertia depends on mass and two objects of the same size can have different masses. An object with more mass will have greater inertia

13. 1,500 kg·m/s north

14. The sports car will be easier to stop. It has a lower mass and less inertia, so it is easier to change its motion.

15. The ball's momentum decreases because some of it is transferred to the bowling pins.

16. The ball slows down, and the pins speed up.

17. 12 m/s

18. 410 km

Part 1 Multiple Choice

Record your answers on the answer sheet provided by your teacher or on a sheet of paper.

1. What is the distance traveled divided by the time taken to travel that distance?
   A. acceleration   **C.** speed
   B. velocity   **D.** inertia

2. Sound travels at a speed of 330 m/s. How long does it take for the sound of thunder to travel 1,485 m?
   A. 45 s   **C.** 4,900 s
   B. 4.5 s   **D.** 0.22 s

Use the figure below to answer questions 3 and 4.

3. During which time period is the ball's instantaneous speed the fastest?
   A. between 0 and 1 s
   B. between 1 and 2 s
   C. between 2 and 3 s
   D. between 3 and 4 s

4. What is the average speed of the ball?
   A. 0.8 m/s   **C.** 10 m/s
   B. 1 m/s   **D.** 0.7 m/s

5. A car accelerates from 30 m/s to 45 m/s in 3.0 s. What is the car's acceleration?
   A. 10 m/s^2 **C.** 15 m/s^2
   B. 25 m/s^2 **D.** 5.0 m/s^2

6. Which of the following can occur when an object is accelerating?
   A. it speeds up   **C.** it changes direction
   B. it slows down   **D.** all of the above

7. What is the momentum of a 21-kg bicycle traveling west at 3.0 m/s?
   A. 7 kg · m/s west   **C.** 18 kg · m/s west
   B. 63 kg · m/s west   **D.** 24 kg · m/s west

Use the figure below to answer questions 8–10.

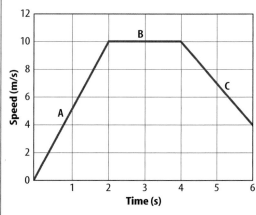

Speed v. Time

8. What is the acceleration between 0 and 2 s?
   A. 10 m/s^2 **C.** 0 m/s^2
   B. 5 m/s^2 **D.** −5 m/s^2

9. During what time period does the car have a constant speed?
   A. between 1 and 2 s
   B. between 2 and 3 s
   C. between 4 and 5 s
   D. between 5 and 6 s

10. What is the acceleration between 4 and 6 s?
    A. 10 m/s^2 **C.** 6 m/s^2
    B. 4 m/s^2 **D.** −3 m/s^2

11. An acorn falls from the top of an oak and accelerates at 9.8 m/s^2. It hits the ground in 1.5 s. What is the speed of the acorn when it hits the ground?
    A. 9.8 m/s   **C.** 15 m/s
    B. 20 m/s   **D.** 30 m/s

19. No; because even if the speed is constant, the car could be changing direction, which is also a form of acceleration.

20. The distance she traveled is 8 km. Her displacement is zero because she ends up back at her starting point.

21. Its speed is decreasing as it rises and increasing as it falls. Its velocity is changing the whole time because its speed and direction are changing. The acceleration of the ball is downward, so the ball's path turns in that direction.

22. The ball has positive acceleration when it is falling because it is speeding up. It has negative acceleration when it is rising because it is slowing down.

Part 2 | Short Response/Grid In

Record your answers on the answer sheet provided by your teacher or on a sheet of paper.

12. Do two objects that are the same size always have the same inertia? Why or why not?

13. What is the momentum of a 57 kg cheetah running north at 27 m/s?

14. A sports car and a moving van are traveling at a speed of 30 km/h. Which vehicle will be easier to stop? Why?

Use the figure below to answer questions 15 and 16.

15. What happens to the momentum of the bowling ball when it hits the pins?

16. What happens to the speed of the ball and the speed of the pins?

17. What is the speed of a race horse that runs 1500 m in 125 s?

18. A car travels for 5.5 h at an average speed of 75 km/h. How far did it travel?

19. If the speedometer on a car indicates a constant speed, can you be certain the car is not accelerating? Explain.

20. A girl walks 2 km north, then 2 km east, then 2 km south, then 2 km west. What distance does she travel? What is her displacement?

Part 3 | Open Ended

Record your answers on a sheet of paper.

Use the figure below to answer questions 21 and 22.

21. Describe the motion of the ball in terms of its speed, velocity, and acceleration.

22. During which part of its path does the ball have positive acceleration? During which part of its path does it have negative acceleration? Explain.

23. Describe what will happen when a baseball moving to the left strikes a bowling ball that is at rest.

24. A girl leaves school at 3:00 and starts walking home. Her house is 2 km from school. She gets home at 3:30. What was her average speed? Do you know her instantaneous speed at 3:15? Why or why not?

25. Why is it dangerous to try to cross a railroad track when a very slow-moving train is approaching?

Test-Taking Tip

Look for Missing Information Questions sometimes will ask about missing information. Notice what is missing as well as what is given.

Rubrics

The following rubrics are sample scoring devices for short response and open-ended questions.

Short Response

Points	Description
2	The student demonstrates a thorough understanding of the science of the task. The response may contain minor flaws that do not detract from the demonstration of a thorough understanding.
1	The student has provided a response that is only partially correct.
0	The student has provided a completely incorrect solution or no response at all.

Open Ended

Points	Description
4	The student demonstrates a thorough understanding of the science of the task. The response may contain minor flaws that do not detract from the demonstration of a thorough understanding.
3	The student demonstrates an understanding of the science of the task. The response is essentially correct and demonstrates an essential but less than thorough understanding of the science.
2	The student demonstrates only a partial understanding of the science of the task. Although the student may have used the correct approach to a solution or may have provided a correct solution, the work lacks an essential understanding of the underlying science concepts.
1	The student demonstrates a very limited understanding of the science of the task. The response is incomplete and exhibits many flaws.
0	The student provides a completely incorrect solution or no response at all.

Part 3 | Open Ended

23. After the collision, the baseball will bounce off the bowling ball and move in the opposite direction, or to the right, at a lower speed. The bowling ball will move slowly in the direction in which the baseball was originally moving, or to the left.

24. Her average speed was 2 km/0.5 h = 4 km/h. It is impossible to know her instantaneous speed at 3:15 because she may not have been walking at a constant speed. Only her average speed can be found.

25. A train has a huge mass, so its momentum is huge even when it is moving very slowly. The train's large mass makes slowing it down difficult. Even if the engineer sees a vehicle on a track, the train might not be able to stop in time.

Section/Objectives	Standards		Labs/Features
Chapter Opener	**National**	**State/Local**	**Launch Lab:** How do forces affect a ball? p. 35 **Foldables,** p. 35
	See pp. 9T–10T for a Key to Standards.		
Section 1 Newton's First Law ⏱ 2 sessions 📦 1 block 1. **Distinguish** between balanced and net forces. 2. **Describe** Newton's first law of motion. 3. **Explain** how friction affects motion.	National Content Standards: UCP.1–UCP.3, UCP.5, A.1, A.2, B.1, G.2, G.3		**Integrate Life Science,** p. 37 **Science Online,** p. 39 **MiniLAB:** Observing Friction, p. 40
Section 2 Newton's Second Law ⏱ 3 sessions 📦 1.5 blocks 4. **Explain** Newton's second law of motion. 5. **Explain** why the direction of force is important.	National Content Standards: UCP.1–UCP.3, UCP.5, A.1, A.2, B.1–B.3		**Integrate History,** p. 43 **Applying Math:** Acceleration of a Car, p. 45
Section 3 Newton's Third Law ⏱ 4 sessions 📦 2 blocks 6. **Identify** the relationship between the forces that objects exert on each other.	National Content Standards: UCP.1–UCP.3, UCP.5, A.1, B.1–B.3, F.5		**Science Online,** p. 50 **Visualizing Newton's Laws in Sports,** p. 51 **MiniLAB:** Measuring Force Pairs, p. 53 **Lab:** Balloon Races, p. 55 **Lab:** Modeling Motion in Two Directions, pp. 56–57 **Science and Society:** Air Bag Safety, p. 58

Lab Materials	Reproducible Resources	Section Assessment	Technology
Launch Lab: metersticks (2), books (3), marble	**Chapter *Fast File* Resources** Foldables Worksheet, p. 17 Directed Reading Overview, p. 19 Note-taking Worksheets, pp. 33–35	GLENCOE'S ASSESSMENT ADVANTAGE	**TeacherWorks** includes: • Interactive Teacher Edition • Lesson Planner with calendar • Access to all program blacklines • Correlations to standards • Web links
MiniLAB: flat bar of soap, flat eraser, key, hard-sided notebook	**Chapter *Fast File* Resources** Transparency Activity, p. 44 MiniLAB, p. 3 Lab Activity, pp. 9–12 Enrichment, p. 30 Reinforcement, p. 27 Directed Reading, p. 20 Transparency Activity, pp. 47–48 **Home and Community Involvement,** p. 23	Portfolio Assessment, p. 41 Performance MiniLAB, p. 40 Applying Skills, p. 41 Content Section Review, p. 41	Section Focus Transparency Teaching Transparency Guided Reading Audio Program Interactive Chalkboard CD-ROM
Need materials? Contact Science Kit at 1-800-828-7777 or www.sciencekit.com on the Internet.	**Chapter *Fast File* Resources** Transparency Activity, p. 45 Lab Activity, pp. 13–16 Enrichment, p. 31 Reinforcement, p. 28 Directed Reading, p. 21 Transparency Activity, pp. 47–48 **Mathematics Skill Activities,** p. 9	Performance Applying Math, p. 45 Applying Math, p. 48 Content Section Review, p. 48	Section Focus Transparency Virtual Labs CD-ROM Guided Reading Audio Program Interactive Chalkboard CD-ROM
MiniLAB: spring scales (2), **Lab:** balloons of different sizes and shapes, drinking straws, string, tape, meterstick, stopwatch **Lab:** masking tape, stop-watch, meterstick, spring scales (2), plastic lid, golf ball	**Chapter *Fast File* Resources** Transparency Activity, p. 46 MiniLAB, p. 4 Enrichment, p. 32 Reinforcement, p. 29 Directed Reading, pp. 20, 22 Lab Worksheets, pp. 5–6, 7–8 Transparency Activity, pp. 47–48 **Lab Management and Safety,** p. 65	Portfolio MiniLAB Assessment, p. 53 Performance MiniLAB, p. 53 Applying Math, p. 54 Content Section Review, p. 54	Section Focus Transparency Guided Reading Audio Program Interactive Chalkboard CD-ROM Video Lab

End of Chapter Assessment

Blackline Masters	Technology	Professional Series
Chapter *Fast File* Resources Chapter Review, pp. 37–38 Chapter Tests, pp. 39–42 **Standardized Test Practice,** pp. 11–14	MindJogger Videoquiz Virtual Labs CD-ROM ExamView® Pro Testmaker TeacherWorks CD-ROM Interactive Chalkboard CD-ROM	**Performance Assessment in the Science Classroom (PASC)**

Transparencies

Section Focus

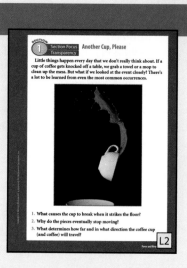

SECTION 1 Section Focus Transparency — **Another Cup, Please**

Little things happen every day that we don't really think about. If a cup of coffee gets knocked off a table, we grab a towel or a mop to clean up the mess. But what if we looked at the event closely? There's a lot to be learned from even the most common occurrences.

1. What causes the cup to break when it strikes the floor?
2. Why do the pieces eventually stop moving?
3. What determines how far and in what direction the coffee cup (and coffee) will travel?

L2

SECTION 2 Section Focus Transparency — **Loop D'loop**

Have you ever gone upside down on a roller coaster? What kept the car on the track? In the cartoon, Calvin is pulling the sled far up the hill so he can get a good start.

CALVIN AND HOBBES © Watterson. Reprinted with permission of UNIVERSAL PRESS SYNDICATE. All rights

1. Does it make a difference where Calvin begins his descent? Explain.
2. How does friction figure into Calvin's scheme?
3. How will gravity affect Calvin if he makes it into the loop?

L2

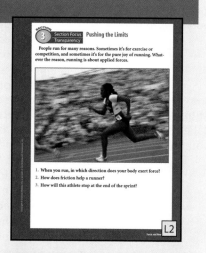

SECTION 3 Section Focus Transparency — **Pushing the Limits**

People run for many reasons. Sometimes it's for exercise or competition, and sometimes it's for the pure joy of running. Whatever the reason, running is about applied forces.

1. When you run, in which direction does your body exert force?
2. How does friction help a runner?
3. How will this athlete stop at the end of the sprint?

L2

This is a representation of key blackline masters available in the Teacher Classroom Resources. See Resource Manager boxes within the chapter for additional information.

Assessment

Assessment Transparency — **Force and Newton's Laws**

Directions: *Carefully review the diagram and answer the following questions.*

A	B	C	D

1. All of these objects have unbalanced forces acting upon them EXCEPT ___.
   A A
   B B
   C C
   D D
2. Rolling friction pushes on an object that is rolling. According to this definition, which of these examples shows rolling friction?
   F A and D
   G B and A
   H C and B
   J D and C
3. A force is a push or pull. Which force is acting on all of the objects in the diagram?
   A Static friction
   B Magnetism
   C Gravity
   D Acceleration

L2

Teaching

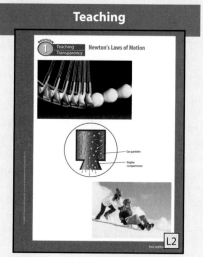

SECTION 1 Teaching Transparency — **Newton's Laws of Motion**

Gas particles

Engine compartment

L2

Key to Teaching Strategies

The following designations will help you decide which activities are appropriate for your students.

L1 Level 1 activities should be appropriate for students with learning difficulties.

L2 Level 2 activities should be within the ability range of all students.

L3 Level 3 activities are designed for above-average students.

ELL ELL activities should be within the ability range of English Language Learners.

COOP LEARN Cooperative Learning activities are designed for small group work.

LS Multiple Learning Styles logos, as described on page 6T, are used throughout to indicate strategies that address different learning styles.

P These strategies represent student products that can be placed into a best-work portfolio.

PBL Problem-Based Learning activities apply real-world situations to learning.

Hands-on Activities

Student Text Lab Worksheet

Activity Balloon Races

Lab Preview
Directions: *Answer these questions before you begin the Activity.*
1. What does Newton's third law of motion state?

2. What will you use to make a path for your rocket?

A balloon and a rocket lifting off the launch pad have something in common. Both use Newton's third law. In this experiment, you will compare different balloon rocket designs. The balloon rocket is powered by escaping air, and its motion is determined by Newton's first, second, and third laws.

What You'll Investigate
How do Newton's laws accelerate different balloon rockets?

Materials
balloons of different sizes and shapes   string
drinking straws   tape   *block
meterstick   stopwatch   *Alternate materials

Goals
• **Measure** the speed of a balloon rocket.
• **Describe** how Newton's laws explain a rocket's motion.

Safety Precautions 🥽 ✋

Procedure
1. Run a string across the classroom to make a rocket path. Leave one end loose so you can place the rockets on the string easily.
2. Make a balloon rocket according to the diagram. Don't tie the balloon. Let it run down the track. Measure the distance it travels and the time it takes.
3. Repeat step 2 with different balloons.

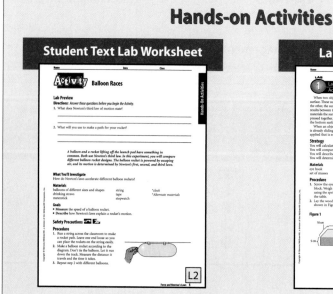

L2

Force and Newton's Laws 5

Laboratory Activities

LAB 1 Laboratory Activity — **Static and Sliding Friction**

When two objects are in contact, the molecules on one surface can attract molecules on the other surface. These surfaces are not smooth; small bumps and grooves exist. When one object slides over the other, the surfaces catch and stick as these bumps and grooves nestle together. The force that results between the surfaces is called friction. Many factors affect the force of friction, including the materials the surfaces are made from, how smooth the surfaces are, and how hard the surfaces are pressed together. For a block sliding on a level horizontal surface, the weight of the block pushes the bottom surface of the block against the horizontal surface.

When an object is at rest, static friction must be overcome to move the object. When one object is already sliding over another, sliding friction occurs. To keep the object moving, a force must be applied that is equal to the sliding friction force.

Strategy
You will calculate coefficients of static and sliding friction.
You will compare static friction to sliding friction.
You will describe the effect of weight on the force of friction.
You will determine the effect of surface area on friction.

Materials
eye hook   spring scale calibrated in newtons
set of masses   wood block (about 5 cm × 10 cm × 26 cm)

Procedure
1. Screw the eye hook into the end of the block. Weigh the wood block and eye hook using the spring scale. Record the weight in the table.
2. Lay the wood block on a flat surface as shown in Figure 1.
3. Find the force required to move the block from rest. Pull on the spring scale and notice the highest reading that occurs before the block moves. That is the static friction force.

Figure 1

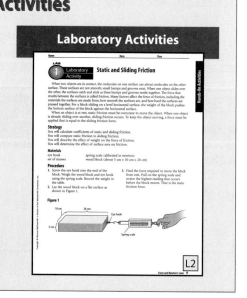

L2

Force and Newton's Laws 9

Resource Manager

Meeting Different Ability Levels

Content Outline

L2

Reinforcement

L2

Enrichment
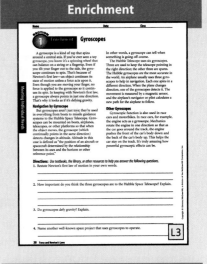
L3

Directed Reading (English/Spanish)

L1

Study Guide

L2

Reading Essentials
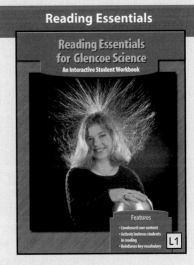
L1

Assessment

Test Practice Workbook

L2

Chapter Review

L2

Chapter Tests

L2

Science Content Background

section 1 **Newton's First Law**
Force
A force is a push or a pull. If two objects must be in contact to exert forces on each other, it is a contact force, like friction between two surfaces. Other forces, such as the gravitational force, are long-ranged forces.

Newton's First Law of Motion
According to Newton's first law of motion, a change in motion, or acceleration, is caused by a force. Because forces cause a change in motion, an object can be moving even if there are no forces acting on it. Then the object's velocity will be constant, and the object will move in a straight line with constant speed. When more than one force is acting on an object, the combination of the forces, is called the net force.

Friction
Friction is a force that acts between any two surfaces in contact. Electromagnetic forces act between the atoms and molecules on the two surfaces. These electromagnetic forces cause bonds to be formed that weld the surfaces together in some places. These welds must be broken before the surfaces can slide past each other. This is the source of static friction.

section 2 **Newton's Second Law**
Gravity
Gravity acts between all objects and causes them to be attracted to each other. According to Newton's law of universal gravitation, the gravitational force between two objects is $F = G\, m_1 m_2/d_2$, where G is the universal gravitational constant, m_1 and m_2 are the masses of the objects, and d is the distance between them. Near Earth's surface, this equation gives the force between Earth and any other object as $F = m(9.8 \text{ m/s}^2)$.

section 3 **Newton's Third Law**
Action and Reaction
According to Newton's third law, forces always act in action-reaction pairs. When one object exerts a force on another, the second object always exerts a force of the same size, but in the opposite direction, on the first object. For example, the force of gravity between two objects is exerted on both objects. The size of the force is the same on both objects, and the direction of the force on one object is opposite to the direction of the force on the other.

chapter content resources

Internet Resources
For additional content background, visit
bookm.msscience.com to:
- access your book onlineonline
- find references to related articles in popular science magazines
- access Web links with related content background
- access current events with science journal topics

Print Resources
The Spinning Blackboard, by Paul Doherty, Don Rothjen, The Exploratorium Teacher Institute, John Wiley and Sons, 1996
Hands-on Physics Activities with Real-Life Applications, by James Cunningham, Norman Herr, Jossey-Bass, 2002
Turning the World Inside Out and 174 Other Simple Physics Demonstrations, by Robert Ehrlich, Jearl Walker, Princeton University Press, 1990

IDENTIFYING ◆ Misconceptions

Find Out What Students Think

Students may think that . . .

An object at rest resists acceleration only because of friction.
Students have probably learned about friction in the past and view it as the thing that works against motion.

Demonstration

Place a small cart or car on your desk. Give it a push and give a humorous grunt to show that it is hard work to get it going. Once it is moving make the pushing seem effortless. Ask students whether they have ever had to help push a stalled car. Did they notice that it takes a lot of effort to get the car going and less effort to keep it going?

Ask students why it takes a larger force to move a stopped car than it does to push a moving car. Give students a few minutes to think about the question. Then have them share their thoughts with a partner. Ask some of the pairs to share their answers with the whole class. Finally, see if the class can come to consensus about the correct answer to this question.

Promote Understanding

Activity

Give each group a cart, a hanging spring scale that reads force in Newtons, five objects with different masses, and string. Show them how to find the amount of force needed to pull the cart as shown in the diagram below.

- Have students practice slowly pulling the cart and measuring the maximum force needed to get the cart moving. Then have them practice measuring the force needed to move the cart with constant velocity.

  Once students are proficient in these techniques, ask them to investigate how increasing the cart's mass affects these two forces.

- They will need to know or measure the mass of the cart and the masses of each of the added objects.

- Suggest students graph their data with mass on the x-axis and force on the y-axis.

After students complete the activity, discuss with them the following questions:

- What is the relationship between the mass of the cart and the maximum force needed to get the cart moving? The greater the mass, the greater the force needed.

- Why is a force needed to have the cart move with constant velocity? to overcome friction

- Why is the force needed to start the cart moving always greater than the force to keep it moving? The friction between the cart and the table is greater when the cart is at rest.

Assess

After completing the chapter, see *Identifying Misconceptions* in the Study Guide at the end of the chapter.

Chapter Vocabulary

force, p. 36
net force, p. 37
balanced forces, p. 37
unbalanced forces, p. 37
Newton's first law of motion,
  p. 38
friction, p. 38
Newton's second law of motion,
  p. 42
weight, p. 43
terminal velocity, p. 48
Newton's third law of motion,
  p. 49

Science Journal Possible answers: pulling a sled—a person supplied the force to overcome the sled's inertia; pulling an anchored boat closer to the dock—a person supplied the force to overcome the boat's inertia

PowerPoint® Presentations

This CD-ROM is an editable Microsoft® PowerPoint® presentation that includes:

- a pre-made presentation for every chapter
- interactive graphics
- animations
- audio clips
- image bank
- all new section and chapter questions
- Standardized Test Practice
- transparencies
- pre-lab questions for all labs
- Foldables directions
- links to bookm.msscience.com

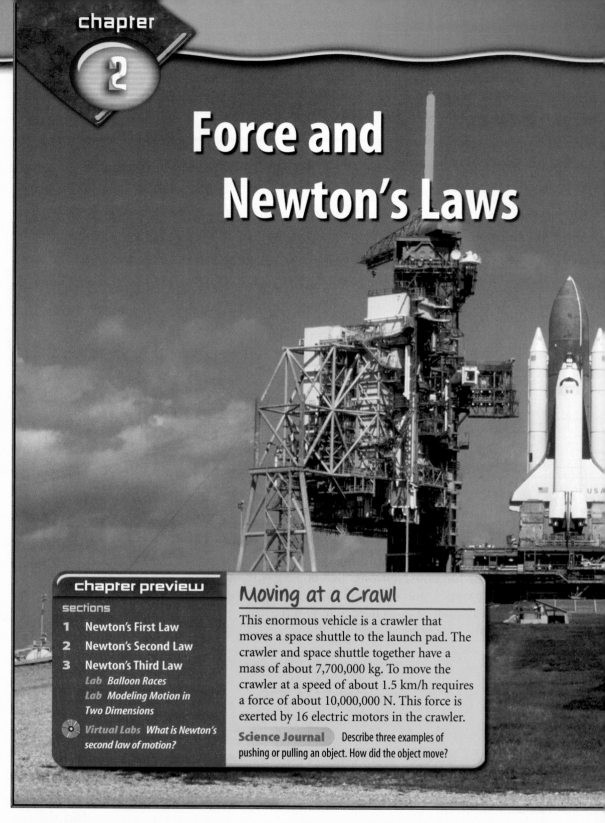

Force and Newton's Laws

chapter preview

sections

1 Newton's First Law

2 Newton's Second Law

3 Newton's Third Law
  Lab Balloon Races
  Lab Modeling Motion in
  Two Dimensions

  Virtual Labs What is Newton's
  second law of motion?

Moving at a Crawl

This enormous vehicle is a crawler that moves a space shuttle to the launch pad. The crawler and space shuttle together have a mass of about 7,700,000 kg. To move the crawler at a speed of about 1.5 km/h requires a force of about 10,000,000 N. This force is exerted by 16 electric motors in the crawler.

Science Journal Describe three examples of pushing or pulling an object. How did the object move?

Theme Connection

Systems and Interactions Newton's laws of motion form a system that can be used to determine an object's future motions. Objects interacting with each other also follow these laws. If you know the forces acting between objects, you can determine the changes in the objects' future motion.

About the Photo

Crawlers When these crawlers were built, they were the largest tracked vehicles ever made. One crawler requires eleven drivers. The electric motors are powered by huge diesel engines that use 350 liters of diesel per kilometer.

Start-Up Activities

Forces and Motion

Imagine being on a bobsled team speeding down an icy run. Forces are exerted on the sled by the ice, the sled's brakes and steering mechanism, and gravity. Newton's laws predict how these forces cause the bobsled to turn, speed up, or slow down. Newton's Laws tell how forces cause the motion of any object to change.

1. Lean two metersticks parallel, less than a marble width apart on three books as shown on the left. This is your ramp.

2. Tap a marble so it rolls up the ramp. Measure how far up the ramp it travels before rolling back.

3. Repeat step 2 using two books, one book, and zero books. The same person should tap with the same force each time.

4. **Think Critically** Make a table to record the motion of the marble for each ramp height. What would happen if the ramp were perfectly smooth and level?

 Newton's Laws Make the following Foldable to help you organize your thoughts about Newton's laws.

STEP 1 Fold a sheet of paper in half lengthwise. Make the back edge about 5 cm longer than the front edge.

STEP 2 Turn the paper so the fold is on the bottom. Then fold it into thirds.

STEP 3 Unfold and cut only the top layer along both folds to make three tabs.

STEP 4 Label the foldable as shown.

Newton's Law
| 1st Law | 2nd Law | 3rd Law |

Make a Concept Map As you read the chapter, record what you learn about each of Newton's laws in your concept map.

 Preview this chapter's content and activities at bookm.msscience.com

Purpose Use the Launch Lab to help students see the effect the steepness of a ramp has on the motion of a marble. L2 ELL LS **Kinesthetic**

Preparation Make sure that the books used are of similar thickness.

Materials 3 books, 2 metersticks, 1 marble

Teaching Strategies To make sure the initial speed of the marble is constant, use a flexible strip to make a launch ramp. Always release the marble from the same point on the ramp, and be sure there isn't a significant bump where the ramps join.

Thinking Critically

Students' data should show that the flatter the incline, the longer the distance traveled by the marble. If the ramp were perfectly smooth and flat, the marble would roll forever.

Assessment

Oral Show students a picture of a bobsled track, ski run, or slide. Ask them to identify the points at which a rider would have maximum speed. Ask students to write a sentence or two defending their choices. Use **Performance Assessment in the Science Classroom**, p. 159.

 Dinah Zike Study Fold

Student preparation materials for this Foldable are available in the **Chapter** *Fast File* **Resources**.

M ◆ 35

1 Motivate

Bellringer

INTERACTIVE CHALKBOARD PowerPoint® Presentations

Section Focus Transparencies also are available on the Interactive Chalkboard CD-ROM.

L2 ELL

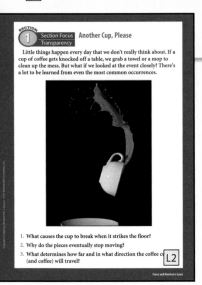

Section Focus Transparency — **Another Cup, Please**

Little things happen every day that we don't really think about. If a cup of coffee gets knocked off a table, we grab a towel or a mop to clean up the mess. But what if we looked at the event closely? There's a lot to be learned from even the most common occurrences.

1. What causes the cup to break when it strikes the floor?
2. Why do the pieces eventually stop moving?
3. What determines how far and in what direction the coffee cup (and coffee) will travel?

L2

Tie to Prior Knowledge

Forces on a Book Push a book across your desk. Ask a volunteer to describe the motion of the book. Tell students that in this section they will learn to describe the motion of the book in terms of the forces acting on it and Newton's first law of motion.

Newton's First Law

as you read

What You'll Learn
- **Distinguish** between balanced and net forces.
- **Describe** Newton's first law of motion.
- **Explain** how friction affects motion.

Why It's Important
Newton's first law explains why objects change direction.

Review Vocabulary
velocity: the speed and direction of a moving object

New Vocabulary
- force
- net force
- balanced forces
- unbalanced forces
- Newton's first law of motion
- friction

Force

A soccer ball sits on the ground, motionless, until you kick it. Your science book sits on the table until you pick it up. If you hold your book above the ground, then let it go, gravity pulls it to the floor. In every one of these cases, the motion of the ball or book was changed by something pushing or pulling on it. An object will speed up, slow down, or turn only if something is pushing or pulling on it.

A **force** is a push or a pull. Examples of forces are shown in **Figure 1.** Think about throwing a ball. Your hand exerts a force on the ball, and the ball accelerates forward until it leaves your hand. After the ball leaves your hand, the force of gravity causes its path to curve downward. When the ball hits the ground, the ground exerts a force, stopping the ball.

A force can be exerted in different ways. For instance, a paper clip can be moved by the force a magnet exerts, the pull of Earth's gravity, or the force you exert when you pick it up. These are all examples of forces acting on the paper clip.

The magnet on the crane pulls the pieces of scrap metal upward.

Figure 1 A force is a push or a pull.

This golf club exerts a force by pushing on the golf ball.

Section 1 Resource Manager

Chapter FAST FILE Resources
Transparency Activity, pp. 44, 47–48
Directed Reading for Content Mastery, pp. 19, 20
Note-taking Worksheets, pp. 33–35
Enrichment, p. 30

Lab Activity, pp. 9–12
MiniLAB, p. 3
Reinforcement, p. 27
Home and Community Involvement, p. 23

This door is not moving because the forces exerted on it are equal and in opposite directions.

The door is closing because the force pushing the door closed is greater than the force pushing it open.

Combining Forces More than one force can act on an object at the same time. If you hold a paper clip near a magnet, you, the magnet, and gravity all exert forces on the paper clip. The combination of all the forces acting on an object is the **net force.** When more than one force is acting on an object, the net force determines the motion of the object. In this example, the paper clip is not moving, so the net force is zero.

How do forces combine to form the net force? If the forces are in the same direction, they add together to form the net force. If two forces are in opposite directions, then the net force is the difference between the two forces, and it is in the direction of the larger force.

Balanced and Unbalanced Forces A force can act on an object without causing it to accelerate if other forces cancel the push or pull of the force. Look at **Figure 2.** If you and your friend push on a door with the same force in opposite directions, the door does not move. Because you both exert forces of the same size in opposite directions on the door, the two forces cancel each other. Two or more forces exerted on an object are **balanced forces** if their effects cancel each other and they do not cause a change in the object's motion. If the forces on an object are balanced, the net force is zero. If the forces are **unbalanced forces,** their effects don't cancel each other. Any time the forces acting on an object are unbalanced, the net force is not zero and the motion of the object changes.

Figure 2 When the forces on an object are balanced, no change in motion occurs. A change in motion occurs only when the forces acting on an object are unbalanced.

Biomechanics Whether you run, jump, or sit, forces are being exerted on different parts of your body. Biomechanics is the study of how the body exerts forces and how it is affected by forces acting on it. Research how biomechanics has been used to reduce job-related injuries. Write a paragraph on what you've learned in your Science Journal.

Visual Learning

Figure 2 Point out to students the force arrows in **Figure 2.** Ask volunteers to identify the force represented by each arrow. L1 ELL L2 **Visual-Spatial**

Use Science Words

Word Meaning The sum of the forces acting on an object is called the *net force.* Ask students to use a dictionary to find the meaning of the word *net.* Net is what remains after all deductions have been made. What are other familiar uses of *net* in this sense? Possible response: The net profit is the money earned after all expenses have been subtracted.

Biomechanics Researchers have used biomechanics to study such problems as repetitive strain injuries causing carpal tunnel syndrome and lower back pain.

Resisting Acceleration Some students may think that an object at rest resists acceleration only because of friction. See the beginning of this chapter for teaching strategies related to this misconception.

Curriculum Connection

Art Mobiles are based on the principle of balanced forces. Have each student make a mobile with at least three arms. The only criterion students must follow is that each arm must be balanced. Hang students' mobiles in the classroom. L2 KS **Kinesthetic**

Newton's First Law of Motion

If you stand on a skateboard and someone gives you a push, then you and your skateboard will start moving. You will begin to move when the force was applied. An object at rest—like you on your skateboard—remains at rest unless an unbalanced force acts on it and causes it to move.

Because a force had to be applied to make you move when you and your skateboard were at rest, you might think that a force has to be applied continually to keep an object moving. Surprisingly, this is not the case. An object can be moving even if the net force acting on it is zero.

The Italian scientist Galileo Galilei, who lived from 1564 to 1642, was one of the first to understand that a force doesn't need to be constantly applied to an object to keep it moving.

Galileo's ideas helped Isaac Newton to better understand the nature of motion. Newton was able to explain the motion of objects in three rules called Newton's laws of motion.

Newton's first law of motion describes how an object moves when the net force acting on it is zero. According to **Newton's first law of motion,** if the net force acting on an object is zero, the object remains at rest, or if the object is already moving, continues to move in a straight line with constant speed.

Friction

Galileo realized the motion of an object doesn't change until an unbalanced force acts on it. Every day you see moving objects come to a stop. The force that brings nearly everything to a stop is **friction,** which is the force that acts to resist sliding between two touching surfaces, as shown in **Figure 3.** Friction is why you never see objects moving with constant velocity unless a net force is applied. Friction is the force that eventually brings your skateboard to a stop unless you keep pushing on it. Friction also acts on objects that are sliding or moving through substances such as air or water.

Figure 3 When two objects in contact try to slide past each other, friction keeps them from moving or slows them down.

Without friction, the rock climber would slide down the rock.

Force due to friction

Force due to friction

Force due to friction

Force due to gravity

Friction slows down this sliding baseball player.

Force due to friction

Opposing Sliding Although several different forms of friction exist, they all have one thing in common. If two objects are in contact, frictional forces always try to prevent one object from sliding on the other object. If you rub your hand against a tabletop, you can feel the friction push against the motion of your hand. If you rub the other way, you can feel the direction of friction change so it is again acting against your hand's motion. Friction always will slow an object down.

✓ Reading Check *What do the different forms of friction have in common?*

Older Ideas About Motion It took a long time for people to understand motion. One reason was that people did not understand the behavior of friction or understand that friction was a force. Because friction causes moving objects to stop, people thought the natural state of an object was to be at rest. For an object to be in motion, something had to be pushing or pulling it continuously. As soon as the force stopped, nature would bring the object to rest.

Galileo understood that an object in constant motion is as natural as an object at rest. It was usually friction that made moving objects slow down and eventually come to a stop. To keep an object moving, a force had to be applied to overcome the effects of friction. If friction could be removed, an object in motion would continue to move in a straight line with constant speed. **Figure 4** shows motion where there is almost no friction.

Science Online

Topic: Galileo and Newton
Visit bookm.msscience.com for Web links to information about the lives of Galileo and Newton.

Activity Make a time line showing important events in the lives of either Galileo or Newton.

Figure 4 In an air hockey game, the puck floats on a layer of air, so that friction is almost eliminated. As a result, the puck moves in a straight line with nearly constant speed after it's been hit.
Infer *how the puck would move if there was no layer of air.*

✓ Reading Check

Answer different forms of friction always slow an object down

Activity

Curling Have students investigate the sport of curling and the role friction plays in it. Curling is played on ice. Each player hurls a stone at fixed goals, and uses a broom to try to clear the path in front of the stone, thereby reducing the friction. [L2] [IS] **Linguistic**

Discussion

Fundamental Forces Physicists hypothesize there are only four fundamental forces of nature. What do you think these forces are, and which kind is friction? The forces are gravitational force, electromagnetic force, the weak nuclear force, and the strong nuclear force. Friction is an example of electromagnetic force.

Caption Answer

Figure 4 It would move in a straight line, but it would slow down and stop because of friction.

Differentiated Instruction

Physically Challenged If you have a student in your class who uses a wheelchair, ask the student to explain its braking system and the role friction plays in making it work. Have students compare pushing the chair with the brake off and with it on. [L2] [IS] **Kinesthetic**

Analysis

1. The eraser had the greatest static friction since it was the last to slide. The soap had the least since it was the first to slide.
2. The key slid the fastest, it had the least sliding friction. The eraser slid the slowest, it had the most sliding friction.
3. Increase the friction by pushing the surfaces together. Decrease the friction by placing a lubricant between the surfaces.

Reading Check

Answer Static friction prevents two objects at rest from moving past one another; sliding friction slows down two objects moving against each other.

Observing Friction

Procedure

1. Lay a **bar of soap**, a **flat eraser**, and a **key** side by side on one end of a **hard-sided notebook.**
2. At a constant rate, slowly lift the end of notebook with objects on it. Note the order in which the objects start sliding.

Analysis

1. For which object was static friction the greatest? For which object was it the smallest? Explain, based on your observations.
2. Which object slid the fastest? Which slid the slowest? Explain why there is a difference in speed.
3. How could you increase and decrease the amount of friction between two materials?

Figure 5 Microscopic roughness, even on surfaces that seem smooth, such as the tray and metal shelf, causes sliding friction.

Static Friction If you've ever tried pushing something heavy, like a refrigerator, you might have discovered that nothing happened at first. Then as you push harder and harder, the object suddenly will start to move. When you first start to push, friction between the heavy refrigerator and the floor opposes the force you are exerting and the net force is zero. The type of friction that prevents an object from moving when a force is applied is called static friction.

Static friction is caused by the attraction between the atoms on the two surfaces that are in contact. This causes the surfaces to stick or weld together where they are in contact. Usually, as the surface gets rougher and the object gets heavier, the force of static friction will be larger. To move the object, you have to exert a force large enough to break the bonds holding two surfaces together.

Sliding Friction While static friction keeps an object at rest, sliding friction slows down an object that slides. If you push an object across a room, you notice the sliding friction between the bottom of the object and the floor. You have to keep pushing to overcome the force of sliding friction. Sliding friction is due to the microscopic roughness of two surfaces, as shown in **Figure 5.** A force must be applied to move the rough areas of one surface past the rough areas of the other. A sliding friction force is produced when the brake pads in a car's brakes rub against the wheels. This force slows the car. Bicycle brakes, shown in **Figure 6,** work the same way.

Reading Check *What is the difference between static friction and sliding friction?*

Differentiated Instruction

Challenge Have each student choose a part of an automobile that is affected by some form of friction. Have students state the type of friction, whether the friction decreases or increases the efficiency of the car, and how the friction can be increased or decreased to improve the performance of the car. L3 IS **Logical-Mathematical**

Visually Impaired When these students do the MiniLAB, have them place the objects at the edge of the notebook by feel. Have a sighted student lift the end of the notebook while the first student puts his or her hand at the bottom of the notebook to catch the objects as they slide. Have students repeat the process several times, until they have had a chance to discover by feel the order in which the objects slide.

Figure 6 A bicycle uses sliding friction and rolling friction.

Sliding friction is used to stop this bicycle tire. Friction between the brake pads and the wheel brings the wheel to a stop.

Wheel turning

Force due to friction

Rolling friction with the ground pushes the bottom of the bicycle tire, so it rolls forward.

Force due to friction

Rolling Friction Another type of friction, rolling friction, is needed to make a wheel or tire turn. Rolling friction occurs between the ground and the part of the tire touching the ground, as shown in **Figure 6.** Rolling friction keeps the tire from slipping on the ground. If the bicycle tires are rolling forward, rolling friction exerts the force on the tires that pushes the bicycle forward.

It's usually easier to pull a load on a wagon or cart that has wheels rather than to drag the load along the ground. This is because rolling friction between the wheels and the ground is less than the sliding friction between the load and the ground.

Check for Understanding

Kinesthetic Give each student a paper clip and a magnet. Have students move their paperclip with different types of forces and try to create situations of balanced and unbalanced forces. Have them list the different forces present as they moved their paperclip. magnetic, applied, gravity, and friction

Reteach

Types of Friction Ask students to identify the type of friction in each of the following situations: a bicycle tire rolling along a road; rolling friction a basketball player slipping on a wet spot on the floor; sliding friction a box resting on a ramp. static friction L2 LS **Logical-Mathematical**

✓ Assessment

Process Ask each student to draw an events chain concept map illustrating why the space shuttle heats up to about 3,000°C when it re-enters the atmosphere. The friction of the atmosphere against the shuttle fuselage moving at 28,000 km/h heats it up to that temperature. Use **Performance Assessment in the Science Classroom,** p. 163. P

---

section 1 review

Summary

Force
- A force is a push or a pull.
- The net force on an object is the combination of all the forces acting on the object.
- The forces acting on an object can be balanced or unbalanced. If the forces are balanced, the net force is zero.

Newton's First Law of Motion
- If the net force on an object at rest is zero, the object remains at rest, or if the object is moving, it continues moving in a straight line with constant speed.

Friction
- Friction is the force that acts to resist sliding between two surfaces that are touching.
- Three types of friction are static friction, sliding friction, and rolling friction.

Self Check

1. **Explain** whether a force is acting on a car that is moving at 20 km/h and turns to the left.
2. **Describe** the factors that cause static friction between two surfaces to increase.
3. **Discuss** why friction made it difficult to discover Newton's first law of motion.
4. **Discuss** whether an object can be moving if the net force acting on the object is zero.
5. **Think Critically** For the following actions, explain whether the forces involved are balanced or unbalanced.
   a. You push a box until it moves.
   b. You push a box but it doesn't move.
   c. You stop pushing a box and it slows down.

Applying Skills

6. **Compare and contrast** static, sliding, and rolling friction.

---

section 1 review

1. Yes; a force is needed to keep the car moving and to change direction.
2. Static friction increases if the surface is rougher or the object is heavier.
3. Because friction usually causes objects in motion to eventually stop, it seemed that rest was the natural state of matter.
4. Yes; if an object is already in motion, it will continue at a constant velocity until acted upon by an outside force.
5. a. unbalanced, box starts moving; b. balanced, box doesn't move; c. unbalanced, box slows down
6. All three types of friction act against the direction an object moves. Static friction keeps an object from moving; sliding friction is the friction between two objects moving against each other; rolling friction is the static friction between the rolling object and the surface on which it is rolling.

Newton's Second Law

as you read

What You'll Learn
- **Explain** Newton's second law of motion.
- **Explain** why the direction of force is important.

Why It's Important
Newton's second law of motion explains how any object, from a swimmer to a satellite, moves when acted on by forces.

Review Vocabulary
acceleration: the change in velocity divided by the time over which the change occurred

New Vocabulary
- Newton's second law of motion
- weight
- center of mass

Figure 7 The force needed to change the motion of an object depends on its mass.
Predict *which grocery cart would be easier to stop.*

Force and Acceleration

When you go shopping in a grocery store and push a cart, you exert a force to make the cart move. If you want to slow down or change the direction of the cart, a force is required to do this, as well. Would it be easier for you to stop a full or empty grocery cart suddenly, as in **Figure 7?** When the motion of an object changes, the object is accelerating. Acceleration occurs any time an object speeds up, slows down, or changes its direction of motion. Newton's second law describes how forces cause an object's motion to change.

Newton's second law of motion connects force, acceleration, and mass. According to the second law of motion, an object acted upon by a force will accelerate in the direction of the force. The acceleration is given by the following equation

Acceleration Equation

$$\text{acceleration (in meters/second}^2\text{)} = \frac{\text{net force (in newtons)}}{\text{mass (in kilograms)}}$$

$$a = \frac{F_{net}}{m}$$

In this equation, a is the acceleration, m is the mass, and F_{net} is the net force. If both sides of the above equation are multiplied by the mass, the equation can be written this way:

$$F_{net} = ma$$

Reading Check
What is Newton's second law?

Section 2 Resource Manager

Chapter *FAST FILE* Resources
Transparency Activity, pp. 45, 47–48
Directed Reading for Content Mastery, p. 21
Lab Activity, pp. 13–16
Enrichment, p. 31

Reinforcement, p. 28
Mathematics Skill Activities, p. 9
Physical Science Critical Thinking/ Problem Solving, p. 4

Units of Force
Force is measured in newtons, abbreviated N. Because the SI unit for mass is the kilogram (kg) and acceleration has units of meters per second squared (m/s²), 1 N also is equal to 1 kg·m/s². In other words, to calculate a force in newtons from the equation shown on the prior page, the mass must be given in kg and the acceleration in m/s².

Gravity

One force that you are familiar with is gravity. Whether you're coasting down a hill on a bike or a skateboard or jumping into a pool, gravity is at work pulling you downward. Gravity also is the force that causes Earth to orbit the Sun and the Moon to orbit Earth.

What is gravity? The force of gravity exists between any two objects that have mass. Gravity always is attractive and pulls objects toward each other. A gravitational attraction exists between you and every object in the universe that has mass. However, the force of gravity depends on the mass of the objects and the distance between them. The gravitational force becomes weaker the farther apart the objects are and also decreases as the masses of the objects involved decrease.

For example, there is a gravitational force between you and the Sun and between you and Earth. The Sun is much more massive than Earth, but is so far away that the gravitational force between you and the Sun is too weak to notice. Only Earth is close enough and massive enough to exert a noticeable gravitational force on you. The force of gravity between you and Earth is about 1,650 times greater than between you and the Sun.

Weight The force of gravity causes all objects near Earth's surface to fall with an acceleration of 9.8 m/s². By Newton's second law, the gravitational force on any object near Earth's surface is:

$$F = ma = m \times (9.8 \text{ m/s}^2)$$

This gravitational force also is called the weight of the object. Your **weight** on Earth is the gravitational force between you and Earth. Your weight would change if you were standing on a planet other than Earth, as shown in **Table 1.** Your weight on a different planet would be the gravitational force between you and the planet.

Newton and Gravity
Isaac Newton was the first to realize that gravity—the force that made objects fall to Earth—was also the force that caused the Moon to orbit Earth and the planets to orbit the Sun. In 1687, Newton published a book that included the law of universal gravitation. This law showed how to calculate the gravitational force between any two objects. Using the law of universal gravitation, astronomers were able to explain the motions of the planets in the solar system, as well as the motions of distant stars and galaxies.

Table 1 Weight of 60-kg Person on Different Planets

Place	Weight in Newtons If Your Mass Were 60 kg	Percent of Your Weight on Earth
Mars	221	38
Earth	587	100
Jupiter	1,387	236
Pluto	39	0.7

Curriculum Connection

History Galileo was the first person to understand gravity's effect on objects. Have students learn more about Galileo and his understanding of gravity. Galileo discovered that the rate at which a body falls is independent of its weight or density, as long as air resistance can be neglected. He was also the first person to use mathematics to analyze his results. [L2] [IS] **Linguistic**

Differentiated Instruction

English-Language Learners Explain to students, especially those who are more familiar with seeing their "weight" in kilograms, that weight is a force, not a mass. A pound and a Newton are both forces—these are measurements of weight. A kilogram is a measure of mass. When you step on a scale, it assumes that the acceleration is always 9.8 m/s², but it varies with altitude.

Figure 8 The girl on the sled is speeding up because she is being pushed in the same direction that she is moving.

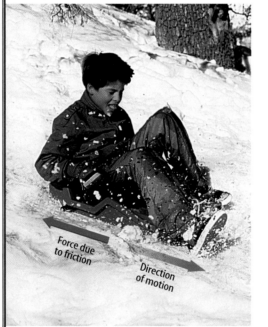

Figure 9 The boy is slowing down because the force exerted by his feet is in the opposite direction of his motion.

Force due to friction

Direction of motion

Force due to friction

Direction of motion

IDENTIFYING Misconceptions

Net Force Students might think that every force produces an acceleration in the direction in which it is applied. However, all of the forces acting on an object are added together to determine the net force on the object. The object accelerates in the direction of this net force. So, for example, if one student pushes an object west while another student pushes it north, the net force on the object will be northwest, and will cause the object to move in that direction.

Discussion

Relationships $F = ma$ describes the relationship between force and acceleration. What is the relationship between force and velocity? A force causes a change in velocity. The magnitude of the change can be calculated if you know the velocity before the force acted, the velocity after the force acted, and how long the change took. L2 IS **Logical-Mathematical**

Visual Learning

Figure 9 Point out that the net force acting on the sled is a combination of gravity pulling the sled down the hill, friction between the sled and the snow, and the force exerted by the boy's feet. Ask students which forces would cause the sled to slow down and which forces would cause the sled to speed up. Gravity would cause the sled to speed up and the other two forces would cause the sled to slow down. L2 IS **Logical-Mathematical**

Weight and Mass Weight and mass are different. Weight is a force, just like the push of your hand is a force, and is measured in newtons. When you stand on a bathroom scale, you are measuring the pull of Earth's gravity—a force. However, mass is the amount of matter in an object, and doesn't depend on location. Weight will vary with location, but mass will remain constant. A book with a mass of 1 kg has a mass of 1 kg on Earth or on Mars. However, the weight of the book would be different on Earth and Mars. The two planets would exert a different gravitational force on the book.

Using Newton's Second Law

How does Newton's second law determine how an object moves when acted upon by forces? The second law tells how to calculate the acceleration of an object if its mass and the forces acting on it are known. You may remember that the motion of an object can be described by its velocity. The velocity tells how fast an object is moving and in what direction. Acceleration tells how velocity changes. If the acceleration of an object is known, then the change in velocity can be determined.

Speeding Up Think about a soccer ball sitting on the ground. If you kick the ball, it starts moving. You exert a force on the ball, and the ball accelerates only while your foot is in contact with the ball. If you look back at all of the examples of objects speeding up, you'll notice that something is pushing or pulling the object in the direction it is moving, as in **Figure 8.** The direction of the push or pull is the direction of the force. It also is the direction of the acceleration.

Slowing Down If you wanted to slow down an object, you would have to push or pull it against the direction it is moving. An example is given in **Figure 9.**

Suppose you push a book across a tabletop. When you start pushing, the book speeds up. Sliding friction also acts on the book. After you stop pushing, sliding friction causes the book to slow down and stop.

Calculating Acceleration Newton's second law of motion can be used to calculate acceleration. For example, suppose you pull a 10-kg sled so that the net force on the sled is 5 N. The acceleration can be found as follows:

$$a = \frac{F_{net}}{m} = \frac{5\ N}{10\ kg} = 0.5\ m/s^2$$

The sled keeps accelerating as long as you keep pulling on it. The acceleration does not depend on how fast the sled is moving. It depends only on the net force and the mass of the sled.

Applying Math   Solving a Simple Equation

ACCELERATION OF A CAR A net force of 4,500 N acts on a car with a mass of 1,500 kg. What is the acceleration of the car?

Solution

1 *This is what you know:*
- net force: $F_{net} = 4,500\ N^2$
- mass: $m = 1,500\ kg$

2 *This is what you need to find:*   acceleration: $a = ?\ m/s^2$

3 *This is the procedure you need to use:*   Substitute the known values for net force and mass into the equation for Newton's second law of motion to calculate the acceleration:

$$a = \frac{F_{net}}{m} = \frac{4,500\ N}{1,500\ kg} = 3.0\ \frac{N}{kg} = 3.0\ m/s^2$$

4 *Check your answer:*   Multiply your answer by the mass, 1,500 kg. The result should be the given net force, 4,500 N.

Practice Problems

1. A book with a mass of 2.0 kg is pushed along a table. If the net force on the book is 1.0 N, what is the book's acceleration?

2. A baseball has a mass of 0.15 kg. What is the net force on the ball if its acceleration is 40 m/s²?

 For more practice visit bookm.msscience.com/math_practice

Science Journal

Forces on You Ask students to calculate their mass in kilograms and write the results in their Science Journals. Then, ask them to calculate the amount of force it would take to accelerate them from standing still to a velocity of 10 km/h in 10 seconds. $a = (v_2 - v_1)/t; v_2 = 10\ km/h = 10,000\ m/3,600\ s = 2.8\ m/s; v_1 = 0;$ therefore, $a = 2.8\ m/s \div 10\ s = 0.28\ m/s^2; F = ma,$ so the force needed will be the student's mass in kilograms times 0.28 m/s². L2 **IS** **Logical-Mathematical**

Activity

Toy Car Have students measure the mass of a toy car, then roll it down a ramp. Have one student measure the distance the car rolled down the ramp, and have another student time how long it takes the car to get to the bottom of the ramp. Add some mass to the car and repeat. Change the mass 5 times. Have students calculate the average speed for each trial by dividing the distance traveled down the ramp by the time. Ask students whether the acceleration depended on the mass of the car. No, because the average speed was the same. Ask students whether the force on each car was different. Yes, because according to $F = ma$ the force will depend on the mass if a is constant. L2 COOP LEARN **IS** **Kinesthetic**

Teacher FYI

Translational and Angular Acceleration This section explains how to calculate the acceleration of an object moving in a straight line. This is called the object's translational acceleration. Acceleration that causes an object to change direction is called angular acceleration. If the object is changing both speed and direction, its total acceleration is the sum of both its translational acceleration and its angular acceleration.

Applying Math

National Math Standards
Correlation to Mathematics Objectives
1, 2, 9

Answers to Practice Problems
1. $a = \frac{F}{m} = \frac{1.0\ N}{2.0\ kg} = .5 m/s^2$
2. $F = ma = 0.15\ kg \times 40\ m/s^2 = 6\ N$

Visual Learning

Figure 10 Ask students to identify the forces acting on the ball as it is being thrown and while it is in the air. Ask them to describe the motion of the ball in both of these situations. The force of the hand accelerates the ball forward and up until it loses contact with the hand. Ignoring air resistance, then only gravity acts on the ball, accelerating it downward. [L2] [LS] **Visual-Spatial**

Discussion

Ball on the Moon Tell students to imagine throwing a baseball on Earth, and then throwing the ball with the same force on the Moon. How would the paths of the ball differ? Why? The ball would travel farther in the horizontal direction before falling to the ground on the Moon. The ball would have the same horizontal force acting on it, but the force pulling it down would be less on the Moon because of the Moon's lower gravity. [L2] [LS] **Logical-Mathematical**

Discussion

Gravity What is the centripetal force that keeps the Moon in orbit around Earth? gravity [L2] [LS] **Logical-Mathematical**

Figure 10 When the ball is thrown, it doesn't keep moving in a straight line. Gravity exerts a force downward that makes it move in a curved path.
Infer *how the ball would move if it were thrown horizontally.*

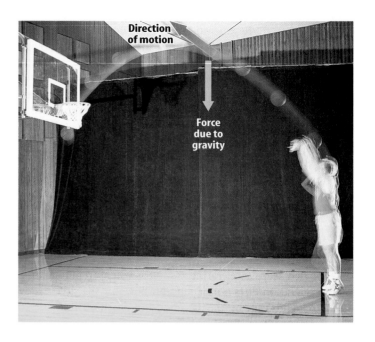

Direction of motion

Force due to gravity

Turning Sometimes forces and motion are not in a straight line. If a net force acts at an angle to the direction an object is moving, the object will follow a curved path. The object might be going slower, faster, or at the same speed after it turns.

For example, when you shoot a basketball, the ball doesn't continue to move in a straight line after it leaves your hand. Instead it starts to curve downward, as shown in **Figure 10.** The force of gravity pulls the ball downward. The ball's motion is a combination of its original motion and the downward motion due to gravity. This causes the ball to move in a curved path.

Circular Motion

A rider on a merry-go-round ride moves in a circle. This type of motion is called circular motion. If you are in circular motion, your direction of motion is constantly changing. This means you are constantly accelerating. According to Newton's second law of motion, if you are constantly accelerating, there must be a force acting on you the entire time.

Think about an object on the end of a string whirling in a circle. The force that keeps the object moving in a circle is exerted by the string. The string pulls on the object to keep it moving in a circle. The force exerted by the string is the centripetal force and always points toward the center of the circle. In circular motion the centripetal force is always perpendicular to the motion.

46 ◆ M CHAPTER 2 Force and Newton's Laws

Active Reading

Jigsaw In this collaborative learning technique, individuals become experts on a portion of a text and share their expertise with a small group, called their home group. Everyone shares responsibility for learning the assigned reading. Assign each person in each home group an expert number (1 through 5, for example). Have students gather into the expert groups that correspond to the number they were assigned. Have them read, discuss, and master chapter concepts and determine how best to teach them to their home groups. Have students return to their home groups and share the content they learned in their expert groups. Have students use the Jigsaw strategy with the material on Newton's laws of motion covered in this chapter.

Satellite Motion Objects that orbit Earth are satellites of Earth. Satellites go around Earth in nearly circular orbits, with the centripetal force being gravity. Why doesn't a satellite fall to Earth like a baseball does? Actually, a satellite is falling to Earth just like a baseball.

Suppose Earth were perfectly smooth and you throw a baseball horizontally. Gravity pulls the baseball downward so it travels in a curved path. If the baseball is thrown faster, its path is less curved, and it travels farther before it hits the ground. If the baseball were traveling fast enough, as it fell, its curved path would follow the curve of Earth's surface as shown in **Figure 11.** Then the baseball would never hit the ground. Instead, it would continue to fall around Earth.

Satellites in orbit are being pulled toward Earth just as baseballs are. The difference is that satellites are moving so fast horizontally that Earth's surface curves downward at the same rate that the satellites are falling downward. The speed at which a object must move to go into orbit near Earth's surface is about 8 km/s, or about 29,000 km/h.

To place a satellite into orbit, a rocket carries the satellite to the desired height. Then the rocket fires again to give the satellite the horizontal speed it needs to stay in orbit.

Figure 11 The faster a ball is thrown, the farther it travels before gravity pulls it to Earth. If the ball is traveling fast enough, Earth's surface curves away from it as fast as it falls downward. Then the ball never hits the ground.

Air Resistance

Whether you are walking, running, or biking, air is pushing against you. This push is air resistance. Air resistance is a form of friction that acts to slow down any object moving in the air. Air resistance is a force that gets larger as an object moves faster. Air resistance also depends on the shape of an object. A piece of paper crumpled into a ball falls faster than a flat piece of paper falls.

When an object falls it speeds up as gravity pulls it downward. At the same time, the force of air resistance pushing up on the object is increasing as the object moves faster. Finally, the upward air resistance force becomes large enough to equal the downward force of gravity.

When the air resistance force equals the weight, the net force on the object is zero. By Newton's second law, the object's acceleration then is zero, and its speed no longer increases. When air resistance balances the force of gravity, the object falls at a constant speed called the terminal velocity.

Use Science Words

Word Meaning Ask students to look up the meaning of the adjective *terminal* and use the definition they find to explain the meaning of the term *terminal velocity*. *Terminal* means "of or relating to an end, extremity, boundary, or terminus." Terminal velocity is the end velocity, or the final velocity with which a particular object falls. It is also the extreme velocity, i.e., the fastest velocity with which the object falls. L2 [LS] **Linguistic**

Make a Model

Parachutes Have each student use coffee filters to make three different models of parachutes. Ask them to make the first parachute using a single coffee filter. Then, have them add coffee filters to make larger parachutes. Have them attach small objects to the parachutes, drop them, and measure the duration of their fall. L2 [LS] **Kinesthetic**

Use an Analogy

Sails Increasing the area of an object to increase air resistance in free fall is analogous to spreading a larger sail on a sailboat to increase the force of the wind against the sail.

Fun Fact

The maximum speed (or terminal velocity) of a sky diver is about 320 km/h.

Science Journal

Skydiving Ask students to draw pictures and write descriptions of what happens from the time a skydiver jumps out of a plane until he or she lands on the ground. Ask students to use the following terms: free fall, terminal velocity, air resistance, gravity, and acceleration due to gravity. Make sure they indicate when the forces on the skydiver are balanced and when they are unbalanced.

Differentiated Instruction

Challenge A 0.15-kg baseball is pitched at 45 m/s and is struck by the bat and sent back toward the pitcher at -45 m/s. If the ball is in contact with the bat for 0.0025 s, how hard does the bat hit the ball? What forces act on the ball after the bat hits it? $F = (0.15 \text{ kg})[(45 \text{ m/s}) - (-45 \text{ m/s})] \div 0.0025 \text{ s} = 5,400$ N. After the bat hits the ball, the only forces acting on the ball are gravity and air resistance. L3 **Logical-Mathematical**

Drop the Ball

Materials sheet of paper, dense ball

Estimated Time five minutes

Procedure Display the sheet of paper and dense ball. Ask which will hit the ground first if both are dropped at the same time, and why. Have students observe as both are dropped. Then, crumple up the paper and drop it and the ball. Explain that the paper fell faster this time because its shape caused it to encounter less air resistance. L2

IS Visual-Spatial

3 Assess

DAILY INTERVENTION

Check for Understanding

Logical-Mathematical A weight lifter lifts a 150-kg weight at a maximum acceleration of 0.25 m/s² as he lifts the weight. What was the maximum force the weight lifter exerted to lift the weight? $F = (150 \text{ kg})(0.25 \text{ m/s}^2) = 37.5 \text{ N}$

Reteach

Many Forces Have students identify the forces acting on them as they sit in a car that is speeding up. Gravity pulls down, the seat pushes up; the back of the seat pushes you forward, static friction between the students' bodies and the seat keeps you from sliding off the seat. L2 IS

Logical-Mathematical

☑ Assessment

Process Have students calculate the force of Earth's gravity acting on a person with a mass of 50 kg. $F = ma = 50 \text{ kg} \times 9.8 \text{ m/s}^2 = 490 \text{ N}$ Use **Performance Assessment in the Science Classroom,** p. 101.

Figure 12 The wrench is spinning as it slides across the table. The center of mass of the wrench, shown by the dots, moves as if the force of friction is acting at that point.

Center of Mass

When you throw a stick, the motion of the stick might seem to be complicated. However, there is one point on the stick, called the center of mass, that moves in a smooth path. The **center of mass** is the point in an object that moves as if all the object's mass were concentrated at that point. For a symmetrical object, such as a ball, the center of mass is at the object's center. However, for any object the center of mass moves as if the net force is being applied there.

Figure 12 shows how the center of mass of a wrench moves as it slides across a table. The net force on the wrench is the force of friction between on the wrench and the table. This causes the center of mass to move in a straight line with decreasing speed.

section 2 review

Summary

Force and Acceleration

● According to Newton's second law, the net force on an object, its mass, and its acceleration are related by

$$F_{net} = ma$$

Gravity

● The force of gravity between any two objects is always attractive and depends on the masses of the objects and the distance between them.

Using Newton's Second Law

● A moving object speeds up if the net force is in the direction of the motion.

● A moving object slows down if the net force is in the direction opposite to the motion.

● A moving object turns if the net force is at an angle to the direction of motion.

Circular Motion

● A centripetal force exerted toward the center of the circle keeps an object moving in circular motion.

Self Check

1. **Make a diagram** showing the forces acting on a coasting bike rider traveling at 25 km/h on a flat roadway.

2. **Analyze** how your weight would change with time if you were on a space ship traveling away from Earth toward the Moon.

3. **Explain** how the force of air resistance depends on an object's speed.

4. **Infer** the direction of the net force acting on a car as it slows down and turns right.

5. **Think Critically** Three students are pushing on a box. Under what conditions will the motion of the box change?

Applying Math

6. **Net Force** A car has a mass of 1,500 kg. If the car has an acceleration of 2.0 m/s², what is the net force acting on the car?

7. **Mass** During a softball game, a softball is struck by a bat and has an acceleration of 1,500 m/s². If the net force exerted on the softball by the bat is 300 N, what is the softball's mass?

Sciencenline bookm.msscience.com/self_check_quiz

---

section 2 review

1. Check students' diagrams. The downward force of gravity is balanced by the upward force exerted by the ground. Rolling friction will cause the bike to slow down and stop.

2. The force of Earth's gravity will decrease so your weight will decrease.

3. The greater the speed, the greater the air resistance, but air resistance remains constant at terminal velocity.

4. The net force is pushing diagonally (at some angle) on the car and to the right.

5. When their forces are unbalanced.

6. $F = ma; F = 1,500 \text{ kg} \times 2.0 \text{ m/s}^2 = 3,000 \text{ N}$

7. $F = ma; m = F/a = 300 \text{ N}/1,500 \text{ m/s}^2 = 0.2 \text{ kg}$

section 3

Newton's Third Law

Action and Reaction

Newton's first two laws of motion explain how the motion of a single object changes. If the forces acting on the object are balanced, the object will remain at rest or stay in motion with constant velocity. If the forces are unbalanced, the object will accelerate in the direction of the net force. Newton's second law tells how to calculate the acceleration, or change in motion, of an object if the net force acting on it is known.

Newton's third law describes something else that happens when one object exerts a force on another object. Suppose you push on a wall. It may surprise you to learn that if you push on a wall, the wall also pushes on you. According to **Newton's third law of motion**, forces always act in equal but opposite pairs. Another way of saying this is for every action, there is an equal but opposite reaction. This means that when you push on a wall, the wall pushes back on you with a force equal in strength to the force you exerted. When one object exerts a force on another object, the second object exerts the same size force on the first object, as shown in **Figure 13.**

as you read

What You'll Learn

■ **Identify** the relationship between the forces that objects exert on each other.

Why It's Important

Newton's third law can explain how birds fly and rockets move.

⊙ **Review Vocabulary**
force: a push or a pull

New Vocabulary
● Newton's third law of motion

1 Motivate

Bellringer

Section Focus Transparencies also are available on the Interactive Chalkboard CD-ROM.
L2 ELL

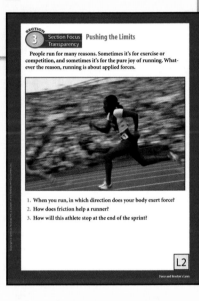

Figure 13 The car jack is pushing up on the car with the same amount of force with which the car is pushing down on the jack.
Identify *the other force acting on the car.*

Tie to Prior Knowledge

Force Pairs Ask students to describe the force exerted on them by their chairs. The force of the chairs pushes up on them, countering the force of gravity pulling them down. Ask students if they exert a force on their chairs. Explain that according to Newton's third law of motion, all forces act in pairs. They will learn more about these pairs of forces in this section.

Caption Answer
Figure 13 gravity

Section 3 Resource Manager

Chapter *FAST FILE* Resources
Transparency Activity, pp. 46, 47–48
Directed Reading for Content Mastery, pp. 20, 22
MiniLAB, p. 4
Enrichment, p. 32
Reinforcement, p. 29

Lab Worksheets, pp. 5–6, 7–8
Cultural Diversity, p. 63
Performance Assessment in the Science Classroom, p. 36
Lab Management and Safety, p. 65

Caption Answer

Figure 14 The car with the smaller mass accelerates more.

Inquiry Lab

Describing the Motion of Balls

Purpose to explore how mass, velocity, and size affect balls' interactions

Possible Materials at least ten balls having different mass and size; such as marbles, bowling, table-tennis, golf, tennis, and wiffle balls, volleyballs, raquetballs, softballs, and basketballs

Estimated Time 20 minutes

Teaching Strategies

• Students can experiment with the ways different balls interact.
• Students can plan how they want the balls to collide (one at rest, both in motion, three at a time, etc.), and then draw a diagram of the planned motion (have students indicate with arrow thickness or length the velocity of the balls).
• Student can test their plans and draw a diagram of how their balls interacted.
• Students can compare and contrast their plans with their tests.

For additional inquiry activities, see *Science Inquiry Labs.*

Figure 14 In this collision, the first car exerts a force on the second. The second exerts the same force in the opposite direction on the first car.
Explain *whether both cars will have the same acceleration.*

Science nline

Topic: How Birds Fly
Visit bookm.msscience.com for Web links to information about how birds and other animals fly.

Activity Make a diagram showing the forces acting on a bird as it flies.

Figure 15 When the child pushes against the wall, the wall pushes against the child.

Reaction force
Action force

Action and Reaction Forces Don't Cancel The forces exerted by two objects on each other are often called an action-reaction force pair. Either force can be considered the action force or the reaction force. You might think that because action-reaction forces are equal and opposite that they cancel. However, action and reaction force pairs don't cancel because they act on different objects. Forces can cancel only if they act on the same object.

For example, imagine you're driving a bumper car and are about to bump a friend in another car, as shown in **Figure 14.** When the two cars collide, your car pushes on the other car. By Newton's third law, that car pushes on your car with the same force, but in the opposite direction. This force causes you to slow down. One force of the action-reaction force pair is exerted on your friend's car, and the other force of the force pair is exerted on your car. Another example of an action-reaction pair is shown in **Figure 15.**

You constantly use action-reaction force pairs as you move about. When you jump, you push down on the ground. The ground then pushes up on you. It is this upward force that pushes you into the air. **Figure 16** shows some examples of how Newton's laws of motion are demonstrated in sporting events.

INTEGRATE Life Science Birds and other flying creatures also use Newton's third law. When a bird flies, its wings push in a downward and a backward direction. This pushes air downward and backward. By Newton's third law, the air pushes back on the bird in the opposite directions—upward and forward. This force keeps a bird in the air and propels it forward.

Teacher FYI

How Birds Fly Newton's third law helps birds to fly, but most birds would not fly very well with Newton's third law alone. Other factors such as lift (due to Bernoulli's Principle), air currents, and air resistance help birds to fly as well.

Differentiated Instruction

Physically Challenged Have a student in a wheelchair with the brakes off push against a student in rollerskates (or in another wheelchair or on a skate board) to demonstrate Newton's third law. Have them repeat with one student in motion, if desired.

Figure 16

Although it is not obvious, Newton's laws of motion are demonstrated in sports activities all the time. According to the first law, if an object is in motion, it moves in a straight line with constant speed unless a net force acts on it. If an object is at rest, it stays at rest unless a net force acts on it. The second law states that a net force acting on an object causes the object to accelerate in the direction of the force. The third law can be understood this way—for every action force, there is an equal and opposite reaction force.

◀ **NEWTON'S SECOND LAW** As Tiger Woods hits a golf ball, he applies a force that will drive the ball in the direction of that force—an example of Newton's second law.

▲ **NEWTON'S FIRST LAW** According to Newton's first law, the diver does not move in a straight line with constant speed because of the force of gravity.

▶ **NEWTON'S THIRD LAW** Newton's third law applies even when objects do not move. Here a gymnast pushes downward on the bars. The bars push back on the gymnast with an equal force.

SECTION 3 Newton's Third Law **M** ◆ **51**

Visualizing Newton's Laws in Sports

Have students examine the pictures and read the captions. Then ask the following questions.

A shot put has a much greater mass than a discus. How does Newton's second law explain why a discus can be thrown about twice as far as a shot put? Because of its greater mass, the shot put must be thrown with much more force than the discus to reach the same acceleration.

How does Newton's third law explain the direction a boat crew must move the oars in order to move the boat forward? The crew applies a backward force to the water through the oars. The water applies an equal and opposite force on the oars. This force propels the oars and thus the boat through the water.

Activity

Motion in Sports Have groups of students cut out magazine pictures showing examples of Newton's laws of motion in sports. Have them mount each picture on poster board. Ask each group to present their pictures to the class, explaining the forces at work in each example. **LS** **Visual-Spatial**

Cultural Diversity

Lacrosse The game of lacrosse is derived from an Iroquois game known as Galahs. This game involves catching and tossing a ball using a thin basket on a stick. Have students learn more about this game and describe it in relation to Newton's laws.

Discussion

Space Shuttle Two minutes after the space shuttle's launch, all fuel in the solid rocket boosters is used up, and these boosters drop off and fall back to Earth. This makes the shuttle lighter and easier to accelerate. Predict what happens to keep the shuttle accelerating smoothly. The rate of combustion in the engine is decreased.

L3 | IS | Logical-Mathematical

Visual Learning

Figure 18 Review with students the action-reaction force pairs between the gas molecules and the rocket. Tell students that the force on the rocket, called the thrust, is equal to the mass ejected per second times the velocity of the expelled gases. How is this equivalent to $F = ma$? Thrust $= (m/t)v = m(v/t) = ma = f$

L2 | IS | Logical-Mathematical

Quick Demo

Thrust in Action-Reaction

Materials CO_2 cartridge, nail to puncture cartridge, apparatus that rotates like a helicopter wing

Estimated Time five minutes

Procedure Attach the CO_2 cartridge to the end of the 'wing'. Puncture the CO_2 cartridge and release it to allow the apparatus to spin. Have the students explain what caused the spinning. Action-reaction similar to a rocket caused the motion.

Figure 17 The force of the ground on your foot is equal and opposite to the force of your foot on the ground. If you push back harder, the ground pushes forward harder.
Determine *In what direction does the ground push on you if you are standing still?*

Large and Small Objects Sometimes it's easy not to notice an action-reaction pair is because one of the objects is often much more massive and appears to remain motionless when a force acts on it. It has so much inertia, or tendency to remain at rest, that it hardly accelerates. Walking is a good example. When you walk forward, you push backward on the ground. Your shoe pushes Earth backward, and Earth pushes your shoe forward, as shown in **Figure 16.** Earth has so much mass compared to you that it does not move noticeably when you push it. If you step on something that has less mass than you do, like a skateboard, you can see it being pushed back.

A Rocket Launch The launching of a space shuttle is a spectacular example of Newton's third law. Three rocket engines supply the force, called thrust, that lifts the rocket. When the rocket fuel is ignited, a hot gas is produced. As the gas molecules collide with the inside engine walls, the walls exert a force that pushes them out of the bottom of the engine, as shown in **Figure 18.** This downward push is the action force. The reaction force is the upward push on the rocket engine by the gas molecules. This is the thrust that propels the rocket upward.

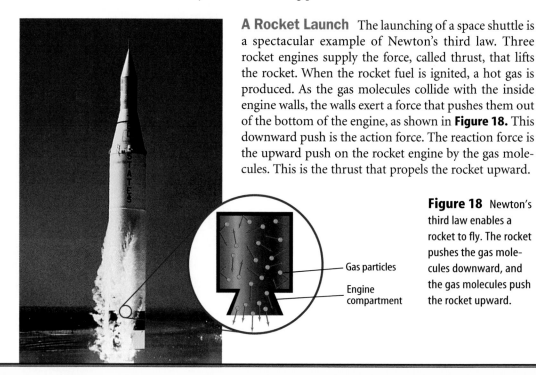

Figure 18 Newton's third law enables a rocket to fly. The rocket pushes the gas molecules downward, and the gas molecules push the rocket upward.

Gas particles

Engine compartment

Cultural Diversity

Chinese Rockets The Chinese were the first to fire rockets. Have students find out more about Chinese rockets. By the 1200s, the Chinese were filling sections of bamboo tubing with gunpowder and shooting them off as fireworks and as weapons. They knew how to weight the rockets to make them fly farther. With time, they learned to make multistage rockets, in which one set of rockets lit the next set. L3 | IS | **Linguistic**

Differentiated Instruction

Challenge Two ice-skaters push off each other. The first skater has a mass of 50 kg and is accelerated 10 m/s^2 by the push. The second is accelerated 15 m/s^2 by the push. What is the mass of the second skater? $F_1 = F_2$, so $m_1a_1 = m_2a_2$, and $m_2 = m_1a_1/a_2 = (50 \text{ kg} \times 10 \text{ m/s}^2) \div 15 \text{ m/s}^2 = 33.3 \text{ kg}$ L3 | IS |
Logical-Mathematical

Force
exerted
by scale

Weight of student

Weight of student

Figure 19 Whether you are standing on Earth or falling, the force of Earth's gravity on you doesn't change. However, your weight measured by a scale would change.

Weightlessness

You might have seen pictures of astronauts floating inside a space shuttle as it orbits Earth. The astronauts are said to be weightless, as if Earth's gravity were no longer pulling on them. Yet the force of gravity on the shuttle is almost 90 percent as large as at Earth's surface. Newton's laws of motion can explain why the astronauts float as if there were no forces acting on them.

Measuring Weight Think about how you measure your weight. When you stand on a scale, your weight pushes down on the scale. This causes the scale pointer to point to your weight. At the same time, by Newton's third law the scale pushes up on you with a force equal to your weight, as shown in **Figure 19.** This force balances the downward pull of gravity on you.

Free Fall and Weightlessness Now suppose you were standing on a scale in an elevator that is falling, as shown in **Figure 19.** A falling object is in free fall when the only force acting on the object is gravity. Inside the free-falling elevator, you and the scale are both in free fall. Because the only force acting on you is gravity, the scale no longer is pushing up on you. According to Newton's third law, you no longer push down on the scale. So the scale pointer stays at zero and you seem to be weightless. Weightlessness is the condition that occurs in free fall when the weight of an object seems to be zero.

However, you are not really weightless in free fall because Earth is still pulling down on you. With nothing to push up on you, such as your chair, you would have no sensation of weight.

Action and Reaction Have students perform or act out various activities that demonstrate action and reaction, while other students describe how the activities demonstrate Newton's third law. For example, a student might pretend to swim or row a boat, and other students would describe how pushing the water propels a person through the water as the water pushes back.

3 Assess

DAILY INTERVENTION

Check for Understanding

Visual-Spatial Working with a partner, have students draw a diagram of a satellite as it climbs to orbit level around Earth, is in orbit around Earth, and as its orbit degenerates toward Earth.

Reteach

Sports Action Ask students to cut sports action photos out of magazines or newspapers and paste them into their Science Journals. Then, ask them to identify the action-reaction force pairs that appear in each picture. **L2** **LS**
Visual-Spatial

✔ Assessment

Process Suppose a canoe has a mass of 45 kg and a person has a mass of 75 kg. If the person jumps out of the back end of the canoe into the water, will the canoe or the person have a greater acceleration? Explain. The canoe; because the forces on the canoe and the person are the same and the canoe has less mass, it will have a greater acceleration. Use **Performance Assessment in the Science Classroom,** p. 101.

Figure 20 These oranges seem to be floating because they are falling around Earth at the same speed as the space shuttle and the astronauts. As a result, they aren't moving relative to the astronauts in the cabin.

Weightlessness in Orbit To understand how objects move in the orbiting space shuttle, imagine you were holding a ball in the free-falling elevator. If you let the ball go, the position of the ball relative to you and the elevator wouldn't change, because you, the ball, and the elevator are moving at the same speed.

However, suppose you give the ball a gentle push downward. While you are pushing the ball, this downward force adds to the downward force of gravity. According to Newton's second law, the acceleration of the ball increases. So while you are pushing, the acceleration of the ball is greater than the acceleration of both you and the elevator. This causes the ball to speed up relative to you and the elevator. After it speeds up, it continues moving faster than you and the elevator, and it drifts downward until it hits the elevator floor.

When the space shuttle orbits Earth, the shuttle and all the objects in it are in free fall. They are falling in a curved path around Earth, instead of falling straight downward. As a result, objects in the shuttle appear to be weightless, as shown in **Figure 20.** A small push causes an object to drift away, just as a small downward push on the ball in the free-falling elevator caused it to drift to the floor.

section 3 review

Summary

Action and Reaction

- According to Newton's third law, when one object exerts a force on another object, the second object exerts the same size force on the first object.
- Either force in an action-reaction force pair can be the action force or the reaction force.
- Action and reaction force pairs don't cancel because they are exerted on different objects.
- When action and reaction forces are exerted by two objects, the accelerations of the objects depend on the masses of the objects.

Weightlessness

- A falling object is in free fall if the only force acting on it is gravity.
- Weightlessness occurs in free fall when the weight of an object seems to be zero.
- Objects orbiting Earth appear to be weightless because they are in free fall in a curved path around Earth.

Self Check

1. **Evaluate** the force a skateboard exerts on you if your mass is 60 kg and you push on the skateboard with a force of 60 N.

2. **Explain** why you move forward and a boat moves backward when you jump from a boat to a pier.

3. **Describe** the action and reaction forces when a hammer hits a nail.

4. **Infer** You and a child are on skates and you give each other a push. If the mass of the child is half your mass, who has the greater acceleration? By what factor?

5. **Think Critically** Suppose you are walking in an airliner in flight. Use Newton's third law to describe the effect of your walk on the motion on the airliner.

Applying Math

6. **Acceleration** A person standing in a canoe exerts a force of 700 N to throw an anchor over the side. Find the acceleration of the canoe if the total mass of the canoe and the person is 100 kg.

 Science Online bookm.msscience.com/self_check_quiz

section 3 review

1. reaction force against your weight—588 N; reaction force against the applied force—60 N
2. You push on the boat, causing it to move backward. The boat pushes forward on you, causing you to move forward.

3. The action force is the hammer pushing down on the nail. The reaction force is the nail pushing up on the hammer, causing it to stop.
4. The child will have twice the acceleraton that you have.
5. You push backward on the airliner

and the airliner pushes you forward. Because the mass of the airliner is so large, your backward push has a negligible effect on the airliner's motion.
6. $a = F/m = 700\,\text{N}/100\,\text{kg} = 7\,\text{m/s}^2$

BALLOON *RACES*

◉ Real-World Question

The motion of a rocket lifting off a launch pad is determined by Newton's laws of motion. Here you will make a balloon rocket that is powered by escaping air. How do Newton's laws of motion explain the motion of balloon rockets?

Goals

■ **Measure** the speed of a balloon rocket.
■ **Describe** how Newton's laws explain a rocket's motion.

Materials

balloons	meterstick
drinking straws	stopwatch
string	*clock
tape	*Alternate materials

Safety Precautions

◉ Procedure

1. Make a rocket path by threading a string through a drinking straw. Run the string across the classroom and fasten at both ends.

2. Blow up a balloon and hold it tightly at the end to prevent air from escaping. Tape the balloon to the straw on the string.

3. Release the balloon so it moves along the string. Measure the distance the balloon travels and the time it takes.

4. Repeat steps 2 and 3 with different balloons.

◉ Analyze Your Data

1. **Compare and contrast** the distances traveled. Which rocket went the greatest distance?

2. **Calculate** the average speed for each rocket. Compare and contrast them. Which rocket has the greatest average speed?

◉ Conclude and Apply

1. **Infer** which aspects of these rockets made them travel far or fast.

2. **Draw** a diagram showing all the forces acting on a balloon rocket.

3. Use Newton's laws of motion to explain the motion of a balloon rocket from launch until it comes to a stop.

*C*ommunicating Your Data

Discuss with classmates which balloon rocket traveled the farthest. Why? **For more help, refer to the** Science Skill Handbook.

LAB **M** ◆ **55**

Real-World Question

Purpose Students observe how to move an object from any point to another point using only two forces at right angles to each other. L2 IS **Kinesthetic**

Process Skills observe and infer, communicate, interpret data, diagram, hypothesize, compare and contrast, form a hypothesis, design an experiment, predict, separate and control variables, recognize cause and effect

Time Required 45 minutes

Possible Materials Any small ball can be used for the activity, but heavier balls, such as a golf ball, work best.

Form a Hypothesis

Possible Hypothesis Students might hypothesize that one person can move the skid in one direction and two people can move the sled diagonally by pulling at right angles to each other.

Design Your Own

MODELING MOTION IN TWO DIRECTIONS

Goals
- **Move** the skid across the ground using two forces.
- **Measure** how fast the skid can be moved.
- **Determine** how smoothly the direction can be changed.

Possible Materials
masking tape
stopwatch
* *watch or clock with a second hand*
meterstick
*metric tape measure
spring scales marked in newtons (2)
plastic lid
golf ball
*tennis ball
*Alternate materials

Safety Precautions

Real-World Question

When you move a computer mouse across a mouse pad, how does the rolling ball tell the computer cursor to move in the direction that you push the mouse? Inside the housing for the mouse's ball are two or more rollers that the ball rubs against as you move the mouse. They measure up-and-down and back-and-forth motions. The motion of the cursor on the screen is based on the movement of the up-and-down rollers and the back-and-forth rollers. Can any object be moved along a path by a series of motions in only two directions?

Form a Hypothesis

How can you combine forces to move in a straight line, along a diagonal, or around corners? Place a golf ball on something that will slide, such as a plastic lid. The plastic lid is called a skid. Lay out a course to follow on the floor. Write a plan for moving your golf ball along the path without having the golf ball roll away.

Test Your Hypothesis

Make a Plan

1. Lay out a course that involves two directions, such as always moving forward or left.

2. Attach two spring scales to the skid. One always will pull straight forward. One always will pull to one side. You cannot turn the skid. If one scale is pulling toward the door of your classroom, it always must pull in that direction. (It can pull with zero force if needed, but it can't push.)

3. How will you handle movements along diagonals and turns?

4. How will you measure speed?

Alternative Inquiry Lab

Motion in All Directions Make this Lab an Inquiry Lab by building on their experience. Have students make groups of four. Give each group masking tape to make their own course that moves through all four directions. Connect the courses and time each group in an "obstacle course" race. Make sure each group stays within the taped off area, has all four members of the group at right angles, and that the students stay in the same direction.

5. **Experiment** with your skid. How hard do you have to pull to counteract sliding friction at a given speed? How fast can you accelerate? Can you stop suddenly without spilling the golf ball, or do you need to slow down?

6. **Write** a plan for moving your golf ball along the course by pulling only forward or to one side. Be sure you understand your plan and have considered all the details.

Follow Your Plan

1. Make sure your teacher approves your plan before you start.

2. Move your golf ball along the path.

3. Modify your plan, if needed.

4. **Organize** your data so they can be used to run your course and write them in your Science Journal.

5. **Test** your results with a new route.

⊚ Analyze Your Data

1. What was the difference between the two routes? How did this affect the forces you needed to use on the golf ball?

2. How did you separate and control variables in this experiment?

3. Was your hypothesis supported? Explain.

⊚ Conclude and Apply

1. What happens when you combine two forces at right angles?

2. If you could pull on all four sides (front, back, left, right) of your skid, could you move anywhere along the floor? Make a hypothesis to explain your answer.

Communicating
Your Data

Compare your conclusions with those of other students in your class. **For more help, refer to the** Science Skill Handbook.

LAB M ◆ 57

⊚ Test Your Hypothesis

Teaching Strategies Suggest that students try moving the skid by applying forces in one direction followed by the other, and then by applying forces in the two directions at the same time.

Expected Outcome Students will find it much easier to move the skid by moving one direction at a time. Moving the skid in both directions simultaneously requires them to be more responsive to what they see happening as they pull.

⊚ Analyze Your Data

Answers to Questions

1. Students should find the new route easier than the first if they have learned from their experience.

2. The variables were the forces in each direction. The two spring scales enabled each force to be measured separately.

3. Check students' explanations.

Error Analysis Have students discuss problems they may have had moving the skid through their courses.

⊚ Conclude and Apply

1. The object moves on a diagonal between the two forces.

2. Yes; forces in these four directions can be combined to move an object along any line.

✓ Assessment

Performance Ask students to examine a computer mouse and determine how it tells the screen how to move the cursor. Most have one roller for horizontal motion, one for vertical motion, and a third roller for stability. The information from the rollers is combined to move the cursor on the screen in any direction. Use **Performance Assessment in the Science Classroom**, p. 89.

Communicating
Your Data

Encourage students to discuss how Newton's three laws affected the results of the activity. Ask them to describe how the activity would have differed if it had been done on an almost frictionless surface such as ice.

TIME) SCIENCE AND
Society
SCIENCE ISSUES THAT AFFECT YOU!

Air Bag Safety

After complaints and injuries, air bags in cars are helping all passengers

The car in front of yours stops suddenly. You hear the crunch of car against car and feel your seat belt grab you. Your mom is covered with, not blood, thank goodness, but with a big white cloth. Your seat belts and air bags worked perfectly.

Popcorn in the Dash

Air bags have saved more than a thousand lives since 1992. They are like having a giant popcorn kernel in the dashboard that pops and becomes many times its original size. But unlike popcorn, an air bag is triggered by impact, not heat. In a crash, a chemical reaction produces a gas that expands in a split second, inflating a balloonlike bag to cushion the driver and possibly the front-seat passenger. The bag deflates quickly so it doesn't trap people in the car.

Newton and the Air Bag

When you're traveling in a car, you move with it at whatever speed it is going. According to Newton's first law, you are the object in motion, and you will continue in motion unless acted upon by a force, such as a car crash.

Unfortunately, a crash stops the car, but it doesn't stop you, at least, not right away. You continue moving forward if your car doesn't have air bags or if you haven't buckled your seat belt. You stop when you strike the inside of the car. You hit the dashboard or steering wheel while traveling at the speed of the car. When an air bag inflates, you come to a stop move slowly, which reduces the force that is exerted on you.

A test measures the speed at which an air bag deploys.

Measure Hold a paper plate 26 cm in front of you. Use a ruler to measure the distance. That's the distance drivers should have between the chest and the steering wheel to make air bags safe. Inform adult drivers in your family about this safety distance.

Science online

For more information, visit
bookm.msscience.com/time

Reviewing Main Ideas

Section 1 Newton's First Law

1. A force is a push or a pull.

2. Newton's first law states that objects in motion tend to stay in motion and objects at rest tend to stay at rest unless acted upon by a nonzero net force.

3. Friction is a force that resists motion between surfaces that are touching each other.

Section 2 Newton's Second Law

1. Newton's second law states that an object acted upon by a net force will accelerate in the direction of this force.

2. The acceleration due to a net force is given by the equation $a = F_{net}/m$.

3. The force of gravity between two objects depends on their masses and the distance between them.

4. In circular motion, a force pointing toward the center of the circle acts on an object.

Section 3 Newton's Third Law

1. According to Newton's third law, the forces two objects exert on each other are always equal but in opposite directions.

2. Action and reaction forces don't cancel because they act on different objects.

3. Objects in orbit appear to be weightless because they are in free fall around Earth.

Visualizing Main Ideas

Copy and complete the following concept map on Newton's laws of motion.

Newton's Laws of Motion
- First — An object at rest will remain at rest until a force is applied
- Third — Forces act in equal, but opposite pairs
- Second — Force = (mass) × (acceleration)

 Science Online bookm.msscience.com/interactive_tutor

CHAPTER STUDY GUIDE **M** ◆ **59**

Reviewing Main Ideas

Summary statements can be used by students to review the major concepts of the chapter.

Visualizing Main Ideas

See student page.

Science Online

Visit bookm.msscience.com
/self_check_quiz
/interactive_tutor
/vocabulary_puzzlemaker
/chapter_review
/standardized_test

Assessment Transparency

For additional assessment questions, use the *Assessment Transparency* located in the transparency book.

◆ Identifying Misconceptions   Assess

Use the assessment as a follow up to page F at the beginning of the chapter.
Procedure Ask students to imagine a bowling ball and a table-tennis ball in outer space so far from other objects that they experience almost no gravity. Will the force required to move the bowling ball be greater than the force required to move the ping pong ball? Why? yes, because it has more mass How do we know friction does not play a part? In outer space there is no air and thus no friction.

Expected Outcome Students should begin to realize that a larger mass has more inertia, and thus a greater tendency to remain at rest.

Using Vocabulary

1. force—a push or pull; inertia—resistance to change in motion; weight—a force due to gravity

2. Newton's first law—a body has inertia; Newton's third law—for every force there is an equal and opposite force

3. Friction is a type of force.

4. net force—total of all forces on an object; balanced forces—net force equals zero

5. weight

6. balanced forces—object does not accelerate; unbalanced forces—object accelerates

7. friction—opposing force; weight—force due to gravity

8. Newton's first law of motion—a body has inertia; Newton's second law—*a = F/m*

9. friction—opposing force; unbalanced force—accelerates an object

10. net force—sum of forces; Newton's third law—for every force there is an equal and opposite force

Checking Concepts

11. B	14. C	17. D
12. C	15. A	18. D
13. B	16. B	

Thinking Critically

19. acceleration due to gravity increases the speed

20. Yes; the ball changed direction

21. Because Earth is so massive, the forces people exert on it cause very little acceleration.

22. The car is held on the hill by static friction. When the car moves at a constant speed, rolling friction and air resistance balance the force exerted on the wheels by the motor. When the brakes are applied, sliding friction between the brake pads and the wheels slows down the car.

Using Vocabulary

balanced forces p. 37	Newton's second law of
center of mass p. 48	motion p. 42
force p. 36	Newton's third law of
friction p. 38	motion p. 49
net force p. 37	unbalanced forces p. 37
Newton's first law of	weight p. 43
motion p. 38	

Explain the differences between the terms in the following sets.

1. force—inertia—weight

2. Newton's first law of motion—Newton's third law of motion

3. friction—force

4. net force—balanced forces

5. weight—weightlessness

6. balanced forces—unbalanced forces

7. friction—weight

8. Newton's first law of motion—Newton's second law of motion

9. friction—unbalanced force

10. net force—Newton's third law of motion

Checking Concepts

Choose the word or phrase that best answers the question.

11. Which of the following changes when an unbalanced force acts on an object?
   A) mass
   C) inertia
   B) motion
   D) weight

12. Which of the following is the force that slows a book sliding on a table?
   A) gravity
   B) static friction
   C) sliding friction
   D) inertia

Use the illustration below to answer question 13.

13. Two students are pushing on the left side of a box and one student is pushing on the right. The diagram above shows the forces they exert. Which way will the box move?
   A) up
   C) down
   B) left
   D) right

14. What combination of units is equivalent to the newton?
   A) m/s^2
   C) $kg \cdot m/s^2$
   B) $kg \cdot m/s$
   D) kg/m

15. Which of the following is a push or a pull?
   A) force
   C) acceleration
   B) momentum
   D) inertia

16. An object is accelerated by a net force in which direction?
   A) at an angle to the force
   B) in the direction of the force
   C) in the direction opposite to the force
   D) Any of these is possible.

17. You are riding on a bike. In which of the following situations are the forces acting on the bike balanced?
   A) You pedal to speed up.
   B) You turn at constant speed.
   C) You coast to slow down.
   D) You pedal at constant speed.

18. Which of the following has no direction?
   A) force
   C) weight
   B) acceleration
   D) mass

ScienceOnline bookm.msscience.com/vocabulary_puzzlemaker

Use the ExamView® Pro Testmaker CD-ROM to:
- create multiple versions of tests
- create modified tests with one mouse click for inclusion students
- edit existing questions and add your own questions
- build tests aligned with state standards using built-in State Curriculum Tags
- change English tests to Spanish with one mouse click and vice versa

Thinking Critically

19. **Explain** why the speed of a sled increases as it moves down a snow-covered hill, even though no one is pushing on the sled.

20. **Explain** A baseball is pitched east at a speed of 40 km/h. The batter hits it west at a speed of 40 km/h. Did the ball accelerate?

21. **Form a Hypothesis** Frequently, the pair of forces acting between two objects are not noticed because one of the objects is Earth. Explain why the force acting on Earth isn't noticed.

22. **Identify** A car is parked on a hill. The driver starts the car, accelerates until the car is driving at constant speed, drives at constant speed, and then brakes to put the brake pads in contact with the spinning wheels. Explain how static friction, sliding friction, rolling friction, and air resistance are acting on the car.

23. **Draw Conclusions** You hit a hockey puck and it slides across the ice at nearly a constant speed. Is a force keeping it in motion? Explain.

24. **Infer** Newton's third law describes the forces between two colliding objects. Use this connection to explain the forces acting when you kick a soccer ball.

25. **Recognize Cause and Effect** Use Newton's third law to explain how a rocket accelerates upon takeoff.

26. **Predict** Two balls of the same size and shape are dropped from a helicopter. One ball has twice the mass of the other ball. On which ball will the force of air resistance be greater when terminal velocity is reached?

Use the figure below to answer question 27.

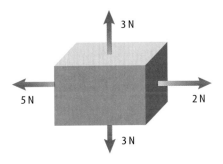

27. **Interpreting Scientific Illustrations** Is the force on the box balanced? Explain.

Performance Activities

28. **Oral Presentation** Research one of Newton's laws of motion and compose an oral presentation. Provide examples of the law. You might want to use a visual aid.

29. **Writing in Science** Create an experiment that deals with Newton's laws of motion. Document it using the following subject heads: *Title of Experiment, Partners' Names, Hypothesis, Materials, Procedures, Data, Results,* and *Conclusion.*

Applying Math

30. **Acceleration** If you exert a net force of 8 N on a 2-kg object, what will its acceleration be?

31. **Force** You push against a wall with a force of 5 N. What is the force the wall exerts on your hands?

32. **Net Force** A 0.4-kg object accelerates at 2 m/s². Find the net force.

33. **Friction** A 2-kg book is pushed along a table with a force of 4 N. Find the frictional force on the book if the book's acceleration is 1.5 m/s².

 Science Online bookm.msscience.com/chapter_review

CHAPTER REVIEW M ◆ **61**

23. When the puck is sliding on the ice, there is no force being exerted on the puck to keep it moving forward. Instead, inertia keeps the puck moving forward. Friction between the puck and the ice gradually slows the puck down.

24. When the foot connects with the ball, the foot accelerates the ball forward (ball has low mass) and the ball accelerates the foot backward, slowing its forward motion somewhat (foot attached to body has high mass).

25. The fuel inside the rocket explodes. The gas particles that are formed push against the rocket, and the rocket pushes against them. This pushes the rocket up and the gases out the bottom.

26. the ball with the greater mass

27. No; the net force is pushing to the left with a strength of 3 N

Performance Activities

28. Check students' work. Use **PASC,** p. 143.

29. Check students' work. Use **PASC,** p. 159.

Applying Math

National Math Standards
1, 2, 9

30. $a = F/m = 8\,N/2\,kg = 4\,m/s^2$

31. 5 N

32. $F = ma = 0.4\,kg \times 2\,m/s^2 = 0.8\,N$

33. $F = ma = (2\,kg)(1.5\,m/s^2) = 3\,N$; $4\,N - 3\,N = 1\,N$

☑ **Assessment** **Resources**

📁 **Reproducible Masters**
Chapter *Fast File* Resources
 Chapter Review, pp. 39–40
 Chapter Tests, pp. 41–44
 Assessment Transparency Activity, p. 51
Glencoe Science Web site
 Chapter Review Test
 Standardized Test Practice

Glencoe Technology
 Assessment Transparency
 Exam*View*® Pro Testmaker
 MindJogger Videoquiz
 Interactive Chalkboard

FAST FILE

Answer Sheet A practice answer sheet can be found at bookm.msscience.com/answer_sheet.

SAMPLE

Part 1 Multiple Choice

1. B **4.** B **7.** C
2. D **5.** B **8.** C
3. C **6.** A

Part 2 Short Response

9. Newton's first law of motion

10. gravity and air resistance

11. 45.7 N

12. The forces are equal and opposite.

13. The accelerations will vary due to the masses of the vehicles.

14. No, acceleration does not depend on the speed of an object. It depends only on the net force and the mass of the object.

15. 0.78 kg

16. $[(9.8 \text{ m/s}^2) \times (1.4 \text{ kg})] - 2.5 \text{ N} = 11.2 \text{ N}$

17. speed up, slow down, or change direction

Part 1 Multiple Choice

Record your answers on the answer sheet provided by your teacher or on a sheet of paper.

1. Which of the following descriptions of gravitational force is *not* true?
A. It depends on the mass of objects.
B. It is a repulsive force.
C. It depends on the distance between objects.
D. It exists between all objects.

Use the table below to answer questions 2 and 3.

Mass of Common Objects	
Object	**Mass (g)**
Cup	380
Book	1,100
Can	240
Ruler	25
Stapler	620

2. Which object would have an acceleration of 0.89 m/s² if you pushed on it with a force of 0.55 N?
A. book **C.** ruler
B. can **D.** stapler

3. Which object would have the greatest acceleration if you pushed on it with a force of 8.2 N?
A. can **C.** ruler
B. stapler **D.** book

Test-Taking Tip

Check Symbols Be sure you understand all symbols on a table or graph before answering any questions about the table or graph.

Question 3 The mass of the objects are given in grams, but the force is given in newtons which is a kg·m/s². The mass must be converted from grams to kilograms.

62 ◆ M STANDARDIZED TEST PRACTICE

---

4. What is the weight of a book that has a mass of 0.35 kg?
A. 0.036 N **C.** 28 N
B. 3.4 N **D.** 34 N

5. If you swing an object on the end of a string around in a circle, the string pulls on the object to keep it moving in a circle. What is the name of this force?
A. inertial **C.** resistance
B. centripetal **D.** gravitational

6. What is the acceleration of a 1.4-kg object if the gravitational force pulls downward on it, but air resistance pushes upward on it with a force of 2.5 N?
A. 11.6 m/s², downward
B. 11.6 m/s², upward
C. 8.0 m/s², downward
D. 8.0 m/s², upward

Use the figure below to answer questions 7 and 8.

7. The figure above shows the horizontal forces that act on a box that is pushed from the left with a force of 12 N. What force is resisting the horizontal motion in this illustration?
A. friction **C.** inertia
B. gravity **D.** momentum

8. What is the acceleration of the box?
A. 27 m/s² **C.** 4.3 m/s²
B. 4.8 m/s² **D.** 0.48 m/s²

Part 3 Open Ended

18. The force of gravity causes the astronauts and the spaceship to fall toward Earth with the same acceleration. Because the spaceship doesn't exert a force on the astronauts, their weight relative to the spaceship is zero and they are able to float. However, the weight of the astronauts relative to Earth is their mass multiplied by the gravitational pull they experience from Earth.

19. A satellite's forward motion tends to keep it traveling in a straight line, but gravity continually pulls it in toward Earth. Satellites move so fast horizontally that Earth's surface curves downward at the same rate that the satellites fall downward.

20. The initial force on the ball causes it to move outward and upward. The force of gravity on the ball pulls it downward. These forces combined cause the ball to travel along a curved path.

21. If the ball were thrown harder, the initial direction of the ball would be the same, but it would travel

Part 2 | Short Response/Grid In

Record your answers on the answer sheet provided by your teacher or on a sheet of paper.

9. A skater is coasting along the ice without exerting any apparent force. Which law of motion explains the skater's ability to continue moving?

10. After a soccer ball is kicked into the air, what force or forces are acting on it?

11. What is the force on an 8.55-kg object that accelerates at 5.34 m/s^2.

Use the figure below to answer questions 12 and 13.

12. Two bumper cars collide and then move away from each other. How do the forces the bumper cars exert on each other compare?

13. After the collision, determine whether both bumper cars will have the same acceleration.

14. Does acceleration depend on the speed of an object? Explain.

15. An object acted on by a force of 2.8 N accelerates 3.6 m/s^2. What is the mass of the object?

16. What is the acceleration a 1.4-kg object falling through the air if the force of air on the object is 2.5 N?

17. Name three ways you could accelerate if you were riding a bicycle.

Part 3 | Open Ended

Record your answers on a sheet of paper.

18. When astronauts orbit Earth, they float inside the spaceship because of weightlessness. Explain this effect.

19. Describe how satellites are able to remain in orbit around Earth.

Use the figure below to answer questions 20 and 21.

20. The figure above shows the path a ball thrown into the air follows. What causes the ball to move along a curved path?

21. What effect would throwing the ball harder have on the ball's path? Explain.

22. How does Newton's second law determine the motion of a book as you push it across a desktop?

23. A heavy box sits on a sidewalk. If you push against the box, the box moves in the direction of the force. If the box is replaced with a ball of the same mass, and you push with the same force against the ball, will it have the same acceleration as the box? Explain.

24. According to Newton's third law of motion, a rock sitting on the ground pushes against the ground, and the ground pushes back against the rock with an equal force. Explain why this force doesn't cause the rock to accelerate upward from the ground according to Newton's second law.

24. Newton's second law states that an object's acceleration equals the force on the object divided by the object's mass. However, this refers to the *net* force on the object. The rock experiences an upward force from the ground and an equal downward force due to gravity. The net force on the rock is zero. According to Newton's second law, the acceleration of the rock is therefore zero.

Rubrics

For more help evaluating open-ended assessment questions, see the rubric on p. 4T.

faster. Gravity would still pull the ball downward with the same force. However, the ball would travel a greater horizontal distance in the time required for the ball to fall down. The ball's path would be a wider arc.

22. Newton's second law describes how to calculate the acceleration of an object if you know the object's mass and the force acting on the object. The book has no vertical motion because the gravitational force acting down on it equals the upward force on the book by the desktop. The horizontal acceleration of the book equals the mass of the book divided by the force you exert upon the book.

23. No, the ball will have a greater acceleration. The sliding friction resisting the motion of the box is greater than the rolling friction resisting the motion of the ball. The box therefore has a smaller net force, resulting in a smaller acceleration.

Section/Objectives	Standards		Labs/Features
Chapter Opener	**National**	**State/Local**	**Launch Lab:** Forces and Air Pressure, p. 65 **Foldables,** p. 65
	See pp. 9T–10T for a Key to Standards.		
Section 1 Pressure ⏱ 2 sessions 🗂 1 block 1. **Define and calculate** pressure. 2. **Model** how pressure varies in a fluid.	National Content Standards: UCP.1–UCP.3, UCP.5, A.1, A.2, B.1, B.2, D.1		**Science Online,** p. 67 **Applying Math:** Calculating Pressure, p. 67 **MiniLAB:** Interpreting Footprints, p. 68 **Integrate Astronomy,** p. 69 **Visualizing Pressure at Varying Elevations,** p. 72
Section 2 Why do objects float? ⏱ 2 sessions 🗂 1 block 3. **Explain** how the pressure in a fluid produces a buoyant force. 4. **Define** density. 5. **Explain** floating and sinking using Archimedes' principle.	National Content Standards: UCP.1–UCP.3, UCP.5, A.1, A.2, B.1, B.2, G.3		**Integrate Career,** p. 78 **Applying Science:** Layering Liquids, p. 78 **Lab:** Measuring Buoyant Force, p. 81
Section 3 Doing Work with Fluids ⏱ 4 sessions 🗂 2 blocks 6. **Explain** how forces are transmitted through fluids. 7. **Describe** how a hydraulic system increases force. 8. **Describe** Bernoulli's principle.	National Content Standards: UCP.1–UCP.3, UCP.5, A.1, A.2, B.1, B.2, F.3		**Science Online,** p. 84 **MiniLAB:** Observing Bernoulli's Principle, p. 85 **Lab:** Barometric Pressure and Weather, pp. 88–89 **Science and Language Arts:** Hurricane, p. 90

Lab Materials	Reproducible Resources	Section Assessment	Technology
Launch Lab: water, drinking straw, cup or glass for water	**Chapter FAST FILE Resources** Foldables Worksheet, p. 17 Directed Reading Overview, p. 19 Note-taking Worksheets, pp. 33–35	GLENCOE'S ASSESSMENT ADVANTAGE	TeacherWorks includes: • Interactive Teacher Edition • Lesson Planner with calendar • Access to all program blacklines • Correlations to standards • Web links
MiniLAB: an area of dirt, sand or snow; metric ruler *Need materials?* Contact Science Kit at 1-800-828-7777 or www.sciencekit.com on the Internet.	**Chapter FAST FILE Resources** Transparency Activity, p. 44 MiniLAB, p. 3 Lab Activity, pp. 9–12 Enrichment, p. 30 Reinforcement, p. 27 Directed Reading, p. 20 **Life Science Critical Thinking/ Problem Solving,** p. 14	**Portfolio** Active Reading, p. 69 **Performance** Applying Math, p. 67 MiniLAB, p. 68 Applying Math, p. 73 **Content** Section Review, p. 73	Section Focus Transparency Guided Reading Audio Program Interactive Chalkboard CD-ROM
Lab: aluminum pan, spring scale, 500-mL beaker, graduated cylinder, funnel, metal object	**Chapter FAST FILE Resources** Transparency Activity, p. 45 Enrichment, p. 31 Reinforcement, p. 28 Directed Reading, p. 20 Lab Worksheet, pp. 5–6 **Reading and Writing Skill Activities,** p. 19	**Portfolio** Curriculum Connection, p. 79 **Performance** Applying Science, p. 78 Applying Math, p. 80 **Content** Section Review, p. 80	Section Focus Transparency Virtual Labs CD-ROM Guided Reading Audio Program Interactive Chalkboard CD-ROM Video Lab
MiniLAB: string, plastic spoon, stream of water from a faucet **Lab:** no materials needed	**Chapter FAST FILE Resources** Transparency Activity, p. 46 MiniLAB, p. 4 Lab Activity, pp. 13–16 Enrichment, p. 32 Reinforcement, p. 29 Directed Reading, pp. 21, 22 Lab Worksheet, pp. 7–8 Transparency Activity, pp. 47–48 **Lab Management and Safety,** p. 38	**Portfolio** Assessment, p. 85 **Performance** MiniLAB, p. 85 Applying Math, p. 87 **Content** Section Review, p. 87	Section Focus Transparency Teaching Transparency Guided Reading Audio Program Interactive Chalkboard CD-ROM

GLENCOE'S ASSESSMENT ADVANTAGE	End of Chapter Assessment		
Blackline Masters	**Technology**	**Professional Series**	
Chapter FAST FILE Resources Chapter Review, pp. 37–38 Chapter Tests, pp. 39–42 **Standardized Test Practice,** pp. 15–18	MindJogger Videoquiz Virtual Labs CD-ROM ExamView® Pro Testmaker TeacherWorks CD-ROM Interactive Chalkboard CD-ROM	**Performance Assessment in the Science Classroom (PASC)**	

Transparencies

Section Focus

SECTION 1 Section Focus Transparency Well, This Is Deep

Have you ever felt your ears pop as you reached for the bottom at the deep end of a pool? This happens because factors affecting your body change as you go deeper. In the ocean, divers need to be aware of this, too. For the deepest dives, a hard suit, like the one being tested below, is necessary for protection.

1. When might people feel their ears pop?
2. Describe the two diving suits you see in the picture. What advantages are there to the hard suit? Disadvantages?
3. How might conditions change as you dive far beneath the surface of the sea? How might conditions change as you climb a mountain?

L2

SECTION 2 Section Focus Transparency Connecticut floats?

Icebergs can be pretty big, but even the largest icebergs float. The pieces shown below were once part of an iceberg roughly the size of Connecticut! This monster iceberg, known as B15, broke off the Ross Ice Shelf in Antarctica.

1. Does shape affect whether or not an object will float? Illustrate your answer with an example.
2. What happens to the water level when a person gets into a bath tub?
3. How is a blimp filled with helium gas similar to an iceberg floating in the ocean?

L2

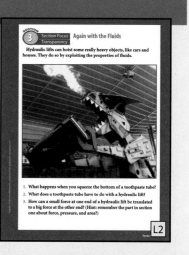

SECTION 3 Section Focus Transparency Again with the Fluids

Hydraulic lifts can hoist some really heavy objects, like cars and houses. They do so by exploiting the properties of fluids.

1. What happens when you squeeze the bottom of a toothpaste tube?
2. What does a toothpaste tube have to do with a hydraulic lift?
3. How can a small force at one end of a hydraulic lift be translated to a big force at the other end? (Hint: remember the part in section one about force, pressure, and area?)

L2

This is a representation of key blackline masters available in the Teacher Classroom Resources. See Resource Manager boxes within the chapter for additional information.

Assessment

Assessment Transparency Forces and Fluids

Directions: *Carefully review the diagram and answer the following questions.*

1. Archimedes' principle states that the buoyant force on an object is equal to the weight of the fluid that object displaces. If a scientist puts an ice cube into one of the graduated cylinders of water and the water level increases by 5 mL, then _____.
   A the ice cube would decrease the pressure exerted by the graduated cylinder of water
   B the ice cube would take a longer time to melt than if it were placed on the table
   C the water could exert more pressure on the side of the ice cube than on the bottom
   D the scientist could conclude that the buoyant force on the ice cube is equal to the weight of 5 mL of water
2. Each graduated cylinder contains 50 mL of water. In which cylinder would a marble on the bottom experience the greatest pressure?
   F cylinder A   G cylinder B   H cylinder C   J cylinder D

L2

Teaching

SECTION 3 Teaching Transparency Diagram of a Wing

Action Force

Reaction Force

L2

Key to Teaching Strategies

The following designations will help you decide which activities are appropriate for your students.

L1 Level 1 activities should be appropriate for students with learning difficulties.

L2 Level 2 activities should be within the ability range of all students.

L3 Level 3 activities are designed for above-average students.

ELL ELL activities should be within the ability range of English Language Learners.

COOP LEARN Cooperative Learning activities are designed for small group work.

LS Multiple Learning Styles logos, as described on page 6T, are used throughout to indicate strategies that address different learning styles.

P These strategies represent student products that can be placed into a best-work portfolio.

PBL Problem-Based Learning activities apply real-world situations to learning.

Hands-on Activities

Student Text Lab Worksheet

Activity Measuring Buoyant Force

Lab Preview
Directions: *Answer these questions before you begin the Activity.*
1. What will you measure with the spring scale in this activity?

2. How do you calculate the weight of the displaced water?

Because the buoyant force is an upward force, the weight of an object in a fluid is decreased. In this activity, you will measure the buoyant force on an object and compare it to the weight of the water displaced.

What You'll Investigate
How is the buoyant force related to the weight of the water that an object displaces?

Materials
aluminum pan   graduated cylinder
spring scale   funnel
500-mL beaker   metal object

Goals
- **Measure** the buoyant force on an object.
- **Compare** the buoyant force to the weight of the water displaced by the object.

Safety Precautions

Procedure
1. Place the beaker in the aluminum pan and fill the beaker to the brim with water.
2. Hang the object from the spring scale and record its weight.
3. With the object hanging from the spring scale, completely submerge the object in the water. The object should not be touching the bottom or the sides of the beaker.
4. Record the object's weight while it is in the water in the Data and Observations section. Calculate the buoyant force by subtracting the object's weight in water from its weight out of water.
5. Use the funnel to carefully pour the water from the pan into the graduated cylinder. Record the volume of this water in cm³.
6. **Calculate** the weight of the water displaced by multiplying the volume of the water by 0.0098 N.

L2

Laboratory Activities

LAB 1 Laboratory Activity Atmospheric Pressure

You live at the bottom of an "ocean" of air. Just as water has weight, air also has weight. The weight of the air above you causes atmospheric pressure. About 1 kg of air presses on each cm² of your body. For an average-size person, the net downward force due to atmospheric pressure can be equal to the weight of several small automobiles pressing against his or her body. In this activity, you can examine how strong atmospheric pressure can be.

Strategy
You will observe the effects of air pressure.
You will describe your observation in terms of differences in air pressure.

Materials
2 wide-mouth jars
2 plastic sandwich bags
masking tape
small suction cup
water
plastic drinking glass
clay
bowl
large basin or sink

Procedure
Part A
1. Place your hand inside a plastic bag. Then push the bag into a wide-mouth jar. Push the bag open inside the jar so there is little air space between the jar and the bag.
2. Turn back the open ends of the bag over the edge of the jar mouth, as shown in Figure 1. Tape the edges of the bag to the jar, being careful to completely seal any openings.
3. Reach into the jar and take hold of the plastic bag. Pull on the bag to turn it inside out and bring the bottom of the bag out of the jar. Observe what happens and record your observations in Table 1.

Figure 1 — Tape

Figure 2 — Tape

Part B
4. Blow a little air into a second plastic bag. Hold the bag upside-down over the mouth of a second wide-mouth jar as the opening of the bag just covers the neck of the jar, as shown in Figure 2.

L2

Resource Manager

Meeting Different Ability Levels

Content Outline

Reinforcement

Enrichment

Directed Reading (English/Spanish)

Study Guide

Reading Essentials
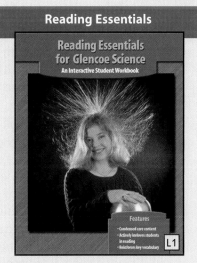

Assessment

Test Practice Workbook

Chapter Review

Chapter Tests

Science Content Background

section 1 Pressure

What is pressure?

Forces exerted on an object sometimes can cause the object to deform. For example, the force exerted by your hand on a thin piece of metal can cause it to bend or deform. For most materials the deformation depends not on the force exerted, but on the pressure exerted. The pressure on an object is the force exerted on the object divided by the area over which the force is exerted, or $P = F/A$. By making the area over which the force is exerted very small, a large pressure can be exerted. For example, an ice pick has a narrow tip with a small area. This enables an ice pick to exert a large pressure on an ice surface that can cause the ice to crack.

Pressure in Fluid

In any material the atoms and molecules that make up the material are in constant motion. In a fluid, these particles can move from place to place. When a fluid is placed in a container, particles continually collide with the surfaces of the container. Each collision causes a force to be exerted on the container surface. The total force on a surface due to the collisions is the sum of forces exerted by all the collisions. Because the particles are moving randomly, the components of the forces in all directions—except those perpendicular to the surface—cancel out. As a result, the force and the pressure exerted by the fluid is always perpendicular to the surface, regardless of the orientation of the surface. This is true for any surface placed in the fluid.

Atmospheric Pressure

Atmospheric pressure on a surface is caused by the weight of the atmosphere above the surface. Just as for any other fluid, the atmospheric pressure on a surface is perpendicular to the surface. The atmosphere becomes more diffuse with altitude. At sea level, the weight of the atmosphere above a surface with an area of 1 m² is about 100,000 N, corresponding to a pressure of about 100,000 Pa. The pressure exerted by water at a depth of only about 10 m is equal to atmospheric pressure at sea level.

section 2 Why do objects float?

The Buoyant Force

An upward force, called the buoyant force, acts on an object placed in a fluid. The buoyant force results from the increase in pressure with depth in the fluid. The pressure on a surface at any depth in a fluid equals the weight of the fluid above the surface divided by the surface area.

If the object is totally submerged, the pressure on the object's bottom surface is greater than the pressure on the top surface. Because the fluid forces exerted on the vertical sides cancel, the net force exerted by the fluid is upward.

Archimedes' Principle

An object floats if the buoyant force on the object equals the object's weight. When an object is placed in a fluid it begins to sink. As the object sinks and is not totally submerged, the buoyant force on the object increases. When the object's bottom surface is at a depth where the buoyant force equals the object's weight, the object stops moving downward and floats.

Bill Brooks/Masterfile

At a given depth, the force exerted by a fluid on a surface is the weight of the fluid above the force. If an object floats, the weight of the fluid above the bottom surface of the object is the same as the weight of the fluid the object displaced. This is Archimedes' principle—the buoyant force on an object in a fluid equals the weight of the fluid displaced by the object.

section 3 Doing Work with Fluids

Hydraulic systems use Pascal's principle to increase an applied force. A force applied to a small piston increases the pressure in a fluid. This pressure increase is transmitted through the fluid to the bottom of a larger piston, increasing the force applied on the piston. However, by the conservation of energy, the work done by the smaller piston is the same as the work done by the larger piston. As a result, the larger piston moves a shorter distance than the smaller piston.

Teacher to Teacher
Pam Griffiths
Havelock High School
Havelock, NC

"Ask the students to tape together two strips of paper that measure 5″ × 1/2″ to form a ring. Have students place the ring in front of them. With a straw, blow outside the ring about midway on the side. Practice different positions until the correct placement of air is achieved. The ring of paper will move toward the straw because of the decrease in pressure from the moving air."

Pam Griffiths

Wings and Flight

The lift on an airplane wing is often explained by Bernoulli's principle. According to this explanation, the curved shape of the upper surface of a wing makes air flow faster over the upper surface, reducing the pressure on the upper surface. However, planes can fly upside down and some wings have identical upper and lower surfaces. The shape of the wing surfaces has little to do with creating lift.

Instead, lift is produced primarily by the angle a wing makes with the airflow. When the wing is at an angle it deflects the air flow downward. Most of the deflection is caused by the upper surface. By Newton's third law, the downward force exerted on the air by the wing results in an upward force exerted by the air on the wing. This is the source of lift.

chapter content resources

Internet Resources
For additional content background, visit
bookm.msscience.com to:
- access your book online
- find references to related articles in popular science magazines
- access Web links with related content background
- access current events with science journal topics

Print Resources
An Introduction to Fluid Dynamics, by G.K. Batchelor, Cambridge University Press, 2000
Introduction to Fluid Mechanics, by Robert W. Fox, Alan T. McDonald, and Philip J. Prichard, John Wiley & Sons, 2003
The Works of Archimedes, by Thomas L. Heath (editor), Dover Publications, Inc., 2002
On Shoulders of Giants: Great Scientists and their Discoveries: From Archimedes to Watson and Crick, by Melvyn Bragg, John Wiley & Sons, 1999

Chapter Vocabulary

pressure, p. 66
fluid, p. 69
buoyant force, p. 74
Archimedes' principle, p. 77
density, p. 78
Pascal's principle, p. 83
hydraulic system, p. 83
Bernoulli's principle, p. 85

Science Journal Student responses will vary. Possible answer: objects that float—leaves, lily pads, corks, boats, and gliders; objects that sink—coins, rocks, ship anchors, lead weights, and concreate blocks

INTERACTIVE CHALKBOARD
with Image Bank

PowerPoint® Presentations

This CD-ROM is an editable Microsoft® PowerPoint® presentation that includes:
- a pre-made presentation for every chapter
- interactive graphics
- animations
- audio clips
- image bank
- all new section and chapter questions
- Standardized Test Practice
- transparencies
- pre-lab questions for all labs
- Foldables directions
- links to bookm.msscience.com

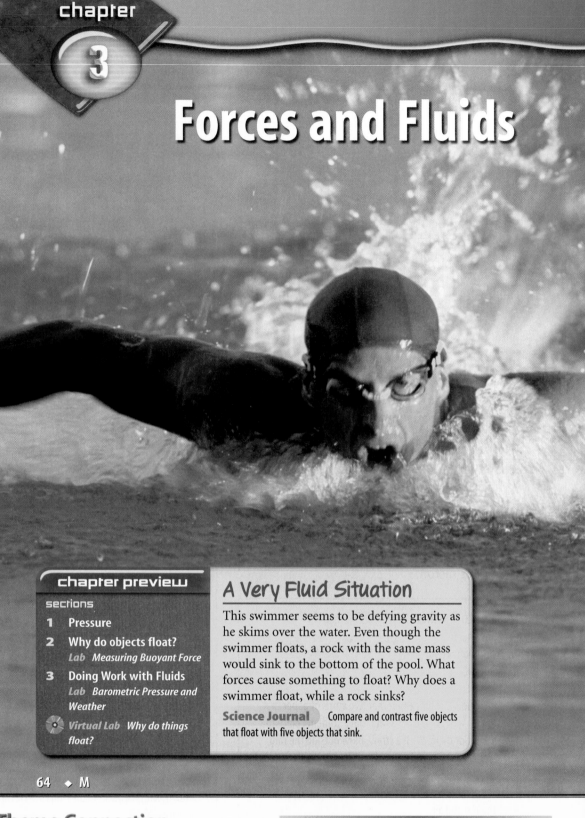

Forces and Fluids

chapter preview

sections

1 Pressure

2 Why do objects float?
 Lab Measuring Buoyant Force

3 Doing Work with Fluids
 Lab Barometric Pressure and Weather

 Virtual Lab Why do things float?

A Very Fluid Situation

This swimmer seems to be defying gravity as he skims over the water. Even though the swimmer floats, a rock with the same mass would sink to the bottom of the pool. What forces cause something to float? Why does a swimmer float, while a rock sinks?

Science Journal Compare and contrast five objects that float with five objects that sink.

Theme Connection

Fluids and Forces Fluids exert forces. These forces enable ships to float and aircraft to fly. Understanding the dynamics of fluids can lead to improvements in vessel design and to advances in aviation technology.

About the Photo

Human Floating On average the human body has a density very close to the density of water. As a result, most people will float only if they are submerged almost totally. Fat tissue has a density of about 0.8 g/cm^3, so bodies with more fat tissue float more easily. Also, the density of the body is decreased by inhaling air.

Start-Up Activities

Forces Exerted by Air

When you are lying down, something is pushing down on you with a force equal to the weight of several small cars. What is the substance that is applying all this pressure on you? It's air, a fluid that exerts forces on everything it is in contact with.

1. Suck water into a straw. Try to keep the straw completely filled with water.

2. Quickly cap the top of the straw with your finger and observe what happens to the water.

3. Release your finger from the top of the straw for an instant and replace it as quickly as possible. Observe what happens to the water.

4. Release your finger from the top of the straw and observe.

5. **Think Critically** Write a paragraph describing your observations of the water in the straw. When were the forces acting on the water in the straw balanced and when were they unbalanced?

Fluids Make the following Foldable to compare and contrast the characteristics of two types of fluids—liquids and gases.

 STEP 1 Fold one sheet of paper lengthwise.

 STEP 2 Fold into thirds.

 STEP 3 Unfold and draw overlapping ovals. Cut the top sheet along the folds.

 STEP 4 Label the ovals as shown.

Liquids Fluids Gases

Construct a Venn Diagram As you read the chapter, list the characteristics of liquids under the left tab, those characteristics of gases under the right tab, and those characteristics common to both under the middle tab.

 Preview this chapter's content and activities at
bookm.msscience.com

Launch LAB

Purpose Students explore the concept of air pressure. L2 LS **Kinesthetic**

Preparation Purchase straws.

Materials water, drinking straw, cup or glass for water

Teaching Strategies To avoid a mess, be certain students experiment with their straws while holding the bottom ends of the straws over the drinking glasses. Have paper towels available to clean up spills.

Think Critically

When the straw is capped, the downward force of gravity on the water is balanced by the upward force exerted by air pressure on the water surface at the bottom of the straw. When the straw is uncapped, the forces on the water are unbalanced. The force exerted by air pressure on the upper and lower water surfaces are balanced, and gravity pulls the water downward.

Assessment

Performance Tell students that the density of air is about 1.3 kg/m^3. Have them measure the dimensions of the classroom and calculate its volume, and then calculate the mass of the air in the room. Use **Performance Assessment in the Science Classroom,** p. 101.

FOLDABLES Study Organizer **Dinah Zike Study Fold**

Student preparation materials for this Foldable are available in the **Chapter *FAST FILE* Resources.**

1 **Motivate**

Pressure

Bellringer

INTERACTIVE CHALKBOARD
PowerPoint® Presentations

Section Focus Transparencies also are available on the Interactive Chalkboard CD-ROM.

L2 ELL

Tie to Prior Knowledge

Force and Weight Review the concepts of force and weight, including the fact that a force has a direction. You may also want to review the states of matter (solid, liquid, gas, plasma) and calculating area.

as you read

What **You'll Learn**
- **Define and calculate** pressure.
- **Model** how pressure varies in a fluid.

Why **It's Important**
Some of the processes that help keep you alive, such as inhaling and exhaling, depend on differences in pressure.

⊙ **Review Vocabulary**
weight: on Earth, the gravitational force between an object and Earth

New Vocabulary
- pressure
- fluid

What is pressure?

What happens when you walk in deep, soft snow or dry sand? Your feet sink into the snow or sand and walking can be difficult. If you rode a bicycle with narrow tires over these surfaces, the tires would sink even deeper than your feet.

How deep you sink depends on your weight as well as the area over which you make contact with the sand or snow. Like the person in **Figure 1,** when you stand on two feet, you make contact with the sand over the area covered by your feet. However, if you were to stand on a large piece of wood, your weight would be distributed over the area covered by the wood.

In both cases, your weight exerted a downward force on the sand. What changed was the area of contact between you and the sand. By changing the area of contact, you changed the pressure you exerted on the sand due to your weight. **Pressure** is the force per unit area that is applied on the surface of an object. When you stood on the board, the area of contact increased, so that the same force was applied over a larger area. As a result, the pressure that was exerted on the sand decreased and you didn't sink as deep.

Figure 1 When your weight is distributed over a larger area, the pressure you exert on the sand decreases.

Weight   Weight

Section 1 Resource Manager

Chapter *FAST FILE* Resources

Transparency Activity, p. 44

Directed Reading for Content Mastery, pp. 19, 20

Note-taking Worksheets, pp. 33–35

MiniLAB, p. 3

Lab Activity, pp. 9–12

Enrichment, p. 30

Reinforcement, p. 27

Calculating Pressure What would happen to the pressure exerted by your feet if your weight increased? You might expect that you would sink deeper in the sand, so the pressure also would increase. Pressure increases if the force applied increases, and decreases if the area of contact increases. Pressure can be calculated from this formula.

Pressure Equation

$$\text{Pressure (in pascals)} = \frac{\text{force (in newtons)}}{\text{area (in meters squared)}}$$

$$P = \frac{F}{A}$$

The unit of pressure in the SI system is the pascal, abbreviated Pa. One pascal is equal to a force of 1 N applied over an area of 1 m², or 1 Pa = 1 N/m². The weight of a dollar bill resting completely flat on a table exerts a pressure of about 1 Pa on the table. Because 1 Pa is a small unit of pressure, pressure sometimes is expressed in units of kPa, which is 1,000 Pa.

Science Online

Topic: Snowshoes

Visit bookm.msscience.com for Web links to information about the history and use of snowshoes. These devices have been used for centuries in cold, snowy climates.

Activity Use simple materials, such as pipe cleaners, string, or paper, to make a model of a snowshoe.

Applying Math — Solve One-Step Equations

CALCULATING PRESSURE A water glass sitting on a table weighs 4 N. The bottom of the water glass has a surface area of 0.003 m². Calculate the pressure the water glass exerts on the table.

Solution

1 *This is what you know:*
- force: $F = 4$ N
- area: $A = 0.003$ m²

2 *This is what you need to find out:*
- pressure: $P = ?$ Pa

3 *This is the procedure you need to use:*

Substitute the known values for force and area into the pressure equation and calculate the pressure:

$$P = \frac{F}{A} = \frac{(4 \text{ N})}{(0.003 \text{ m}^2)}$$

$$= 1{,}333 \text{ N/m}^2 = 1{,}333 \text{ Pa}$$

4 *Check your answer:*

Multiply pressure by the given area. You should get the force that was given.

Practice Problems

1. A student weighs 600 N. The student's shoes are in contact with the floor over a surface area of 0.012 m². Calculate the pressure exerted by the student on the floor.

2. A box that weighs 250 N is at rest on the floor. If the pressure exerted by the box on the floor is 25,000 Pa, over what area is the box in contact with the floor?

 For more practice, visit bookm.msscience.com/math_practice

Curriculum Connection

History The pascal is named for Blaise Pascal (1623–1662) a French scientist, philosopher and mathematician. Pascal carried out a number of experiments on the behavior of fluids, and also is credited with constructing the first digital calculator. Ask students to find out more about the life of Blaise Pascal.

2 Teach

Discussion

Pressure Phrases What do people mean when they say they are under pressure? that they are being pushed; or are being stressed What do they mean when they say the pressure is letting up? Pressure lets up when the stress is reduced. L2 [IS] **Linguistic**

Activity

Inverse Relationships Some students have trouble with inverse relationships such as $P = F/A$. Have each student make a pair of tables and graphs showing what happens to pressure when area is held constant and force varies, and what happens to pressure when force is held constant and area varies. L2 [IS] **Visual-Spatial**

Discussion

Snow Walking Why is it easier to walk in snow when you are wearing skis or snowshoes than when you are wearing winter boots? Skis and snowshoes increase the area in contact with the snow, reducing the pressure so you don't sink as far into the snow when you stand or walk. L2 [IS] **Logical-Mathematical**

Applying Math

National Math Standards

Correlation to Mathematics Objectives

1, 2, 9

Answers to Practice Problems

1. $(600 \text{ N})/(0.012 \text{ m}^2) = 50{,}000$ Pa
2. $A = \frac{F}{P} = \frac{250 \text{ N}}{25{,}000 \text{ N/m}^2} = 0.01$ m²

Mini LAB

Purpose Students compare and contrast the pressures exerted by different types of movement. [L2] [IS] **Kinesthetic**

Materials metric ruler, outside area that will take tracks

Teaching Strategy Try the ground before class to make sure it will take tracks, and observe how detailed the tracks are. A dusting of snow, for example, won't make tracks with varying depth. Slightly damp sand will hold clearer tracks than dry sand.

Analysis

1. Students should measure to the 0.10 cm.
2. Possible answers: A running person puts more pressure on the ball of the foot than the heel. A person carrying a load puts more pressure on the whole foot. A person walking backward puts more pressure on the heel than on the ball of the foot.
3. Answers should include some reasoning such as the tracks are deep at the ball of the foot and shallow at the heel, so the person was running.

Assessment

Process Ask students how a naturalist would use animal tracks to study animals. Possible answer: Look at the depths of different parts of the track and the distance between tracks to determine if the animal was walking or running. Use **Performance Assessment in the Science Classroom**, p. 89.

Mini LAB

Interpreting Footprints

Procedure

1. Go outside to **an area of dirt, sand, or snow** where you can make footprints. Smooth the surface.
2. Make tracks in several different ways. Possible choices include walking forward, walking backward, running, jumping a short or long distance, walking carrying a load, and tiptoeing.

Analysis

1. Measure the depth of each type of track at two points: the ball of the foot and the heel. Compare the depths of the different tracks.
2. The depth of the track corresponds to the pressure on the ground. In your **Science Journal,** explain how different means of motion put pressure on different parts of the sole.
3. Have one person make a track while the other looks away. Then have the second person determine what the motion was.

Figure 2 The force applied to the head of the nail by the hammer is the same as the force that the tip of the nail applies to the wood. However, because the area of the tip is small, the pressure applied to the wood is large.

Pressure and Weight To calculate the pressure that is exerted on a surface, you need to know the force and the area over which it is applied. Sometimes the force that is exerted is the weight of an object, such as when you are standing on sand, snow, or a floor. Suppose you are holding a 2-kg book in the palm of your hand. To find out how much pressure is being exerted on your hand, you first must know the force that the book is exerting on your hand—its weight.

$$\text{Weight} = \text{mass} \times \text{acceleration due to gravity}$$
$$W = (2 \text{ kg}) \times (9.8 \text{ m/s}^2)$$
$$W = 19.6 \text{ N}$$

If the area of contact between your hand and the book is 0.003 m^2, the pressure that is exerted on your hand by the book is:

$$P = \frac{F}{A}$$
$$P = \frac{(19.6 \text{ N})}{(0.003 \text{ m}^2)}$$
$$P = 6,533 \text{ Pa} = 6.53 \text{ kPa}$$

Pressure and Area One way to change the pressure that is exerted on an object is to change the area over which the force is applied. Imagine trying to drive a nail into a piece of wood, as shown in **Figure 2.** Why is the tip of a nail pointed instead of flat? When you hit the nail with a hammer, the force you apply is transmitted through the nail from the head to the tip. The tip of the nail comes to a point and is in contact with the wood over a small area. Because the contact area is so small, the pressure that is exerted by the nail on the wood is large—large enough to push the wood fibers apart. This allows the nail to move downward into the wood.

Teacher FYI

Kinetic Theory of Matter According to the kinetic theory of matter, all matter is composed of small particles (atoms and molecules) in constant motion. The pressure of a fluid is due to the movement of the molecules in it. When the molecules of a fluid collide with the walls of a container or with objects submerged in the fluid, they exert pressure. Pressure depends on the mass of the molecules, their velocity, and how often collisions occur.

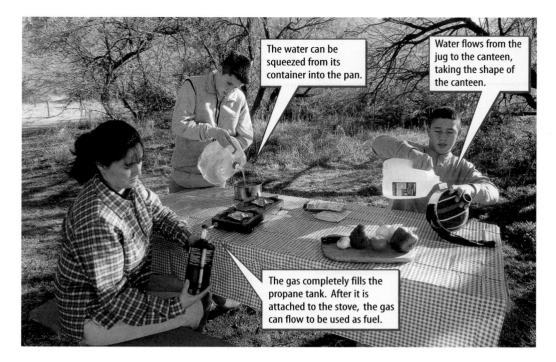

The water can be squeezed from its container into the pan.

Water flows from the jug to the canteen, taking the shape of the canteen.

The gas completely fills the propane tank. After it is attached to the stove, the gas can flow to be used as fuel.

Fluids

What do the substances in **Figure 3** have in common? Each takes the shape of its container and can flow from one place to another. A **fluid** is any substance that has no definite shape and has the ability to flow. You might think of a fluid as being a liquid, such as water or motor oil. But gases are also fluids. When you are outside on a windy day, you can feel the air flowing past you. Because air can flow and has no definite shape, air is a fluid. Gases, liquids, and the state of matter called plasma, which is found in the Sun and other stars, are fluids and can flow.

Pressure in a Fluid

Suppose you placed an empty glass on a table. The weight of the glass exerts pressure on the table. If you fill the glass with water, the weight of the water and glass together exert a force on the table. So the pressure exerted on the table increases.

Because the water has weight, the water itself also exerts pressure on the bottom of the glass. This pressure is the weight of the water divided by the area of the glass bottom. If you pour more water into the glass, the height of the water in the glass increases and the weight of the water increases. As a result, the pressure exerted by the water increases.

Figure 3 Fluids all have the ability to flow and take the shape of their containers.
Classify *What are some other examples of fluids?*

Plasma The Sun is a star with a core temperature of about 16 million°C. At this temperature, the particles in the Sun move at tremendous speeds, crashing into each other in violent collisions that tear atoms apart. As a result, the Sun is made of a type of fluid called a plasma. A plasma is a gas made of electrically charged particles.

SECTION 1 Pressure **M** ◆ **69**

Discussion

Water Level Explain that air pressure is also important to water level in a system. What happens to the level of water if the air pressure over the top of one tube is lower than the air pressure over the top of a second tube connected to the first? The water will be pushed farther up the tube on which the pressure is lower. L2 IS

Logical-Mathematical

Observing Pressure

Purpose To explore and observe pressure in fluids, have students design an experiment showing that, as the height of a fluid increases, the pressure at the bottom of the fluid increases.

Possible Materials water, recycled materials such as cans or plastic containers

Estimated Time one week outside class time

Teaching Strategies

• Students can make simple lab set-ups that show that the pressure increases at the bottom of a container as the height of the fluid increases.

• Encourage students to use inexpensive items such as recycled containers from home.

• Have students show their set-ups to the class.

• Allow students to explore other questions that arise.

For additional inquiry activities, see *Science Inquiry Labs.*

Caption Answer

Figure 4 The pressure becomes greater as the water column becomes narrower because the height of the column increases.

Figure 4 Even though each graduated cylinder contains the same volume of water, the pressure exerted by the higher column of water is greater.
Infer *how the pressure exerted by a water column would change as the column becomes narrower.*

Figure 5 Pressure depends only on the height of the fluid above a surface, not on the shape of the container. The pressure at the bottom of each section of the tube is the same.

Pressure and Fluid Height Suppose you poured the same amount of water into a small and a large graduated cylinder, as shown in **Figure 4.** Notice that the height of the water in the small cylinder is greater than in the large cylinder. Is the water pressure the same at the bottom of each cylinder? The weight of the water in each cylinder is the same, but the contact area at the bottom of the small cylinder is smaller. Therefore, the pressure is greater at the bottom of the small cylinder.

The height of the water can increase if more water is added to a container or if the same amount of water is added to a narrower container. In either case, when the height of the fluid is greater, the pressure at the bottom of the container is greater. This is always true for any fluid or any container. The greater the height of a fluid above a surface, the greater the pressure exerted by the fluid on that surface. The pressure exerted at the bottom of a container doesn't depend on the shape of the container, but only on the height of the fluid above the bottom, as **Figure 5** shows.

Pressure Increases with Depth If you swim underwater, you might notice that you can feel pressure in your ears. As you go deeper, you can feel this pressure increase. This pressure is exerted by the weight of the water above you. As you go deeper in a fluid, the height of the fluid above you increases. As the height of the fluid above you increases, the weight of the fluid above you also increases. As a result, the pressure exerted by the fluid increases with depth.

Height

Differentiated Instruction

Challenge Deep-sea diving is challenging because of the high pressures that divers must contend with. Have students research what methods are used for deep-sea diving and what equipment is used. Have students present their reports to their class. L3

Visual Learning

Figure 5 The height of the water in the vertical tubes in this closed system is constant even though the shapes of the tubes are different. If the center section of the tube is sealed so that the two sides are independent, what will happen? The water in the left two vertical tubes would be isolated from the water in the right two tubes, so the water would behave independently on each side. L3 IS **Visual-Spatial**

Pressure in All Directions If the pressure that is exerted by a fluid is due to the weight of the fluid, is the pressure in a fluid exerted only downward? **Figure 6** shows a small, solid cube in a fluid. The fluid exerts a pressure on each side of this cube, not just on the top. The pressure on each side is perpendicular to the surface, and the amount of pressure depends only on the depth in the fluid. As shown in **Figure 6,** this is true for any object in a fluid, no matter how complicated the shape. The pressure at any point on the object is perpendicular to the surface of the object at that point.

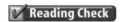 **Reading Check** *In what direction is pressure exerted by a fluid on a surface?*

Atmospheric Pressure

Even though you don't feel it, you are surrounded by a fluid that exerts pressure on you constantly. That fluid is the atmosphere. The atmosphere at Earth's surface is only about one-thousandth as dense as water. However, the thickness of the atmosphere is large enough to exert a large pressure on objects at Earth's surface. For example, look at **Figure 7.** When you are sitting down, the force pushing down on your body due to atmospheric pressure can be equal to the weight of several small cars. Atmospheric pressure is approximately 100,000 Pa at sea level. This means that the weight of Earth's atmosphere exerts about 100,000 N of force over every square meter on Earth.

Why doesn't this pressure cause you to be crushed? Your body is filled with fluids such as blood that also exert pressure. The pressure exerted outward by the fluids inside your body balances the pressure exerted by the atmosphere.

Going Higher As you go higher in the atmosphere, atmospheric pressure decreases as the amount of air above you decreases. The same is true in an ocean, lake, or pond. The water pressure is highest at the ocean floor and decreases as you go upward. The changes in pressure at varying heights in the atmosphere and depths in the ocean are illustrated in **Figure 8.**

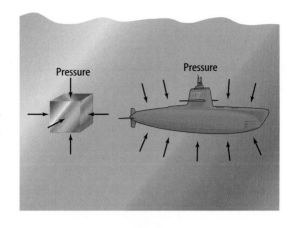

Figure 6 The pressure on all objects in a fluid is exerted on all sides, perpendicular to the surface of the object, no matter what its shape.

Figure 7 Atmospheric pressure on your body is a result of the weight of the atmosphere exerting force on your body.
Infer *Why don't you feel the pressure exerted by the atmosphere?*

Reading Check

Answer perpendicular to the surface

Use an Analogy

Air and Water Atmospheric pressure is like water pressure. Both fluids have weight, and the more fluid there is above you, the greater the force on you.

Quick Demo

Atmospheric Pressure

Materials one full double page sheet of newspaper, ruler or paint stirrer

Estimated Time five minutes

Procedure Open the newspaper and place it flat on a desk. Slip the ruler underneath the newspaper allowing it to hang over the edge about halfway. Ask the students to predict what will happen if you strike the ruler quickly in a downward motion. Test their predictions by striking the ruler with your hand. The newspaper holds the ruler down because of the atmospheric pressure pushing down on the newspaper. Warning: The ruler may break.

Caption Answer

Figure 7 It is balanced by the pressure of fluids in your body.

LAB DEMONSTRATION

Purpose to observe that water and oil come to rest at different levels when balanced in a closed system

Materials clear plastic tube, water colored with food coloring, funnel, vegetable oil

Procedure Fill the tube partway with water and hang it in a U-shape. Mark the water level on each side. Pour some water out, and add oil to one side. Hang the tube in a U. Mark the level of the liquid on each side.

Expected Outcome When the tube contains only water, the liquid rises to the same level on each side. When the tube contains water and oil, the levels differ.

Assessment

Why are the levels different with oil on one side of the tube and water on the other? Oil is less dense than water, so oil at a depth of, for example, 10 cm exerts less pressure than water at a depth of 10 cm. The water pushes the oil up until equilibrium is reached.

Visualizing Pressure at Varying Elevations

Have students examine the pictures and read the captions. Then ask the following questions.

Commercial jets often fly 10 km above sea level. Why is air added to the passenger cabins of the planes to pressurize them? People would find it difficult or impossible to breathe the air at that altitude.

What could happen to a submarine if it went too deep in the ocean? It could be crushed by the water pressure.

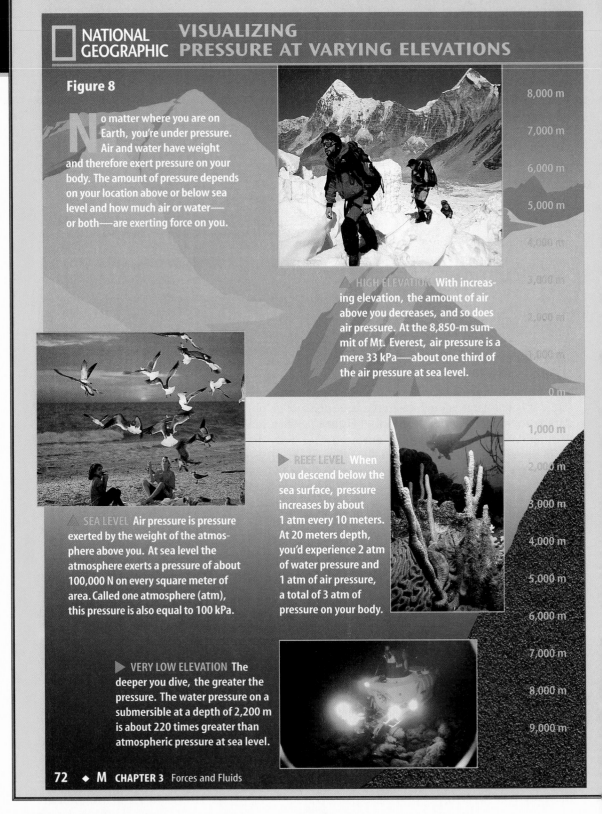

NATIONAL GEOGRAPHIC

VISUALIZING PRESSURE AT VARYING ELEVATIONS

Figure 8

No matter where you are on Earth, you're under pressure. Air and water have weight and therefore exert pressure on your body. The amount of pressure depends on your location above or below sea level and how much air or water—or both—are exerting force on you.

HIGH ELEVATION With increasing elevation, the amount of air above you decreases, and so does air pressure. At the 8,850-m summit of Mt. Everest, air pressure is a mere 33 kPa—about one third of the air pressure at sea level.

SEA LEVEL Air pressure is pressure exerted by the weight of the atmosphere above you. At sea level the atmosphere exerts a pressure of about 100,000 N on every square meter of area. Called one atmosphere (atm), this pressure is also equal to 100 kPa.

REEF LEVEL When you descend below the sea surface, pressure increases by about 1 atm every 10 meters. At 20 meters depth, you'd experience 2 atm of water pressure and 1 atm of air pressure, a total of 3 atm of pressure on your body.

VERY LOW ELEVATION The deeper you dive, the greater the pressure. The water pressure on a submersible at a depth of 2,200 m is about 220 times greater than atmospheric pressure at sea level.

8,000 m
7,000 m
6,000 m
5,000 m
4,000 m
3,000 m
2,000 m
1,000 m
0 m
1,000 m
2,000 m
3,000 m
4,000 m
5,000 m
6,000 m
7,000 m
8,000 m
9,000 m

72 ◆ **M CHAPTER 3** Forces and Fluids

Differentiated Instruction

Learning Disabled Have students copy the meter measurements given in the above page on notebook paper using one line for each number. Have students label and draw brackets around the elevations above sea level, at sea level, and below sea level. Reread the captions and mark the atmospheric pressure given in the passage beside the correct elevation. Use the same units, such as atmospheres, for each entry. Students should see that atmospheric pressure increases as you go toward the center of the Earth.

Barometer An instrument called a barometer is used to measure atmospheric pressure. A barometer has something in common with a drinking straw. When you drink through a straw, it seems like you pull your drink up through the straw. But actually, atmospheric pressure pushes your drink up the straw. By removing air from the straw, you reduce the air pressure in the straw. Meanwhile, the atmosphere is pushing down on the surface of your drink. When you pull the air from the straw, the pressure in the straw is less than the pressure pushing down on the liquid, so atmospheric pressure pushes the drink up the straw.

One type of barometer works in a similar way, as shown in **Figure 9.** The space at the top of the tube is a vacuum. Atmospheric pressure pushes liquid up a tube. The liquid reaches a height where the pressure at the bottom of the column of liquid balances the pressure of the atmosphere. As the atmospheric pressure changes, the force pushing on the surface of the liquid changes. As a result, the height of the liquid in the tube increases as the atmospheric pressure increases.

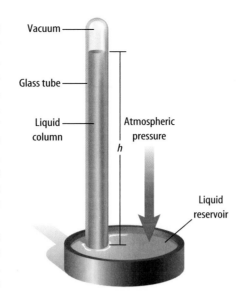

Figure 9 In this type of barometer, the height of the liquid column increases as the atmospheric pressure increases.

section ① review

Summary

Pressure

● Pressure is the force exerted on a unit area of a surface. Pressure can be calculated from this equation:

$$P = \frac{F}{A}$$

● The SI unit for pressure is the pascal, abbreviated Pa.

Pressure in a Fluid

● The pressure exerted by a fluid depends on the depth below the fluid surface.

● The pressure exerted by a fluid on a surface is always perpendicular to the surface.

Atmospheric Pressure

● Earth's atmosphere exerts a pressure of about 100,000 Pa at sea level.

● A barometer is an instrument used to measure atmospheric pressure.

Self Check

1. **Compare** One column of water has twice the diameter as another water column. If the pressure at the bottom of each column is the same, how do the heights of the two columns compare?

2. **Explain** why the height of the liquid column in a barometer changes as atmospheric pressure changes.

3. **Classify** the following as fluids or solids: warm butter, liquid nitrogen, paper, neon gas, ice.

4. **Explain** how the pressure at the bottom of a container depends on the container shape and the fluid height.

5. **Think Critically** Explain how the diameter of a balloon changes as it rises higher in the atmosphere.

Applying Math

6. **Calculate Force** The palm of a person's hand has an area of 0.0135 m². If atmospheric pressure is 100,000 N/m², find the force exerted by the atmosphere on the person's palm.

section ① review

1. The heights must be equal if the pressures are equal.

2. When atmospheric pressure changes, the force pushing on the open reservoir of liquid changes. This causes the pressure exerted by the fluid in the reservoir on the fluid in the tube to change. If atmos-pheric pressure increases, the upward force on the liquid in the tube increases and the liquid rises.

3. fluids—warm butter, liquid nitrogen, neon gas; solids—paper, ice

4. Pressure depends only on the height of the fluid above a surface, not on the shape of the container.

5. The balloon will expand and its diameter will increase. As the altitude of the balloon increases, the pressure exerted by the air surrounding the balloon decreases. Because the pressure inside the balloon is greater, the balloon expands. As the balloon expands, the surface area of the balloon increases. This causes the pressure exerted by the air inside the balloon to decrease. The balloon expands until the air pressure inside and outside the balloon are the same.

6. $F = PA = (100{,}000 \text{ N/m}^2) \times (0.0135 \text{ m}^2) = 1{,}350 \text{ m}^2$

3 Assess

DAILY INTERVENTION

Check for Understanding

Logical-Mathematical Suppose a gas is contained in a cylinder with a piston at one end. Ask students what happens to the pressure the gas exerts if you pull on the piston to increase the volume. Pressure decreases. What happens to the pressure if you push on the piston, making the volume smaller? Pressure increases. L3

Reteach

Fluids Ask students to identify all the fluids in the classroom. Make sure they include such things as sealed containers that have air inside. L1 IS **Visual-Spatial**

☑ Assessment

Performance Have students place a small amount of hot water in a plastic soda bottle and screw on the cap. Have them describe the forces at work as they observe what happens when they submerge the bottle in ice water. As the gases inside the bottle cool, they exert less pressure on the container walls. When the outside pressure becomes so much larger than the inside pressure that the walls of the bottle are no longer strong enough to balance the force pushing inward, the bottle is crushed. Use **Performance Assessment in the Science Classroom,** p. 89.

Why do objects float?

as you read

What You'll Learn

- **Explain** how the pressure in a fluid produces a buoyant force.
- **Define** density.
- **Explain** floating and sinking using Archimedes' principle.

Why It's Important

Knowing how fluids exert forces helps you understand how boats can float.

Review Vocabulary

Newton's second law of motion: the acceleration of an object is in the direction of the total force and equals the total force divided by the object's mass

New Vocabulary

- buoyant force
- Archimedes' principle
- density

Figure 10 When you float, the forces on you are balanced. Gravity pulls you downward and is balanced by the buoyant force pushing you upward.
Infer *What is the acceleration of the person shown here?*

The Buoyant Force

Can you float? Think about the forces that are acting on you as you float motionless on the surface of a pool or lake. You are not moving, so according to Newton's second law of motion, the forces on you must be balanced. Earth's gravity is pulling you downward, so an upward force must be balancing your weight, as shown in **Figure 10.** This force is called the buoyant force. The **buoyant force** is an upward force that is exerted by a fluid on any object in the fluid.

What causes the buoyant force?

The buoyant force is caused by the pressure that is exerted by a fluid on an object in the fluid. **Figure 11** shows a cube-shaped object submerged in a glass of water. The water exerts pressure everywhere over the surface of the object. Recall that the pressure exerted by a fluid has two properties. One is that the direction of the pressure on a surface is always perpendicular to the surface. The other is that the pressure exerted by a fluid increases as you go deeper into the fluid.

Buoyant force

Gravity

Buoyant Force and Unbalanced Pressure The pressure that is exerted by the water on the cube is shown in **Figure 11.** The bottom of the cube is deeper in the water. Therefore, the pressure that is exerted by the water at the bottom of the cube is greater than it is at the top of the cube. The higher pressure near the bottom means that the water exerts an upward force on the bottom of the cube that is greater than the downward force that is exerted at the top of the cube. As a result, the force that is exerted on the cube due to water pressure is not balanced, and a net upward force is acting on the cube due to the pressure of the water. This upward force is the buoyant force. A buoyant force acts on all objects that are placed in a fluid, whether they are floating or sinking.

✓ **Reading Check** *When does the buoyant force act on an object?*

Sinking and Floating

If you drop a stone into a pool of water, it sinks. But if you toss a twig on the water, it floats. An upward buoyant force acts on the twig and the stone, so why does one float and one sink?

The buoyant force pushes an object in a fluid upward, but gravity pulls the object downward. If the weight of the object is greater than the buoyant force, the net force on the object is downward and it sinks. If the buoyant force is equal to the object's weight, the forces are balanced and the object floats. As shown in **Figure 12,** the fish floats because the buoyant force on it balances its weight. The rocks sink because the buoyant force acting on them is not large enough to balance their weight.

Pressure

Figure 11 The pressure exerted on the bottom of the cube is greater than the pressure on the top. The fluid exerts a net upward force on the cube.

Figure 12 The weight of a rock is more than the buoyant force exerted by the water, so it sinks to the bottom.
Infer *Why do the fish float?*

Discussion

Diving Forces Ask students to compare the forces on a diver at a depth of 10 m and at a depth of 50 m. The downward force of gravity on the diver and the upward buoyant force don't change with depth. However, the pressure exerted on the diver does increase with depth. **L3** **LS** **Logical-Mathematical**

Figure 13 The buoyant force on a piece of aluminum foil increases as the surface area of the foil increases.

Figure 14 The hull of this oil tanker has a large surface area in contact with the water. As a result, the buoyant force is so large that the ship floats.

Virtual Labs

Floating *Why do things float?*

Changing the Buoyant Force

Whether an object sinks or floats depends on whether the buoyant force is smaller than its weight. The weight of an object depends only on the object's mass, which is the amount of matter the object contains. The weight does not change if the shape of the object changes. A piece of modeling clay contains the same amount of matter whether it's squeezed into a ball or pressed flat.

Buoyant Force and Shape Buoyant force does depend on the shape of the object. The fluid exerts upward pressure on the entire lower surface of the object that is in contact with the fluid. If this surface is made larger, then more upward pressure is exerted on the object and the buoyant force is greater. **Figure 13** shows how a piece of aluminum can be made to float. If the aluminum is crumpled, the buoyant force is less than the weight, so the aluminum sinks. When the aluminum is flattened into a thin, curved sheet, the buoyant force is large enough that the sheet floats. This is how large, metal ships, like the one in **Figure 14,** are able to float. The metal is formed into a curved sheet that is the hull of the ship. The contact area of the hull with the water is much greater than if the metal were a solid block. As a result, the buoyant force on the hull is greater than it would be on a metal block.

Differentiated Instruction

Challenge There is a legend that Archimedes (287–212 B.C.) was asked by King Hiero II whether a crown was made of pure gold or also contained silver. Have students find out how Archimedes is supposed to have solved this problem. Archimedes realized that when submerged in water, equal weights of gold and silver displace different amounts of water because gold and silver have different densities. This allowed him to show that the crown was not pure gold. **L3** **LS** **Linguistic**

The Buoyant Force Doesn't Change with Depth

Suppose you drop a steel cube into the ocean. You might think that the cube would sink only to a depth where the buoyant force on the cube balances its weight. However, the steel sinks to the bottom, no matter how deep the ocean is.

The buoyant force on the cube is the difference between the downward force due to the water pressure on the top of the cube and the upward force due to water pressure on the bottom of the cube. **Figure 15** shows that when the cube is deeper, the pressure on the top surface increases, but the pressure on the bottom surface also increases by the same amount. As a result, the difference between the forces on the top and bottom surfaces is the same, no matter how deep the cube is submerged. The buoyant force on the submerged cube is the same at any depth.

Archimedes' Principle

A way of determining the buoyant force was given by the ancient Greek mathematician Archimedes(ar kuh MEE deez) more than 2,200 years ago. According to **Archimedes' principle,** the buoyant force on an object is equal to the weight of the fluid it displaces.

To understand Archimedes' principle, think about what happens if you drop an ice cube in a glass of water that's filled to the top. The ice cube takes the place of some of the water and causes this water to overflow, as shown in **Figure 16.** Another way to say this is that the ice cube displaced water that was in the glass.

Suppose you caught all the overflow water and weighed it. According to Archimedes' principle, the weight of the overflow, or displaced water, would be equal to the buoyant force on the ice cube. Because the ice cube is floating, the buoyant force is balanced by the weight of the ice cube. So the weight of the water that is displaced, or the buoyant force, is equal to the weight of the ice cube.

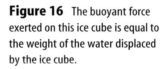

Figure 15 Because the cube on the right is deeper, the pressure on its upper surface is increased due to the weight of the water inside the dashed lines. The pressure on the bottom surface also increases by this amount.

Explain *how the buoyant force on the cube would change if it moved only to the left or right.*

A   **B**

Figure 16 The buoyant force exerted on this ice cube is equal to the weight of the water displaced by the ice cube.

Cultural Diversity

Kayaks Boats come in many shapes and sizes. Have students investigate the boats called kayaks used by the Inuit people of North America. Kayaks, still used by the Inuit, are quiet and fast. They were traditionally used to hunt seals and caribou. Originally made of skins shrunk over a wooden frame, today most are made of plastics. The kayak is completely enclosed except for the center cockpit.

Visual Learning

Figure 15 Point out to students that the weight of the water above the lower cube is greater than the weight of the water above the upper cube. The buoyant force on the cube, however, is due to the difference in the pressure above the cube and the pressure below it. Because pressure increases linearly with depth, the difference in pressure at the top and bottom of the cube is the same at any depth.

Activity

Density Fill a clear glass with warm water and add a grape. The grape will sink to the bottom because it is denser than the water. Remove the grape and stir a tablespoon of salt into the water. Now replace the grape. This time it floats, because it is less dense then the salt water.

L2 IS **Visual-Spatial**

Naval Architect Many universities do not offer a degree in naval architecture. Have students find universities that offer this as a major.

Research Have students research the courses that are required to become an engineer or architect. Have them find the employment outlook for navel architects.

Applying Science

Answers

1. From bottom to top: blue, red, green, purple, yellow; the water layer (clear) would be between the purple and green layers, because the density of water, 1 g/cm³, is between 0.78 and 1.2.

2. A) 76.8 g; B) 43.5 g; C) 24 g; D) 14.4 g; E) 14.8 g

Naval Architect Naval architects design the ships and submarines for the U.S. Naval Fleet, Coast Guard, and Military Sealift Command. Naval architects need math, science, and English skills for designing and communicating design ideas to others.

Density Archimedes' principle leads to a way of determining whether an object placed in a fluid will float or sink. The answer depends on comparing the density of the fluid and the density of the object. The **density** of a fluid or an object is the mass of the object divided by the volume it occupies. Density can be calculated by the following formula:

Density Equation

$$\text{density (in g/cm}^3) = \frac{\text{mass (in g)}}{\text{volume (in cm}^3)}$$

$$D = \frac{m}{V}$$

For example, water has a density of 1.0 g/cm³. The mass of any volume of a substance can be calculated by multiplying both sides of the above equation by volume. This gives the equation

$$\text{mass} = \text{density} \times \text{volume}$$

Then if the density and volume are known, the mass of the material can be calculated.

Applying Science

Layering Liquids

The density of an object or substance determines whether it will sink or float in a fluid. Just like solid objects, liquids also have different densities. If you pour vegetable oil into water, the oil doesn't mix. Instead, because the density of oil is less than the density of water, the oil floats on top of the water.

Identifying the Problem

In science class, a student is presented with five unknown liquids and their densities. He measures the volume of each and organizes his data into the table at the right. He decides to experiment with these liquids by carefully pouring them, one at a time, into a graduated cylinder.

Solving the Problem

1. Assuming the liquids don't mix with each other, draw a diagram and label the colors, illustrating how these liquids would look when poured into a graduated cylinder. If 30 cm³ of water were added to the graduated cylinder, explain how your diagram would change.

2. Use the formula for density to calculate the mass of each of the unknown liquids in the chart.

Liquid Density and Volume			
Liquid	Color	Density (g/cm³)	Volume (cm³)
A	red	2.40	32.0
B	blue	2.90	15.0
C	green	1.20	20.0
D	yellow	0.36	40.0
E	purple	0.78	19.0

Differentiated Instruction

English-Language Learners Have students create an illustrated glossary of the science terms in this chapter. Students should write each new term on an index card. Divide the word into parts (prefix, root word, suffix) if needed. Have students write down the meaning of the word, its pronunciation, an illustration representing the word, and a sentence using the word correctly on the index card. For students with limited English proficiency, pair them with another student to assist in translations.

Sinking and Density Suppose you place a copper block with a volume of 1,000 cm³ into a container of water. This block weighs about 88 N. As the block sinks, it displaces water, and an upward buoyant force acts on it. If the block is completely submerged, the volume of water it has displaced is 1,000 cm³—the same as its own volume. This is the maximum amount of water the block can displace. The weight of 1,000 cm³ of water is about 10 N, and this is the maximum buoyant force that can act on the block. This buoyant force is less than the weight of the copper, so the copper block continues to sink.

The copper block and the displaced water had the same volume. Because the copper block had a greater density, the mass of the copper block was greater than the mass of the displaced water. As a result, the copper block weighed more than the displaced water because its density was greater. Any material with a density that is greater than the density of water will weigh more than the water that it displaces, and it will sink. This is true for any object and any fluid. Any object that has a density greater than the density of the fluid it is placed in will sink.

Floating and Density Suppose you place a block of wood with a volume of 1,000 cm³ into a container of water. This block weighs about 7 N. The block starts to sink and displaces water. However, it stops sinking and floats before it is completely submerged, as shown in **Figure 17.** The density of the wood was less than the density of the water. So the wood was able to displace an amount of water equal to its weight before it was completely submerged. It stopped sinking after it had displaced about 700 cm³ of water. That much water has a weight of about 7 N, which is equal to the weight of the block. Any object with a density less than the fluid it is placed in will float.

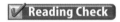 **Reading Check** *How can you determine whether an object will float or sink?*

Figure 17 An object, such as this block of wood, will continue to sink in a fluid until it has displaced an amount of fluid that is equal to its mass. Then the buoyant force equals its weight.

Floating on Water Is it easier to float in salt water or in fresh water? salt water Is salt water more dense or less dense than fresh water? more dense In salt water the buoyant force acting on a swimmer is greater than it is in fresh water—less of the swimmer is submerged in saltwater. A smaller volume of saltwater is displaced which has a weight equal to the swimmer's weight. L2 IS **Logical-Mathematical**

Fun Fact

Archimedes' writings were concerned with calculating the areas and volumes of curved surfaces and solids. His work influenced the development of mathematics and quantitative science in the middle ages as people studied the rediscovered writings of ancient scientists.

Visual Learning

Figure 17 Point out that when the block starts to enter the water, only a small amount of water is displaced. The buoyant force is not large enough to balance the block's weight, so the block continues sinking. As the block displaces more and more water, the buoyant force becomes greater and greater, until it balances the block's weight. L2 IS **Visual-Spatial**

Reading Check

Answer If its density is less than that of the fluid, it will float; if its density is greater than that of the fluid, it will sink.

Science Journal

Weather The density of air is affected by its temperature and by how much water vapor it contains. Have students write short paragraphs in their Science Journals about how this might affect weather cycles. Warm air can hold more water vapor than cool air. Clouds and rain form when warm, moist, less dense air is pushed up from the surface into the colder atmosphere above. L2 IS **Linguistic**

Curriculum Connection

History Have students find out more about the life of Archimedes and make pamphlets illustrating their findings. Archimedes lived from approximately 287–212 B.C. He was a mathematician, engineer, and scientist. He is said to have created several military devices to defend his city of Syracuse, in Greece. The city eventually fell to the Romans in 212 B.C., and Archimedes was killed in the siege. L2 IS **Visual-Spatial** P

Check for Understanding

Visual-Spatial Have students make illustrations showing buoyancy and density for a scenario of their choice. Students should include labels and explanations on their illustrations.

Reteach

Density Place an air-filled ball and a solid ball, such as a marble, into a glass of water. Ask students to explain why the air-filled ball floats and the solid ball sinks. The air-filled ball is less dense than water; the solid ball is more dense than water. L2 IS **Visual-Spatial**

☑ Assessment

Performance Have students make miniposters illustrating why it is easier to float in salt water than in fresh water. Miniposters should indicate that the density of salt water is greater than the density of fresh water. Use **Performance Assessment in the Science Classroom,** p. 145.

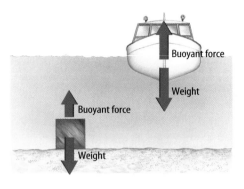

Figure 18 Even though the boat and the cube have the same mass, the boat displaces more water because of its shape. Therefore the boat floats, but the cube sinks.

Boats

Archimedes' principle provides an-other way to understand why boats that are made of metal can float. Look at **Figure 18.** By making a piece of steel into a boat that occupies a large volume, more water is displaced by the boat than by the piece of steel. According to Archimedes' principle, increasing the weight of the water that is displaced increases the buoyant force. By making the volume of the boat large enough, enough water can be displaced so that the buoyant force is greater than the weight of the steel.

How does the density of the boat compare to the density of the piece of steel? The steel now surrounds a volume that is filled with air that has little mass. The mass of the boat is nearly the same as the mass of the steel, but the volume of the boat is much larger. As a result, the density of the boat is much less than the density of the steel. The boat floats when its volume becomes large enough that its density is less than the density of water.

---

section 2 review

Summary

The Buoyant Force

- The buoyant force is an upward force that is exerted by a fluid on any object in the fluid.
- The buoyant force is caused by the increase in pressure with depth in a fluid.
- Increasing the surface area in contact with a fluid increases the buoyant force on an object.

Sinking and Floating

- An object sinks when the buoyant force on an object is less than the object's weight.
- An object floats when the buoyant force on an object equals the object's weight.

Archimedes' Principle

- Archimedes' principle states that the buoyant force on a object equals the weight of the fluid the object displaces.
- According to Archimedes' principle, an object will float in a fluid only if the density of the object is less than the density of the fluid.

Self Check

1. **Explain** whether the buoyant force on a submerged object depends on the weight of the object.
2. **Determine** whether an object will float or sink in water if it has a density of 1.5 g/cm^3. Explain.
3. **Compare** the buoyant force on an object when it is partially submerged and when it's completely submerged.
4. **Explain** how the buoyant force acting on an object placed in water can be measured.
5. **Think Critically** A submarine changes its mass by adding or removing seawater from tanks inside the sub. Explain how this can enable the sub to dive or rise to the surface.

Applying Math

6. **Buoyant Force** A ship displaces 80,000 L of water. One liter of water weighs 9.8 N. What is the buoyant force on the ship?
7. **Density** The density of 14k gold is 13.7 g/cm^3. A ring has a mass of 7.21 g and a volume of 0.65 cm^3. Find the density of the ring. Is it made from 14k gold?

Science Online bookm.msscience.com/self_check_quiz

---

section 2 review

1. No. The buoyant force on the submerged object depends on the object's volume.
2. It will sink because its density is greater than 1 g/cm^3, the density of water.
3. The buoyant force depends on the weight of fluid displaced. When the object is partially submerged it displaces less fluid than when it is fully submerged. So the buoyant force on the partially submerged object is less.
4. One way would be to weigh the object in air, and then weigh the object in the water. The difference between the two weights is the upward buoyant force on the object.
5. When the sub displaces air in its tanks with seawater, its density increases and becomes greater than the surrounding water. Then the sub dives. When the sub expels seawater from its tanks, its density decreases and the sub rises.
6. Water has a density of 1 kg/L, so that 1 L has a weight of 9.8 N. So the buoyant force is (80,000 L)(9.8 N/L) = 784,000 N.
7. The density of the ring is $D = m/V$ = (7.21 g)/(0.65 cm^3) = 11.1 g/cm^3. Because the density of the ring is not the same as the density of 14k gold, the ring cannot be made of pure 14k gold.

Measuring Buoyant Force

The total force on an object in a fluid is the difference between the object's weight and the buoyant force. In this lab, you will measure the buoyant force on an object and compare it to the weight of the water displaced.

▶ Real-World Question

How is the buoyant force related to the weight of the water that an object displaces?

Goals

- **Measure** the buoyant force on an object.
- **Compare** the buoyant force to the weight of the water displaced by the object.

Materials

aluminum pan	graduated cylinder
spring scale	funnel
500-mL beaker	metal object

Safety Precautions

▶ Procedure

1. Place the beaker in the aluminum pan and fill the beaker to the brim with water.

2. Hang the object from the spring scale and record its weight.

3. With the object hanging from the spring scale, completely submerge the object in the water. The object should not be touching the bottom or the sides of the beaker.

4. **Record** the reading on the spring scale while the object is in the water. Calculate the buoyant force by subtracting this reading from the object's weight.

5. Use the funnel to carefully pour the water from the pan into the graduated cylinder. Record the volume of this water in cm3.

6. **Calculate** the weight of the water displaced by multiplying the volume of water by 0.0098 N.

▶ Conclude and Apply

1. **Explain** how the total force on the object changed when it was submerged in water.

2. **Compare** the weight of the water that is displaced with the buoyant force.

3. **Explain** how the buoyant force would change if the object were submersed halfway in water.

*C*ommunicating
Your Data

Make a poster of an empty ship, a heavily loaded ship, and an overloaded, sinking ship. Explain how Archimedes' principle applies in each case. **For more help, refer to the** Science Skill Handbook.

LAB **M** ◆ **81**

*C*ommunicating
Your Data

Posters should show that as more material is loaded onto the boat, it sinks lower into the water. The overloaded ship starts taking in water over the sides, causing it to become even heavier.

▶ Real-World Question

Purpose to measure the buoyant force and compare it to the weight of water displaced by an object L2 LS **Kinesthetic**

Process Skills observe, infer, measure, test a hypothesis, collect data, compare and contrast, recognize cause and effect

Time Required 45 minutes

▶ Procedure

Safety Precautions Caution students not to spill water on the floor.

Teaching Strategy Make sure the objects will sink in water, and are large enough to displace a noticeable amount of water. For example, a hollow metal bead won't sink, and a necklace chain will have too small a volume to displace much water.

▶ Conclude and Apply

1. The total force decreased.
2. The two should be equal.
3. If only half of the object were submerged, only half the volume of water would be displaced, so the buoyant force would be half what it was on the completely submerged object.

✓ Assessment

Oral Ask students to hypothesize why birds that dive and do not fly, such as penguins, tend to have heavier bones than birds that fly. The heavier bones make the birds denser than flying birds of similar shape. This makes it easier for the birds to dive. Use **Performance Assessment in the Science Classroom,** p. 93.

as you read

What You'll Learn
- **Explain** how forces are transmitted through fluids.
- **Describe** how a hydraulic system increases force.
- **Describe** Bernoulli's principle.

Why It's Important
Fluids can exert forces that lift heavy objects and enable aircraft to fly.

Review Vocabulary
work: the product of the force applied to an object and the distance the object moves in the direction of the force

New Vocabulary
- Pascal's principle
- hydraulic system
- Bernoulli's principle

Using Fluid Forces

You might have watched a hydraulic lift raise a car off the ground. It might surprise you to learn that the force pushing the car upward is being exerted by a fluid. When a huge jetliner soars through the air, a fluid exerts the force that holds it up. Fluids at rest and fluids in motion can be made to exert forces that do useful work, such as pumping water from a well, making cars stop, and carrying people long distances through the air. How are these forces produced by fluids?

Pushing on a Fluid The pressure in a fluid can be increased by pushing on the fluid. Suppose a watertight, movable cover, or piston, is sitting on top of a column of fluid in a container. If you push on the piston, the fluid can't escape past the piston, so the height of the fluid in the container doesn't change. As a result, the piston doesn't move. But now the force exerted on the bottom of the container is the weight of the fluid plus the force pushing the piston down. Because the force exerted by the fluid at the bottom of the container has increased, the pressure exerted by the fluid also has increased. **Figure 19** shows how the force exerted on a brake pedal is transmitted to a fluid.

Figure 19 Because the fluid in this piston can't escape, it transmits the force you apply throughout the fluid.

Pascal's Principle

Suppose you fill a plastic bottle with water and screw the cap back on. If you poke a hole in the bottle near the top, water will leak out of the hole. However, if you squeeze the bottle near the bottom, as shown in **Figure 20,** water will shoot out of the hole. When you squeezed the bottle, you applied a force on the fluid. This increased the pressure in the fluid and pushed the water out of the hole faster.

No matter where you poke the hole in the bottle, squeezing the bottle will cause the water to flow faster out of the hole. The force you exert on the fluid by squeezing has been transmitted to every part of the bottle. This is an example of Pascal's principle. According to **Pascal's principle,** when a force is applied to a fluid in a closed container, the pressure in the fluid increases everywhere by the same amount.

Hydraulic Systems

Pascal's principle is used in building hydraulic systems like the ones used by car lifts. A **hydraulic system** uses a fluid to increase an input force. The fluid enclosed in a hydraulic system transfers pressure from one piston to another. An example is shown in **Figure 21.** An input force that is applied to the small piston increases the pressure in the fluid. This pressure increase is transmitted throughout the fluid and acts on the large piston. The force the fluid exerts on the large piston is the pressure in the fluid times the area of the piston. Because the area of the large piston is greater than the area of the small piston, the output force exerted on the large piston is greater than the input force exerted on the small piston.

Figure 20 When you squeeze the bottle, the pressure you apply is distributed throughout the fluid, forcing the water out the hole.

Force applied on large piston

Force applied on small piston

Figure 21 A hydraulic system uses Pascal's principle to make the output force applied on the large piston greater than the input force applied on the small piston.
Infer how the force on the large piston would change if its area increased.

SECTION 3 Doing Work with Fluids **M** ◆ 83

Differentiated Instruction

Physically Challenged Students with asthma and other breathing problems may not be able to do many of the experiments described in this section. Suggest these students use a hairdryer set to cool to produce a steady, high pressure stream of air.

Figure 22 By blowing on one side of the can, you decrease the air pressure on that side. Because the pressure on the opposite side is now greater, the can moves toward the side you're blowing on.

Increasing Force What is the force pushing upward on the larger piston? For example, suppose that the area of the small piston is 1 m^2 and the area of the large piston is 2 m^2. If you push on the small piston with a force of 10 N, the increase in pressure at the bottom of the small piston is

$$P = F/A$$
$$= (10 \text{ N})/(1 \text{ m}^2)$$
$$= 10 \text{ Pa}$$

According to Pascal's principle, this increase in pressure is transmitted throughout the fluid. This causes the force exerted by the fluid on the larger piston to increase. The increase in the force on the larger piston can be calculated by multiplying both sides of the above formula by A.

$$F = P \times A$$
$$= 10 \text{ Pa} \times 2 \text{ m}^2$$
$$= 20 \text{ N}$$

The force pushing upward on the larger piston is twice as large as the force pushing downward on the smaller piston. What happens if the larger piston increases in size? Look at the calculation above. If the area of the larger piston increases to 5 m^2, the force pushing up on this piston increases to 50 N. So a small force pushing down on the left piston as in **Figure 21** can be made much larger by increasing the size of the piston on the right.

☑ Reading Check *How does a hydraulic system increase force?*

Pressure in a Moving Fluid

What happens to the pressure in a fluid if the fluid is moving? Try the following experiment. Place an empty soda can on the desktop and blow to the right of the can, as shown in **Figure 22.** In which direction will the can move?

When you blow to the right of the can, the can moves to the right, toward the moving air. The air pressure exerted on the right side of the can, where the air is moving, is less than the air pressure on the left side of the can, where the air is not moving. As a result, the force exerted by the air pressure on the left side is greater than the force exerted on the right side, and the can is pushed to the right. What would happen if you blew between two empty cans?

Bernoulli's Principle

The reason for the surprising behavior of the can in **Figure 22** was discovered by the Swiss scientist Daniel Bernoulli in the eighteenth century. It is an example of Bernoulli's principle. According to **Bernoulli's principle,** when the speed of a fluid increases, the pressure exerted by the fluid decreases. When you blew across the side of the can, the pressure exerted by the air on that side of the can decreased because the air was moving faster than it was on the other side. As a result, the can was pushed toward the side you blew across.

Chimneys and Bernoulli's Principle In a fireplace the hotter, less dense air above the fire is pushed upward by the cooler, denser air in the room. Wind outside of the house can increase the rate at which the smoke rises. Look at **Figure 23.** Air moving across the top of the chimney causes the air pressure above the chimney to decrease according to Bernoulli's principle. As a result, more smoke is pushed upward by the higher pressure of the air in the room.

Damage from High Winds You might have seen photographs of people preparing for a hurricane by closing shutters over windows or nailing boards across the outside of windows. In a hurricane, the high winds blowing outside the house cause the pressure outside the house to be less than the pressure inside. This difference in pressure can be large enough to cause windows to be pushed out and to shatter.

Hurricanes and other high winds sometimes can blow roofs from houses. When wind blows across the roof of a house, the pressure outside the roof decreases. If the wind outside is blowing fast enough, the outside pressure can become so low that the roof can be pushed off the house by the higher pressure of the still air inside.

Wings and Flight

You might have placed your hand outside the open window of a moving car and felt the push on it from the air streaming past. If you angled your hand so it tilted upward into the moving air, you would have felt your hand pushed upward. If you increased the tilt of your hand, you felt the upward push increase. You might not have realized it, but your hand was behaving like an airplane wing. The force that lifted your hand was provided by a fluid—the air.

Figure 23 The air moving past the chimney lowers the air pressure above the chimney. As a result, smoke is forced up the chimney faster than when air above the chimney is still.

The Coanda effect describes the tendency of any viscous fluid, such as air, to stick to a surface it flows past. Friction between the fluid and the surface makes the fluid move slower close to the surface. Just as a car that turns to the right when the wheels on the left are rotating faster than the wheels on the right, the fluid turns toward a surface that curves away from the flow direction. As a result, air flow follows the upper surface of the wing.

Reading Check

Answer by increasing the surface area of the wing

Visual Learning

Figure 25 People have made many attempts to fly by building wings, attaching them to their arms, and flapping them. All attempts have been unsuccessful. Why can't humans fly by flapping artificial wings? Birds have a number of adaptations that enable them to fly, including hollow bones that reduce their body mass, and powerful chest muscles to flap their wings. Because of their relatively high body mass, humans would need artificial wings with a large surface area to provide enough lift. However, humans do not have the muscles that would be needed to flap these large wings. L2

IS Logical-Mathematical

Producing Lift How is the upward force, or lift, on an airplane wing produced? A jet engine pushes the plane forward, or a propeller pulls the plane forward. Air flows over the wings as the plane moves. The wings are tilted upward into the airflow, just like your hand was tilted outside the car window. **Figure 24** shows how the tilt of the wing causes air that has flowed over the wing's upper and lower surfaces to be directed downward.

Lift is created by making the air flow downward. To understand this, remember that air is made of different types of molecules. The motion of these molecules is changed only when a force acts on them. When the air is directed downward, a force is being exerted on the air molecules by the wing.

However, according to Newton's third law of motion, for every action force there is an equal but opposite reaction force. The wing exerts a downward action force on the air. So the air must exert an upward reaction force on the wing. This reaction force is the lift that enables paper airplanes and jet airliners to fly.

Airplane Wings Airplanes have different wing shapes, depending on how the airplane is used. The lift on a wing depends on the amount of air that the wing deflects downward and how fast that air is moving. Lift can be increased by increasing the size or surface area of the wing. A larger wing is able to deflect more air downward.

Look at the planes in **Figure 25.** A plane designed to fly at high speeds, such as a jet fighter, can have small wings. A large cargo plane that carries heavy loads needs large wings to provide a great deal of lift. A glider flies at low speeds and uses long wings that have a large surface area to provide the lift it needs.

Reading Check *How can a wing's lift be increased?*

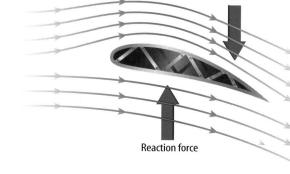

Action force

Reaction force

Figure 24 An airplane wing forces air to be directed downward. As a result, the air exerts an upward reaction force on the wing, producing lift.

Active Reading

Pair of Pairs Have students as partners respond to a question by brainstorming together and recording on one paper their ideas. After a few minutes, have them combine with another pair and share responses. Finally, ask the groups of four to share any responses. Have students use the Pair of Pairs strategy on question 5 in the Section Review for this section.

INTEGRATE Life Science

Birds' Wings A bird's wing provides lift in the same way that an airplane wing does. The wings also act as propellers that pull the bird forward when it flaps its wings up and down. Bird wings also have different shapes depending on the type of flight. Seabirds have long, narrow wings, like the wings of a glider, that help them glide long distances. Forest and field birds, such as pheasants, have short, rounded wings that enable them to take off quickly and make sharp turns. Swallows, swifts, and falcons, which fly at high speeds, have small, narrow, tapered wings like those on a jet fighter.

Figure 25 Different wing shapes are used for different types of planes. Larger wings provide more lift.

3 Assess

DAILY INTERVENTION

Check for Understanding
Linguistic Write the terms *Pascal's Principle* and *Bernoulli's Principle* on the board. Have students write one fact and give two examples for each term. Let students share their facts and examples with the class.

Reteach
Pressure and Moving Air Repeat for students the experiment with the soda cans, and ask students to explain what is happening. Students should recognize that air pressure always acts on the cans, and that the pressure of the moving air is less than that of the still air. L2 IS **Visual-Spatial**

✓ Assessment

Process In a hydraulic lift, a force of 15 N is exerted on a piston with an area of 1 m². How much pressure is exerted on the piston? 15 Pa This pressure is transferred to a piston with an area of 2 m². What is the force on the second piston? 30 N Use **Performance Assessment in the Science Classroom,** p. 101.

section 3 review

1. A larger wing is able to deflect more air downward which results in a greater reaction force pushing upward, resulting in greater lift.
2. The change in pressure is the same throughout the water.
3. The air flowing between the car and the truck is moving faster than the air on the other side of the car. So the pressure exerted by the air between the car and the truck is less than the pressure exerted on the other side of the car.
4. Blowing across the top of a sheet of paper creates a low pressure area above the paper. The higher pressure air below the paper pushes the paper up.
5. The pressure increase is the same on both pistons. The increase in force is greater on the piston with the greater surface area.
6. The increase in pressure in the fluid is $P = F/A = (250\ N)/(0.01\ m^2) = 25{,}000$ Pa. The increase in force on the larger piston is $F = PA = (25{,}000\ Pa)(0.05\ m^2) = 1{,}250$ N.

Real-World Question

Purpose

Internet Students use Internet sites that can be accessed through bookm.msscience.com/internet_lab.

Non-Internet Sources Weather information from a newspaper or other sources.

Time Required

90 minutes spread over five days or more

Make a Plan

Preparation

Internet To run through the steps that the students will follow, visit bookm.msscience.com/internet_lab.

Non-Internet Sources Bring weather information to class.

Follow Your Plan

Teaching Strategies

• **Troubleshooting** Data and observations may not exactly coincide. Students may have a difficult time understanding that meteorology is not an exact science. Depending on the area and season, wide variations may not even occur.

• Direct students to make sure they observe the weather for the prescribed number of days. Incomplete data will make it difficult to draw conclusions.

LAB

Barometric Pressure and Weather

Goals

■ **Collect** barometric pressure and other weather data.

■ **Compare** barometric pressure to weather conditions.

■ **Predict** weather patterns based on barometric pressure, wind speed and direction, and visual conditions.

Data Source

Science Online

Visit bookm.msscience.com/internet_lab for more information about barometric pressure, weather information, and data collected by other students.

Real-World Question

What is the current barometric pressure where you are? How would you describe the weather today where you are? What is the weather like in the region to the west of you? To the east of you? What will your weather be like tomorrow? The atmosphere is a fluid and flows from one place to another as weather patterns change. Changing weather conditions also cause the atmospheric pressure to change. By collecting barometric pressure data and observing weather conditions, you will be able to make a prediction about the next day's weather.

Make a Plan

1. Visit the Web site on the left for links to information about weather in the region where you live.

2. Find and record the current barometric pressure and whether the pressure is rising, falling, or remaining steady. Also record the wind speed and direction.

3. **Observe and record** other weather conditions, such as whether rain is falling, the Sun is shining, or the sky is cloudy.

4. Based on the data you collect and your observations, predict what you think tomorrow's weather will be. Record your prediction.

5. Repeat the data collection and observation for a total of five days.

Alternative Inquiry Lab

Star Gazing To make this Lab an Inquiry Lab, give students a more personal investment in the problem by connecting it to the real world. Tell the students that they are in charge of planning a stargazing party for their class. The class is going into the countryside with telescopes and observing the stars on two consecutive nights. Have students collect weather data and predict which two consecutive nights would be the best for this party. Remind the students that you cannot look at stars on cloudy nights.

Barometric Pressure Weather Data	
Location of weather station	Carlsbad, CA
Barometric pressure	99.7 kPa
Status of barometric pressure	Falling
Wind speed	2 m/s
Wind direction	Variable
Current weather conditions	Cloudy and cool
Predictions of tomorrow's weather conditions	Continue to be cloudy and cool

Follow Your Plan

1. Make sure your teacher approves your plan before you start.
2. Visit the link below to post your data.

Analyze Your Data

1. **Analyze** Look at your data. What was the weather the day after the barometric pressure increased? The day after the barometric pressure decreased? The day after the barometric pressure was steady?
2. **Draw Conclusions** How accurate were your weather predictions?

Conclude and Apply

1. **Infer** What is the weather to the west of you today? How will that affect the weather in your area tomorrow?
2. **Compare** What was the weather to the east of you today? How does that compare to the weather in your area yesterday?
3. **Evaluate** How does increasing, decreasing, or steady barometric pressure affect the weather?

Communicating Your Data

Find this lab using the link below. Use the data on the Web site to predict the weather where you are two days from now.

Science Online
bookm.msscience.com/internet_lab

Expected Outcome If students look broadly at their data, they should notice that lower pressure often brings rain and higher pressure usually brings fairer skies.

Analyze Your Data

Answers to Questions

1. Increasing pressure brings clear skies, decreasing pressure brings rain or clouds, and steady pressure brings no changes.
2. A general trend should be seen, but precise, exact correlations may be difficult to find.

Error Analysis If the expected results are not seen, another series of observations may bring clearer results.

Conclude and Apply

1. Since weather patterns generally move west to east, the weather to the west is an indicator of your weather for tomorrow.
2. The weather to the east should be similar to the weather you experienced yesterday.
3. Increasing pressure brings clear skies, while decreasing pressure brings clouds or rain. Steady pressure means there will not be a change in weather.

✔ Assessment

Performance Have students take additional data and predict the weather for the next day. Do several predictions, list the reasons for the predictions, and assess the accuracy. Use **Performance Assessment in the Science Classroom,** p. 89.

Communicating Your Data

To clearly communicate their recorded data, be sure that students have a large chart that has space for each item to be recorded on each day. If it is not clear what they are to record, students may not take all data needed.

"Hurricane"
by John Balaban

Understanding Literature

Sense Impressions Sample examples: smell: "ozoned light" sight: "day arrived in queer light" sound: "crashed" touch: "sickening August heat"

Respond to the Reading

1. The hurricane destroyed houses, caused trees to snap, and caused other living things such as snakes to die.

2. Elling brought much needed supplies.

3. **Linking Science and Writing** Lead students in a brainstorming activity to think of words that suggest sense impressions.

 Bernoulli's Principle

Daniel Bernoulli was the second son of Johann Bernoulli, who first taught him mathematics. In his important work entitled *Hydrodynamica*, he considered how pressure, density, and velocity of fluids affect fluid flow and established their basic relationship. He put forward what is called Bernoulli's principle, which states that the pressure in a fluid decreases as its velocity increases. He also established the basis for the kinetic theory of gases and heat by demonstrating that the impact of molecules on a surface could explain pressure and that, assuming the constant, random motion of molecules, pressure and motion would increase with temperature.

Near dawn our old live oak sagged over
then crashed on the tool shed
rocketing off rakes paintcans flower pots.

All night, rain slashed the shutters until
it finally quit and day arrived in queer light,
silence, and ozoned air. Then voices calling

as neighbors crept out to see the snapped trees,
leaf mash and lawn chairs driven in heaps
with roof bits, siding, sodden birds, dead snakes.

For days, bulldozers clanked by our houses
in sickening August heat as heavy cranes
scraped the rotting tonnage from the streets.

Then our friend Elling drove in from Sarasota
in his old . . . van packed with candles, with
dog food, cat food, flashlights and batteries . . . .

Understanding Literature

Sense Impressions In this poem, John Balaban uses sense impressions to place the reader directly into the poem's environment. For example, the words *rotting tonnage* evoke the sense of smell. Give examples of other sense impressions mentioned.

Respond to the Reading

1. What kinds of damage did the hurricane cause?

2. Why do you think the poet felt relief when his friend, Elling, arrived?

3. **Linking Science and Writing** Write a poem describing a natural phenomenon involving forces and fluids. Use words that evoke at least one of the five sense impressions.

 In the poem, bits of roofs and siding from houses are part of the debris that is everywhere in heaps. According to Bernoulli's principle, the high winds in a hurricane blowing past a house causes the air pressure outside the house to be less than the air pressure inside. In some cases, the forces exerted by the air inside causes the roof to be pushed off the house, and the walls to be blown outward.

Resources for Teachers and Students

Locust at the Edge of Summer: New and Selected Poems, by John Balaban, Copper Canyon Press, 1997

Blue Mountain, by John Balaban, Unicorn Press, 1982

Reviewing Main Ideas

Section 1 Pressure

1. Pressure equals force divided by area.

2. Liquids and gases are fluids that flow.

3. Pressure increases with depth and decreases with elevation in a fluid.

4. The pressure exerted by a fluid on a surface is always perpendicular to the surface.

Section 2 Why do objects float?

1. A buoyant force is an upward force exerted on all objects placed in a fluid.

2. The buoyant force depends on the shape of the object.

3. According to Archimedes' principle, the buoyant force on the object is equal to the weight of the fluid displaced by the object.

4. An object floats when the buoyant force exerted by the fluid is equal to the object's weight.

5. An object will float if it is less dense than the fluid it is placed in.

Section 3 Doing Work with Fluids

1. Pascal's principle states that the pressure applied at any point to a confined fluid is transmitted unchanged throughout the fluid.

2. Bernoulli's principle states that when the velocity of a fluid increases, the pressure exerted by the fluid decreases.

3. A wing provides lift by forcing air downward.

Visualizing Main Ideas

Copy and complete the following table.

Relationships Among Forces and Fluids

Idea	What does it relate?	How?
Density	mass and volume	
Pressure		force/area
Archimedes' principle	buoyant force and weight of fluid that is displaced	
Bernoulli's principle		velocity increases, pressure decreases
Pascal's principle	pressure applied to enclosed fluid at one point and pressure at other points in a fluid	

Reviewing Main Ideas

Summary statements can be used by students to review the major concepts of the chapter.

Visualizing Main Ideas

See student page.

Visit bookm.msscience.com
/self_check_quiz
/interactive_tutor
/vocabulary_puzzlemaker
/chapter_review
/standardized_test

Assessment Transparency

For additional assessment questions, use the *Assessment Transparency* located in the transparency book.

Assessment

Assessment Transparency   Forces and Fluids

Directions: *Carefully review the diagram and answer the following questions.*

1. Archimedes' principle states that the buoyant force on an object is equal to the weight of the fluid that object displaces. If a scientist puts an ice cube into one of the graduated cylinders of water and the water level increases by 5 mL, then _____.
   A the ice cube would decrease the pressure exerted by the graduated cylinder of water
   B the ice cube would take a longer time to melt than if it were placed on the table
   C the water could exert more pressure on the side of the ice cube than on the bottom
   D the scientist could conclude that the buoyant force on the ice cube is equal to the weight of 5 mL of water

2. Each graduated cylinder contains 50 mL of water. In which cylinder would a marble on the bottom experience the greatest pressure?
   F cylinder A   G cylinder B   H cylinder C   J cylinder D

Forces and Fluids

Using Vocabulary

1. fluid
2. pressure
3. Archimedes' principle
4. hydraulic system
5. density
6. density
7. Bernoulli's principle

Checking Concepts

8. A   11. B
9. C   12. B
10. D   13. B

Thinking Critically

14. When the sandbag is dropped, the weight of the balloon decreases. The buoyant force of air on the balloon remains the same, so the balloon rises.

15. The statement is not correct because the density determines whether or not an object floats, not its weight. A heavy aircraft carrier is less dense than water so it will float, while a much lighter pebble will sink because it is denser than water.

16. The boat takes in water, increasing its mass and its density. Eventually the boat becomes more dense than water and sinks.

17. The forces due to water pressure on either side of the cube balance each other, because they are at the same depth. The top and bottom of the cube are at different depths, and the force at the greater depth, the bottom of the cube, is greater. So the net force is upward.

18. Steel is denser than the material making up the balloon, so the steel tank filled with helium is denser than air while the balloon filled with helium is less dense than air. The balloon rises and the steel tank stays on the ground.

Using Vocabulary

Archimedes' principle p. 77	fluid p. 69
Bernoulli's principle p. 85	hydraulic system p. 83
buoyant force p. 74	Pascal's principle p. 83
density p. 78	pressure p. 66

Answer each of the following questions using complete sentences that include vocabulary from the list above.

1. How would you describe a substance that can flow?

2. When the area over which a force is applied decreases, what increases?

3. What principle relates the weight of displaced fluid to the buoyant force?

4. How is a fluid used to lift heavy objects?

5. If you increase an object's mass but not its volume, what have you changed?

6. How is a log able to float in a river?

7. What principle explains why hurricanes can blow the roof off of a house?

Checking Concepts

Choose the word or phrase that best answers the question.

8. What happens to pressure when the force that is exerted on a surface decreases?
   A) decreases   C) stays the same
   B) increases   D) any of the above

9. The weight of the fluid displaced by an object that is in the fluid is equal to which of the following?
   A) the weight of the object
   B) the density of the object
   C) the buoyant force on the object
   D) the volume of the object

10. If force increased and pressure remained the same, what must have happened?
    A) density decreased
    B) density increased
    C) area decreased
    D) area increased

Use the photo below to answer question 11.

water level

water level

11. Each graduated cylinder contains the same amount of water. Which of the following statements is true?
    A) The pressure is greater at the bottom of the large cylinder.
    B) The pressure is greater at the bottom of the small cylinder.
    C) The pressure is equal at the bottom of both cylinders.
    D) There is zero pressure at the bottom of both cylinders.

12. As you drive down a high mountain, what happens to air pressure?
    A) It decreases.
    B) It increases.
    C) It increases, then decreases.
    D) It stays the same.

13. If the pressure that is exerted by a moving fluid decreases, what happens to its speed?
    A) decreases   C) stays the same
    B) increases   D) any of the above

 Science Online bookm.msscience.com/vocabulary_puzzlemaker

19. The graph should be a curved line from upper left to lower right, showing that pressure decreases as area increases.

20. An upward buoyant force acts on an object in water. As a result, the net downward force due to gravity is less. The upward force needed to lift the object is less when it is in water.

21. The object that sinks has a greater density than the object that floats. Because the objects have identical volumes, the object that sinks has a greater mass.

Use the Exam*View*® Pro Testmaker CD-ROM to:
- customize tests
- create multiple versions of tests
- generate tests in Spanish
- build tests aligned with state standards

Thinking Critically

14. **Explain** A sandbag is dropped from a hot-air balloon and the balloon rises. Explain why this happens.

15. **Determine** whether or not this statement is true: Heavy objects sink, and light objects float. Explain your answer.

16. **Explain** why a leaking boat sinks.

17. **Explain** why the direction of the buoyant force on a submerged cube is upward and not left or right.

18. **Recognizing Cause and Effect** A steel tank and a balloon are the same size and contain the same amount of helium. Explain why the balloon rises and the steel tank doesn't.

19. **Make and Use Graphs** Graph the pressure exerted by a 75-kg person wearing different shoes with areas of 0.01 m², 0.02 m², 0.03 m², 0.04 m², and 0.05 m². Plot pressure on the vertical axis and area on the horizontal axis.

20. **Explain** why it is easier to lift an object that is underwater, than it is to lift the object when it is out of the water.

21. **Infer** Two objects with identical shapes are placed in water. One object floats and the other object sinks. Infer the difference between the two objects that causes one to sink and the other to float.

22. **Compare** Two containers with different diameters are filled with water to the same height. Compare the force exerted by the fluid on the bottom of the two containers.

Performance Activities

23. **Oral Presentation** Research the different wing designs in birds or aircraft. Present your results to the class.

 bookm.msscience.com/chapter_review

24. **Experiment** Partially fill a plastic dropper with water until it floats just below the surface of the water in a bowl or beaker. Place the dropper inside a plastic bottle, fill the bottle with water, and seal the top. Now squeeze the bottle. What happens to the water pressure in the bottle? How does the water level in the dropper change? How does the density of the dropper change? Use your answers to these questions to explain how the dropper moves when you squeeze the bottle.

Applying Math

25. **Buoyant Force** A rock is attached to a spring scale that reads 10 N. If the rock is submerged in water, the scale reads 6 N. What is the buoyant force on the submerged rock?

26. **Hydraulic Force** A hydraulic lift with a large piston area of 0.04 m² exerts a force of 5,000 N. If the smaller piston has an area of 0.01 m², what is the force on it?

Use the table below to answer questions 27 and 28.

Material Density	
Substance	**Density (g/cm³)**
Ice	0.92
Lead	11.34
Balsa wood	0.12
Sugar	1.59

27. **Density** Classify which of the above substances will and will not float in water.

28. **Volume** Find the volumes of each material, if each has a mass of 25 g.

29. **Pressure** What is the pressure due to a force of 100 N on an area 4 m²?

30. **Pressure** A bottle of lemonade sitting on a table weighs 6 N. The bottom of the bottle has a surface area of 0.025 m². Calculate the pressure the bottle of lemonade exerts on the table.

CHAPTER REVIEW M ◆ 93

22. Because the water has the same height, the pressure exerted at the bottom of each container is the same. The container with the larger diameter has a greater surface area at the bottom, so the force exerted by the fluid is greater at the bottom of this container.

Performance Activities

23. Answers will vary. Students should contrast at least two wing designs, listing the benefits and limitations of each. Use **PASC,** p. 143.

24. The water pressure in the bottle increases as you squeeze it, as does the water pressure in the dropper. The air in the dropper is compressed by incoming water. This increased pressure is transferred, by Pascal's principle, to the water and air in the dropper. More water is pushed into the dropper, thus increasing the density of the dropper, so it sinks. Use **PASC,** p. 119.

Applying Math

National Math Standards
1, 2, 3, 5, 9

25. 4 N

26. The pressure equals $F/A = (5,000 \text{ N})/(0.04 \text{ m}^2) = 125,000$ Pa. The force on the smaller piston then is $F = PA = (125,000 \text{ Pa})(0.01 \text{ m}^2) = 1,250$ N.

27. Ice and balsa wood float; lead and sugar do not float.

28. $V = m/D$; ice, 27 cm³; lead, 2.2 cm³; balsa wood, 208 cm³; sugar, 16 cm³

29. $P = F/A = (100 \text{ N})/(4 \text{ m}^2) = 25$ Pa

30. $P = F/A = (6 \text{ N})/(0.025 \text{ m}^2) = 240$ Pa

Answer Sheet A practice answer sheet can be found at bookm.msscience.com/answer_sheet.

S A M P L E

Part 1 Multiple Choice

1. B
2. D
3. B
4. A
5. C
6. A
7. C

Part 2 Short Response

8. Snowshoes turn the bottoms of feet into large, flat surfaces. This increases the area over which the force of body weight is exerted. The pressure is decreased, making it easier to walk without sinking.

9. A fluid is any substance that has no definite shape and has the ability to flow. Gases meet both of these criteria.

10. The fluids in your body exert an outward pressure which balances the inward pressure exerted by the atmosphere.

Part 1 Multiple Choice

Record your answers on the answer sheet provided by your teacher or on a sheet of paper.

1. A force of 15 N is exerted on an area of 0.1 m². What is the pressure?
  A. 150 N
  B. 150 Pa
  C. 1.5 Pa
  D. 0.007 Pa

Use the illustration below to answer questions 2 and 3.

2. Which statement is TRUE?
  A. The contact area between the board and the nail tip is large.
  B. The contact area between the nail tip and the board is greater than the contact area between the nail head and the hammer head.
  C. The nail exerts no pressure on the board because its weight is so small.
  D. The pressure exerted by the nail is large because the contact area between the nail tip and the board is small.

3. If the force exerted by the hammer on the nail stays the same, how does the pressure exerted by the nail on the board change if the diameter of the nail tip increases?
  A. becomes denser **C.** no change
  B. decreases **D.** increases

Test-Taking Tip

Check the Answer Number For each question, double check that you are filling in the correct answer bubble for the question number you are working on.

4. A 15-g block of aluminum has a volume of 5.5 cm³. What is the density?
  A. 2.7 g/cm³
  B. 82.5 g/cm³
  C. 0.37 g/cm³
  D. 2.7 cm³/g

Use the illustration below to answer questions 5 and 6.

5. Assume the boat and cube have the same mass. Which of these is correct?
  A. The boat displaces less water than the cube.
  B. The densities of the boat and cube are equal.
  C. The density of the boat is less than the density of the cube.
  D. The density of the boat is greater than the density of the water.

6. Which of the following would make the cube more likely to float?
  A. increasing its volume
  B. increasing its density
  C. increasing its weight
  D. decreasing its volume

7. Which of the following instruments is used to measure atmospheric pressure?
  A. altimeter
  B. hygrometer
  C. barometer
  D. anemometer

11. The buoyant force increases because the boat displaces more water.

12. Any change in the boat's weight that made it greater than the buoyant force would result in the boat sinking. This could happen if large amounts of water entered the boat through holes in the hull or if the boat was overloaded.

13. High winds blowing across the outside of windows cause the pressure to be less outside of the house than inside. If the difference in pressure is large enough, the windows can be pushed out.

14. Lift is affected by the amount of air deflected downward by the wing and how fast the air is moving.

15. $F = (1,000 \text{ Pa}) \times (0.05 \text{ m}^2) = 50 \text{ N}$

Part 2 | Short Response/Grid In

Record your answers on the answer sheet provided by your teacher or on a sheet of paper.

8. Explain why wearing snowshoes makes it easier to walk over deep, soft snow.

9. Why is a gas, such as air condidered to be a fluid?

10. Explain why the pressure exerted by the atmosphere does not crush your body.

Use the illustration below to answer questions 11 and 12.

11. How does the buoyant force on the boat change if the boat is loaded so that it floats lower in the water?

12. What changes in the properties of this boat could cause it to sink?

13. People sometimes prepare for a coming hurricane by nailing boards over the outside of windows. How can high winds damage windows?

14. What factors influence the amount of lift on an airplane wing?

15. The pressure inside the fluid of a hydraulic system is increased by 1,000 Pa. What is the increase in the force exerted on a piston that has an area of 0.05 m²?

Part 3 | Open Ended

Record your answers on a sheet of paper.

16. Explain why the interior of an airplane is pressurized when flying at high altitude. If a hole were punctured in an exterior wall, what would happen to the air pressure inside the plane?

17. In an experiment, you design small boats using aluminum foil. You add pennies to each boat until it sinks. Sketch several different shapes you might create. Which will likely hold the most pennies? Why?

18. You squeeze a round, air-filled balloon slightly, changing its shape. Describe how the pressure inside the balloon changes.

Use the illustration below to answer questions 19 and 20.

19. Describe the motion of the table tennis balls when air is blown between the two balls. Explain.

20. Describe the motion of the table tennis balls if air blown to the left of the ball on the left and to the right of the ball on the right at the same time. Explain.

21. Compare the pressure you exert on a floor when you are standing on the floor and when you are lying on the floor.

22. In order to drink a milk shake through a straw, how must the air pressure inside the straw change, compared with the air pressure outside the straw?

Part 3 | Open Ended

16. At a high altitude, atmospheric pressure decreases. In order to maintain comfortable air pressure and adequate oxygen supply, cabins are pressurized. Should a puncture occur, the air inside the plane will attempt to move to an area of lower pressure outside the plane. Eventually, the pressures inside and outside the plane would equalize.

17. Shapes might include flat-bottomed boats, hulls which are slightly rounded, and hulls which have steep sides. Boats that hold the most pennies will be those with the largest volume that displace the most water.

18. According to Pascal's principle, the pressure of the gas inside the balloon increases throughout the balloon by the same amount because the force is transmitted to all parts of the fluid.

19. According to Bernoulli's principle, the pressure exerted by the moving air is less than the pressure exerted by the still air. This will cause the balls to move toward each other.

20. The pressure exerted by the moving air is less than the pressure exerted by the still air between the balls. This will cause the balls to move away from each other.

21. The force you exert on the floor equals your weight and is the same in each case. When you are standing, the area in contact with the floor is less, so the pressure is greater.

22. The air pressure in the straw must decrease.

Rubrics

For more help evaluating open-ended assessment questions, see the rubric on p. 10T.

chapter 4 Organizer

Section/Objectives	Standards		Labs/Features
Chapter Opener	**National**	**State/Local**	**Launch Lab:** Compare forces, p. 97
	See pp. 9T–10T for a Key to Standards.		**Foldables,** p. 97
Section 1 Work and Power ⏱ 3 sessions 📦 1.5 blocks 1. **Recognize** when work is done. 2. **Calculate** how much work is done. 3. **Explain** the relationship between work and power.	National Content Standards: UCP.2, UCP.3, A.1, A.2, B.2, B.3		**Integrate History,** p. 100 **Applying Math:** Calculating Work, p. 100 **MiniLAB:** Work and Power, p. 101 **Applying Math:** Calculating Power, p. 101 **Science Online,** p. 102 **Lab:** Building the Pyramids, p. 103
Section 2 Using Machines ⏱ 3 sessions 📦 1.5 blocks 4. **Explain** how a machine makes work easier. 5. **Calculate** the mechanical advantages and efficiency of a machine. 6. **Explain** how friction reduces efficiency.	National Content Standards: UCP.2, UCP.3, A.1, A.2, B.2, B.3		**Science Online,** p. 105 **Applying Math:** Calculating Mechanical Advantage, p. 105 **Integrate Life Science,** p. 107 **Applying Math:** Calculating Efficiency, p. 107
Section 3 Simple Machines ⏱ 4 sessions 📦 2 blocks 7. **Distinguish** among the different simple machines. 8. **Describe** how to find the mechanical advantage of each simple machine.	National Content Standards: UCP.2, UCP.3, A.1, A.2, B.2, B.3		**Visualizing Levers,** p. 113 **MiniLAB:** Observing Pulleys, p. 114 **Lab:** Pulley Power, pp. 116–117 **Science and Society:** Bionic People, p. 118

Lab Materials	Reproducible Resources	Section Assessment	Technology
Launch Lab: ruler, flat eraser, book	**Chapter FAST FILE Resources** Foldables Worksheet, p. 17 Directed Reading Overview, p. 19 Note-taking Worksheets, pp. 33–35	GLENCOE'S ASSESSMENT ADVANTAGE	Teacher**Works** includes: • Interactive Teacher Edition • Lesson Planner with calendar • Access to all program blacklines • Correlations to standards • Web links
MiniLAB: bathroom scale, meterstick, stopwatch, calculator **Lab:** wood block, tape, spring scale, ruler, thin notebooks, meterstick, several books	**Chapter FAST FILE Resources** Transparency Activity, p. 44 MiniLAB, p. 3 Lab Activity, pp. 9–12 Enrichment, p. 30 Reinforcement, p. 27 Directed Reading, pp. 19, 20 Lab Worksheets, pp. 5–6 **Cultural Diversity,** p. 63 **Mathematics Skill Activities,** p. 11	Portfolio Integrate History, p. 100 Performance Applying Math, pp. 100, 101 MiniLAB, p. 101 Applying Math, p. 102 Content Section Review, p. 102	Section Focus Transparency Virtual Labs CD-ROM Guided Reading Audio Program Interactive Chalkboard CD-ROM Video Lab
Need materials? Contact Science Kit at 1-800-828-7777 or www.sciencekit.com on the Internet.	**Chapter FAST FILE Resources** Transparency Activity, p. 45 Enrichment, p. 31 Reinforcement, p. 28 Directed Reading, p. 21 Transparency Activity, pp. 47–48 **Reading and Writing Skill Activities,** p. 35	Portfolio Active Reading, p. 107 Performance Applying Math, pp. 105, 107 Applying Math, p. 108 Content Section Review, p. 108	Section Focus Transparency Teaching Transparency Guided Reading Audio Program Interactive Chalkboard CD-ROM
MiniLAB: 2 broomsticks, rope **Lab:** single- and multiple-pulley systems, nylon rope, steel bar to support the pulley system, meterstick, variety of weights, force spring scale, brick, balance	**Chapter FAST FILE Resources** Transparency Activity, p. 46 MiniLAB, p. 4 Lab Activity, pp. 13–16 Enrichment, p. 32 Reinforcement, p. 29 Directed Reading, pp. 21, 22 Lab Worksheets, pp. 7–8 **Lab Management and Safety,** p. 39	Portfolio Differentiated Instruction, p. 110 Performance MiniLAB, p. 114 Applying Math, p. 115 Content Section Review, p. 115	Section Focus Transparency Guided Reading Audio Program Interactive Chalkboard CD-ROM

End of Chapter Assessment

GLENCOE'S ASSESSMENT ADVANTAGE

Blackline Masters	Technology	Professional Series
Chapter FAST FILE Resources Chapter Review, pp. 37–38 Chapter Tests, pp. 39–42 **Standardized Test Practice,** pp. 19–22	MindJogger Videoquiz Virtual Labs CD-ROM ExamView® Pro Testmaker TeacherWorks CD-ROM Interactive Chalkboard CD-ROM	**Performance Assessment in the Science Classroom (PASC)**

Transparencies

Section Focus

1 Section Focus Transparency **Weighted Down** Chapter 4

A heavy backpack can be a load to carry. Just lifting it can take a lot of effort, but it's easier to take it off your back.

1. What forces are acting on the backpack?
2. Compare the direction the backpack moves when it is lifted by the girl with the direction it moves when the girl is walking.
3. Why is it easier to lower something down than it is to lift it up?

L2

2 Section Focus Transparency **The Puck Stops Here**

If you've ever tried to walk or run on ice, you know how difficult it can be. Because ice can be so slippery, hockey players on skates can move quickly, making hockey a fast and exciting sport.

1. Why do you sometimes slip when you step onto a patch of ice on the sidewalk?
2. Why can a hockey player move faster than a runner?
3. When a player takes a shot, is work being done on the puck? Explain.

L2

3 Section Focus Transparency **Useful?**

A Rube Goldberg contraption uses comically complex methods to perform a fairly simple task. In this case, more effort is expended on the machine than it would take to simply do the job.

1. What do you think this contraption is supposed to do?
2. Do machines usually increase or decrease the amount of effort involved in accomplishing a task? Explain.
3. What parts of this machine could really work? Which parts wouldn't work so well?

L2

This is a representation of key blackline masters available in the Teacher Classroom Resources. See Resource Manager boxes within the chapter for additional information.

Key to Teaching Strategies

The following designations will help you decide which activities are appropriate for your students.

L1 Level 1 activities should be appropriate for students with learning difficulties.

L2 Level 2 activities should be within the ability range of all students.

L3 Level 3 activities are designed for above-average students.

ELL ELL activities should be within the ability range of English Language Learners.

COOP LEARN Cooperative Learning activities are designed for small group work.

LS Multiple Learning Styles logos, as described on page 6T, are used throughout to indicate strategies that address different learning styles.

P These strategies represent student products that can be placed into a best-work portfolio.

PBL Problem-Based Learning activities apply real-world situations to learning.

Assessment

Assessment Transparency **Work and Simple Machines**

Directions: *Carefully review the graph and answer the following questions.*

1. According to the graph, which engine is initially the most efficient?
   A Engine 1   B Engine 2   C Engine 3   D Engine 4
2. According to the graph, the engine that most likely will require the least maintenance is ___.
   A Engine 1   B Engine 2   C Engine 3   D Engine 4

L2

Teaching

2 Teaching Transparency **Schematic Depiction of a Machine**

L2

Hands-on Activities

Student Text Lab Worksheet

Activity Building the Pyramids

Lab Preview
Directions: *Answer these questions before you begin the Activity.*

1. What safety materials does this activity call for? Why might they be needed?

2. Why is it important to measure the height of the books?

Imagine moving 2.3 million blocks of limestone, each weighing more than 1,000 kg. That is exactly what the builders of the Great Pyramid at Giza did. Although no one knows for sure exactly how they did it, they probably pulled the blocks most of the way. What could they have done to make their work easier?

What You'll Investigate
How is the force needed to lift a block related to the distance it travels?

Materials
wood block   thin notebooks
tape   meterstick
spring scale   several books
ruler

Goals
■ **Compare** the force needed to lift a block with the force needed to pull it up a ramp.

Safety Precautions

Procedure
1. Stack several books together on a table-top to model a half-completed pyramid. Measure the height of the stack in centimeters. Record the height on the first row of the data table under *Distance.*
2. Use the wood block as a model for a block of stone. Use tape to attach the block to the spring scale.

3. Place the block on the table and lift it straight up the side of the stack of books until the top of the block is even with the top of the books. Record the force shown on the scale in the data table under *Force.*
4. **Arrange** a notebook so that one end is on the stack of books and the other end is on the table. Measure the length of the notebook and record this length as distance in the second row of the data table under *Distance.*
5. **Measure** the force needed to pull the block up the ramp. Record the force in the data table.

L2

Laboratory Activities

LAB 1 Laboratory Activity **Calculating Work and Power**

When work is done on an object, energy is transferred to the object. When a force acts on an object and moves that object a certain distance, work is done on the object. Work (W) is defined by the following equation.

$$W = F \times d$$

In this equation, F represents a force acting on the object and d represents the distance through which the object moves as that force acts on it. In the metric system, force is measured in newtons (N), and distance is measured in meters (m). If a force of 1 newton acts on an object and the object moves 1 meter while the force is acting on it, the value of $F \times d$ equals 1 newton-meter (N-m), which is the same as to 1 joule (J) of energy being transferred.

Power (P) is the rate at which work is done. It can be calculated by the following equation.

$$P = W/t$$

In this equation, W represents the work done and t represents the amount of time required to do the work. In the metric system, the unit of power is the watt (W). If 1 joule of work is done in 1 second, W/t has a value of 1 J/s, which is equal to 1 watt.

Strategy
You will determine the amount of work required to lift an object.
You will determine the power used while lifting the object.

Materials
spring scale   string   wire tie (plastic-coated)
mass (1-kg)   dowel (wood, about 50 cm long)   meterstick
scissors   masking tape   stopwatch

Procedure
1. Weigh the 1-kg mass using the metric spring scale. Record this value in the Data and Observations section.
2. Cut a 1.5-m length of string. Tightly tie one end of the string to the center of the wood dowel. Secure the knot with a piece of masking tape to prevent the string from slipping.
3. Make a small loop at the other end of the string and knot it. Attach the 1-kg mass to the loop with a plastic-coated wire tie.
4. Measure a 1-m distance along the string from the dowel using the meterstick. Mark this distance on the string with a small strip of masking tape.
5. Hold the dowel at both ends as shown in Figure 1.

Figure 1

L2

Meeting Different Ability Levels

Content Outline

Reinforcement

Enrichment

Directed Reading (English/Spanish)

Study Guide

Reading Essentials

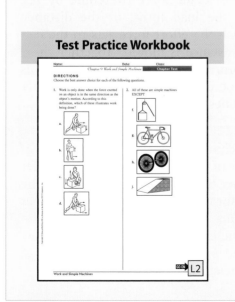

Assessment

Test Practice Workbook

Chapter Review

Chapter Tests

Science Content Background

section 1 ## Work and Power
What is work?

Energy is the ability to produce change. One way to produce change is to do work. Energy is the ability to perform work. When work is done on an object, energy is transferred to the object. The work-energy theorem states that when work is done on an object, the object's kinetic energy changes. The work done is equal to the change in kinetic energy.

Calculating Work

Both energy and work are measured in joules, kg (m²/s²). When an object falls, gravity does work equal to (force)(distance) = (mass)(g) (distance) where g is the acceleration due to gravity, 9.8 m/s². The kinetic energy changes from 0 to $\frac{1}{2}mv^2$ at the end of the fall. By letting $mgd = \frac{1}{2}mv^2$, you can find the velocity of an object when it hits the ground.

The concept of negative work is somewhat abstract. It is most easily grasped in situations where objects slow down. Here, an object is subjected to a force, usually friction, that reduces the object's kinetic energy. When an object is lifted, Earth's gravitational force does negative work. The lifter does positive work, which is stored as potential energy. When the object is held up, the lifter's muscles move microscopically. The object, however, does not move, so no work is done on it.

Teacher to Teacher
Kevin Finnegan
McCord Middle School
Worthington, OH

"When examining compound machines, have students search the classroom, the school, or magazines to identify the compound machine that includes the greatest number of simple machines. Have them identify each simple machine they find and share their information with the class."

Kevin Finnegan

Michael Lichter/International Stock

section 2 ## Using Machines
Mechanical Advantage

Mechanical advantage is a measure of a machine's leverage. It relates either the resistance force overcome by the machine to the load force, or the distance through which the effort force acts to the distance the resistance is moved. Together these quantities form the equality: $F_e d_e = F_r d_r$. This is the equation of balance for a lever and other simple machines.

Efficiency

When a machine leverages a force, the law of conservation of energy states that the smaller force must act through a greater distance. The work to perform a task is the same no matter how it is done. In reality, with a machine, you must do some extra work because some of the work supplied is lost as heat. The lower the loss, the more efficient the machine.

A perpetual-motion machine is a fictitious device that is said to convert all of the input work into an equal or greater amount of output work. An inventor always aspires to make a machine that is 100 percent efficient, but there is always some energy lost to friction. A carefully designed machine can get close. Getting more out of the machine than is put into it would be a clear violation of the law of energy conservation.

The source of energy that allows a machine to work is called the prime mover. Although machines make a job easier, the job may still require a backbreaking effort if you have to supply the energy. The steam engine and the electric motor were invented to ease this burden. They get their energy from coal, oil, electricity, and other sources. An automobile engine has the ability to supply the power of 200 horses, hence the term horsepower for engine capacity.

means of facilitating the move, the ramp needed to drag one of these blocks would require more material than the pyramid itself. Archaeologists discovered the Egyptians used a type of clay called tafla which becomes slippery when wet. Tests indicate that by using tafla as a lubricant, the Egyptians could have made steeper ramps, requiring much less fill.

Wheel and Axle

The wheel and axle discussed in this chapter is a simple machine. Some wheels and axles, such as those in a car, are more complicated.

You may want to point out to students the two uses of wheels. The wheels on a car or wagon are designed to avoid sliding friction: it's easier to push a grocery cart with wheels than without. Wheels that appear as handles, such as faucets and doorknobs, are designed to take advantage of the mechanical advantage of a wheel and axle.

section 3 Simple Machines
Inclined Plane

Archaeologists believe the ancient Egyptians constructed enormous ramps to move the pyramids' limestone blocks into place. Without the use of wheels or other

chapter content resources

Internet Resources
For additional content background, visit bookm.msscience.com to:
- access your book onlineonline
- find references to related articles in popular science magazines
- access Web links with related content background
- access current events with science journal topics

Print Resources
On the Shoulders of Giants: The Great Works of Physics and Astronomy, by Stephen Hawking (Commentary), Running Press Book Publishers, 2003
Work (Early Bird Physics Series), by Sally M. Walker and Roseann Feldmann, Lerner Publications Company, 2001
Physics, by David Halliday, Kenneth S. Krane, and Robert Resnick, John Wiley & Sons, 2001
Physics, by James S. Walker, Prentice Hall, 2003

Chapter Vocabulary

Science Journal Student answers will vary. Accept all reasonable responses.

PowerPoint® Presentations

This CD-ROM is an editable Microsoft® PowerPoint® presentation that includes:

- a pre-made presentation for every chapter
- interactive graphics
- animations
- audio clips
- image bank
- all new section and chapter questions
- Standardized Test Practice
- transparencies
- pre-lab questions for all labs
- Foldables directions
- links to bookm.msscience.com

Work and Simple Machines

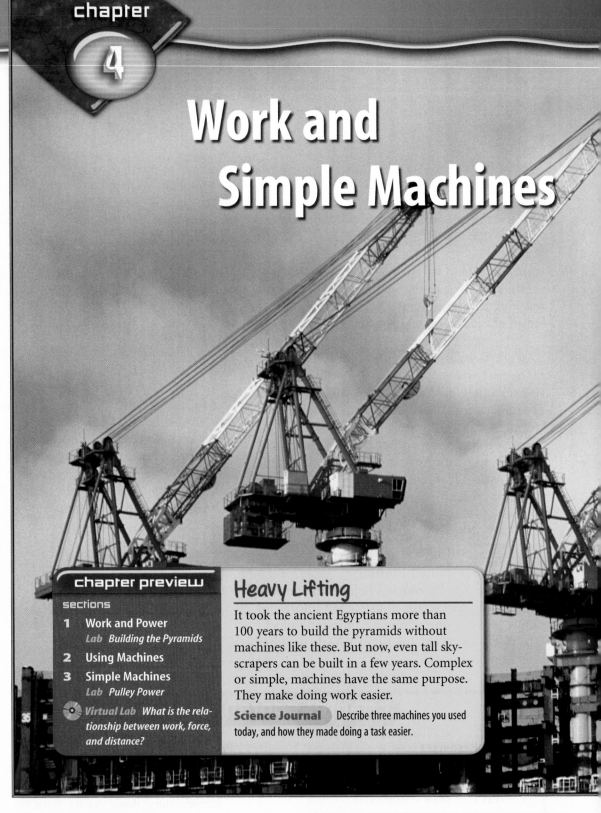

chapter preview

sections

1 **Work and Power**
   Lab Building the Pyramids

2 **Using Machines**

3 **Simple Machines**
   Lab Pulley Power

Virtual Lab What is the relationship between work, force, and distance?

Heavy Lifting

It took the ancient Egyptians more than 100 years to build the pyramids without machines like these. But now, even tall skyscrapers can be built in a few years. Complex or simple, machines have the same purpose. They make doing work easier.

Science Journal Describe three machines you used today, and how they made doing a task easier.

Theme Connection

Systems and Interactions A simple machine interacts with an input force and converts it to an output force. Compound machines are systems of interacting simple machines.

About the Photo

Cranes Pieces of heavy equipment are common on modern construction sites. Cranes often are used to lift support beams and other heavy objects. Cranes were introduced in the nineteenth century when steam engines, internal-combustion engines, and electric motors were developed.

Start-Up Activities

Compare Forces

Two of the world's greatest structures were built using different tools. The Great Pyramid at Giza in Egypt was built nearly 5,000 years ago using blocks of limestone moved into place by hand with ramps and levers. In comparison, the Sears Tower in Chicago was built in 1973 using tons of steel that were hoisted into place by gasoline-powered cranes. How do machines such as ramps, levers, and cranes change the forces needed to do a job?

1. Place a ruler on an eraser. Place a book on one end of the ruler.

2. Using one finger, push down on the free end of the ruler to lift the book.

3. Repeat the experiment, placing the eraser in various positions beneath the ruler. Observe how much force is needed in each instance to lift the book.

4. **Think Critically** In your Science Journal, describe your observations. How did changing the distance between the book and the eraser affect the force needed to lift the book?

Simple Machines Many of the devices that you use every day are simple machines. Make the following Foldable to help you understand the characteristics of simple machines.

STEP 1 Draw a mark at the midpoint of a sheet of paper along the side edge. Then **fold** the top and bottom edges in to touch the midpoint.

STEP 2 **Fold** in half from side to side.

STEP 3 **Turn** the paper vertically. **Open and cut** along the inside fold lines to form four tabs.

STEP 4 **Label** the tabs *Inclined Plane*, *Lever*, *Wheel and Axle*, and *Pulley*.

Read for Main Ideas As you read the chapter, list the characteristics of inclined planes, levers, wheels and axles, and pulleys under the appropriate tab.

Preview this chapter's content and activities at
bookm.msscience.com

Purpose Use the Launch Lab to introduce students to first-class levers and mechanical advantage. L2 ELL IS **Kinesthetic**

Preparation Before students do the lab, find a book that is not too heavy for the ruler.

Materials ruler, eraser, paperback book

Teaching Strategy Make this lab quantitative by using known weights in place of the book and finger. Expect to find (weight on left) × (distance from fulcrum) = (weight on right) × (distance from fulcrum). Have students measure distance from the center of each object.

Think Critically

As the book got farther from the eraser, it took more force to balance it.

Assessment

Process Have students use their results to draw diagrams showing how a small object could be used to balance a heavier object. Use **Performance Assessment in the Science Classroom,** p. 127. L1 IS **Logical-Mathematical**

 Dinah Zike Study Fold

Student preparation materials for this Foldable are available in the **Chapter FAST FILE Resources.**

Section Focus Transparencies also are available on the Interactive Chalkboard CD-ROM.

L2 ELL

SECTION 1 Section Focus Transparency **Weighted Down** Chapter 4

A heavy backpack can be a load to carry. Just lifting it can take a lot of effort, but it's easier to take it off your back.

1. What forces are acting on the backpack?
2. Compare the direction the backpack moves when it is lifted by the girl with the direction it moves when the girl is walking.
3. Why is it easier to lower something down than it is to lift it up?

L2

Work and Simple Machines

Tie to Prior Knowledge

Force and Motion Have students recall what they know about force and motion. Ask students to recall situations where they apply a force to an object and it doesn't move; and situations where they apply a force and an object moves. Ask students how the energy of the object changes in these situations. When the object moves its energy increases. Tell students they will study how work and energy are related in this section.

as you read

What **You'll Learn**
- **Recognize** when work is done.
- **Calculate** how much work is done.
- **Explain** the relation between work and power.

Why **It's Important**
If you understand work, you can make your work easier.

Review Vocabulary
force: push or pull that one body exerts on another

New Vocabulary
- work
- power

What is work?

What does the term *work* mean to you? You might think of household chores; a job at an office, a factory, a farm; or the homework you do after school. In science, the definition of work is more specific. **Work** is done when a force causes an object to move in the same direction that the force is applied.

Can you think of a way in which you did work today? Maybe it would help to know that you do work when you lift your books, turn a doorknob, raise window blinds, or write with a pen or pencil. You also do work when you walk up a flight of stairs or open and close your school locker. In what other ways do you do work every day?

Work and Motion Your teacher has asked you to move a box of books to the back of the classroom. Try as you might, though, you just can't budge the box because it is too heavy. Although you exerted a force on the box and you feel tired from it, you have not done any work. In order for you to do work, two things must occur. First, you must apply a force to an object. Second, the object must move in the same direction as your applied force. You do work on an object only when the object moves as a result of the force you exert. The girl in **Figure 1** might think she is working by holding the bags of groceries. However, if she is not moving, she is not doing any work because she is not causing something to move.

Reading Check *To do work, how must a force make an object move?*

Figure 1 This girl is holding bags of groceries, yet she isn't doing any work. **Explain** *what must happen for work to be done.*

Section 1 Resource Manager

Chapter Fast File Resources
Transparency Activity, p. 44
Directed Reading for Content Mastery, pp. 19, 20
Note-taking Worksheets, pp. 33–35
Enrichment, p. 30
Reinforcement, p. 27

MiniLAB, p. 3
Lab Worksheets, pp. 5–6
Lab Activity, pp. 9–12
Cultural Diversity, p. 63
Mathematics Skill Activities, p. 11

Force

Motion

The boy's arms do work when they exert an upward force on the basket and the basket moves upward.

Force

Motion

The boy's arms still exert an upward force on the basket. But when the boy walks forward, no work is done by his arms.

Figure 2 To do work, an object must move in the direction a force is applied.

Applying Force and Doing Work Picture yourself lifting the basket of clothes in **Figure 2.** You can feel your arms exerting a force upward as you lift the basket, and the basket moves upward in the direction of the force your arms applied. Therefore, your arms have done work. Now, suppose you carry the basket forward. You can still feel your arms applying an upward force on the basket to keep it from falling, but now the basket is moving forward instead of upward. Because the direction of motion is not in the same direction of the force applied by your arms, no work is done by your arms.

Force in Two Directions Sometimes only part of the force you exert moves an object. Think about what happens when you push a lawn mower. You push at an angle to the ground as shown in **Figure 3.** Part of the force is to the right and part of the force is downward. Only the part of the force that is in the same direction as the motion of the mower—to the right—does work.

Forward force

Total force

Downward force

Motion

Figure 3 When you exert a force at an angle, only part of your force does work—the part that is in the same direction as the motion of the object.

M ◆ 99

Caption Answer

Figure 1 A force must move an object in the same direction that the force is applied.

✓ Reading Check

Answer in the direction of the force

Activity

Pushing on a Book To help students understand how one force can be divided into components in two directions, have them push on two sides of a book—for example, left and bottom—using different amounts of force. They will observe how the two forces acting in different directions are added. L2 ELL LS **Kinesthetic**

Quick Demo

Work and a Toy Car

Materials table or another flat space, tape, spring scale, toy car

Estimated Time 15 minutes

Procedure Mark a distance of one or two meters on a tabletop with a tape. Fasten a spring scale to a toy car and pull the car from one tape mark to the other. Read the force on the spring scale as you pull, and calculate the amount of work done on the car. Repeat the demonstration, but increase the force exerted on the car. Calculate the work done on the car. Point out to students that the car was moving faster and had greater kinetic energy when more work was done on the car.

Visual Learning

Figure 3 Point out to students the angle between the handle of the lawn mower and the ground. Ask students whether more of the force applied by the boy would be down or forward if the angle between the handle and the ground were smaller. More of the force would be forward. L2 LS **Visual-Spatial**

James Prescott Joule This British physicist lived from 1818 to 1889. Joule is best known for his research in electricity and thermodynamics. He discovered that heat produced in a wire by an electric current is proportional to the product of the resistance of the wire and the square of the current. This is known as Joule's law. Joule and Lord Kelvin discovered that the temperature of a gas falls without doing work when the gas is allowed to expand. This is known as the Joule-Thomson effect and is the underlying principle of refrigeration.

Research William Thomson, who later became Lord Kelvin, made many contributions to science. Have students prepare a short biography of Lord Kelvin. Have selected students make a short presentation to the class about his life. **P**

Applying Math

National Math Standards

Correlation to Mathematics Objectives

1, 2, 9

Answers to Practice Problems

1. work = force × distance = 300 N × 500 m = 150,000 J

2. work = force × distance = 93 N × 1.5 m = 140 J

Teacher FYI

Power There are two units used to express power—watt and horsepower. One horsepower is equal to the amount of power required to lift 33,000 pounds a distance of 1 foot in 1 minute. There are 746 watts in 1 horsepower.

James Prescott Joule This English physicist experimentally verified the law of conservation of energy. He showed that various forms of energy—mechanical, electrical, and thermal—are essentially the same and can be converted one into another. The SI unit of energy and work, the joule, is named after him. Research the work of Joule and write what you learn in your Science Journal.

Calculating Work

Work is done when a force makes an object move. More work is done when the force is increased or the object is moved a greater distance. Work can be calculated using the work equation below. In SI units, the unit for work is the joule, named for the nineteenth-century scientist James Prescott Joule.

Work Equation

work (in joules) = **force** (in newtons) × **distance** (in meters)

$$W = Fd$$

Work and Distance Suppose you give a book a push and it slides across a table. To calculate the work you did, the distance in the above equation is not the distance the book moved. The distance in the work equation is the distance an object moves while the force is being applied. So the distance in the work equation is the distance the book moved while you were pushing.

Applying Math — Solve a One-Step Equation

CALCULATING WORK A painter lifts a can of paint that weighs 40 N a distance of 2 m. How much work does she do? *Hint: to lift a can weighing 40 N, the painter must exert a force of 40 N.*

Solution

1 *This is what you know:*
- force: $F = 40$ N
- distance: $d = 2$ m

2 *This is what you need to find out:*
work: $W = ?$ J

3 *This is the procedure you need to use:*
Substitute the known values $F = 40$ N and $d = 2$ m into the work equation:

$$W = Fd = (40\ N)(2\ m) = 80\ N \cdot m = 80\ J$$

4 *Check your answer:*
Check your answer by dividing the work you calculated by the distance given in the problem. The result should be the force given in the problem.

Practice Problems

1. As you push a lawn mower, the horizontal force is 300 N. If you push the mower a distance of 500 m, how much work do you do?

2. A librarian lifts a box of books that weighs 93 N a distance of 1.5 m. How much work does he do?

 For more practice, visit bookm.msscience.com/math_practice

Differentiated Instruction

Challenge A 7,500-W engine is used to lift an I beam with a mass of 1,000 kg to a height of 150 m. How much work must be done to lift this mass at constant speed? How long will it take? Have students write down a detailed solution to the problems. $W = F \times d = m \times g \times d = $ (1,000 kg) (9.8 m/s²) (150 m) = 1,470,000 J; $t = W/P = $ 1,470,000 J/7,500 W = 196 s [L3]

Physically Challenged Help students who use hand-powered wheelchairs understand how force and distance affect work by having them think about how much effort they must use to move their wheelchairs in various situations, such as starting, moving up a ramp, or moving at a constant rate along a flat surface. [L1] **Intrapersonal**

What is power?

What does it mean to be powerful? Imagine two weightlifters lifting the same amount of weight the same vertical distance. They both do the same amount of work. However, the amount of power they use depends on how long it took to do the work. **Power** is how quickly work is done. The weightlifter who lifted the weight in less time is more powerful.

Calculating Power Power can be calculated by dividing the amount of work done by the time needed to do the work.

Power Equation

$$\text{power (in watts)} = \frac{\text{work (in joules)}}{\text{time (in seconds)}}$$

$$P = \frac{W}{t}$$

In SI units, the unit of power is the watt, in honor of James Watt, a nineteenth-century British scientist who invented a practical version of the steam engine.

Applying Math   Solve a One-Step Equation

CALCULATING POWER You do 200 J of work in 12 s. How much power did you use?

Solution

1 *This is what you know:*
- work: $W = 200$ J
- time: $t = 12$ s

2 *This is what you need to find out:*
- power: $P = ?$ watts

3 *This is the procedure you need to use:*

Substitute the known values $W = 200$ J and $t = 12$ s into the power equation:

$$P = \frac{W}{t} = \frac{200 \text{ J}}{12 \text{ s}} = 17 \text{ watts}$$

4 *Check your answer:*

Check your answer by multiplying the power you calculated by the time given in the problem. The result should be the work given in the problem.

Practice Problems

1. In the course of a short race, a car does 50,000 J of work in 7 s. What is the power of the car during the race?

2. A teacher does 140 J of work in 20 s. How much power did he use?

 For more practice, visit bookm.msscience.com/math_practice

Mini LAB

Work and Power

Procedure
1. Weigh yourself on a **scale**.
2. Multiply your weight in pounds by 4.45 to convert your weight to newtons.
3. Measure the vertical height of a **stairway**. WARNING: *Make sure the stairway is clear of all objects.*
4. Time yourself walking slowly and quickly up the ramp.

Analysis
Calculate and compare the work and power in each case.

 Try at Home

Mini LAB

Purpose Students measure and compare work and power. L2
ELL **IS** **Kinesthetic**
Materials scale, meterstick, stairway, stopwatch
Analysis
Work will be the same in both cases, but power will be greater when a student runs.

Assessment

Process One dietary Calorie is 4,184 J. Have students calculate the number of Calories used to climb the stairs. Use **Performance Assessment in the Science Classroom**, p. 101.

Try at Home

Discussion

SI Units To help students understand the relationship between force, work, and power, have them express each in terms of their basic SI units. $F = ma = $ kg m/s^2 = N; $W = F \times d = mad = $ kg m/s^2 m = J; $P = W/t = (F \times d)/t = mad/t = $ (kg m/s^2)m/s = watt L2
IS **Logical-Mathematical**

Applying Math

National Math Standards
Correlation to Mathematics Objectives
1, 2, 9

Answers to Practice Problems

1. Power = work done/time needed
   50,000 J/7 s = 7,143 watts
2. $P = W/t = $ 140 J/20 s = 7 watts

Curriculum Connection

History Explain to students that another unit for measuring work is the calorie. One calorie is equal to 4.184 joules. The kilocalorie, written with a capital C as Calorie, is often used when discussing the energy available from food. One Calorie = 4,184 joules. Tell students that walking and running a given distance burn about the same number of Calories. Under what conditions does running result in a greater number of Calories being burned than walking does? A greater number of Calories are burned when running for a given period of time rather than walking for the same time period, because a greater distance is covered and therefore more work is done. Which requires more power, running or walking? Why? running, because it covers the distance in less time. L2 **IS** **Logical-Mathematical**

Topic: James Watt
Visit bookm.msscience.com for Web links to information about James Watt and his steam engine.

Activity Draw a diagram showing how his steam engine worked.

Work and Energy If you push a chair and make it move, you do work on the chair and change its energy. Recall that when something is moving it has energy of motion, or kinetic energy. By making the chair move, you increase its kinetic energy.

You also change the energy of an object when you do work and lift it higher. An object has potential energy that increases when it is higher above Earth's surface. By lifting an object, you do work and increase its potential energy.

Power and Energy When you do work on an object you increase the energy of the object. Because energy can never be created or destroyed, if the object gains energy then you must lose energy. When you do work on an object you transfer energy to the object, and your energy decreases. The amount of work done is the amount of energy transferred. So power is also equal to the amount of energy transferred in a certain amount of time.

Sometimes energy can be transferred even when no work is done, such as when heat flows from a warm to a cold object. In fact, there are many ways energy can be transferred even if no work is done. Power is always the rate at which energy is transferred, or the amount of energy transferred divided by the time needed.

section 1 review

Summary

What is work?

- Work is done when a force causes an object to move in the same direction that the force is applied.

- If the movement caused by a force is at an angle to the direction the force is applied, only the part of the force in the direction of motion does work.

- Work can be calculated by multiplying the force applied by the distance:

$$W = Fd$$

- The distance in the work equation is the distance an object moves while the force is being applied.

What is power?

- Power is how quickly work is done. Something is more powerful if it can do a given amount of work in less time.

- Power can be calculated by dividing the work done by the time needed to do the work:

$$P = \frac{W}{t}$$

Self Check

1. **Describe** a situation in which work is done on an object.

2. **Evaluate** which of the following situations involves more power: 200 J of work done in 20 s or 50 J of work done in 4 s? Explain your answer.

3. **Determine** two ways power can be increased.

4. **Calculate** how much power, in watts, is needed to cut a lawn in 50 min if the work involved is 100,000 J.

5. **Think Critically** Suppose you are pulling a wagon with the handle at an angle. How can you make your task easier?

Applying Math

6. **Calculate Work** How much work was done to lift a 1,000-kg block to the top of the Great Pyramid, 146 m above ground?

7. **Calculate Work Done by an Engine** An engine is used to lift a beam weighing 9,800 N up to 145 m. How much work must the engine do to lift this beam? How much work must be done to lift it 290 m?

section 1 review

1. Answers will vary. The students may describe any situation where a force moves an object in the direction of the force.

2. In the first case, 10 W are used; in the second case, 12.5 W are used. Even though less work is done in the second case, it uses more power because the work is done at a faster rate.

3. increasing the amount of work or decreasing the time

4. $P = 100,000 \text{ J}/[(50 \text{ min}) \times (60 \text{ s/min})] = 100,000 \text{ J}/3,000 \text{ s} = 33 \text{ W}$

5. Pull the wagon by the handle, making as small an angle with the ground as possible.

6. $W = mgh = (1,000 \text{ kg}) \times (9.8 \text{ m/s}^2) \times (146 \text{ m}) = 1,430,800 \text{ J}$

7. $W = mgh = (9,800 \text{ N})(145 \text{ m}) = 1,420,000 \text{ J}$. To lift the beam 290 m, twice as much work, 2,840,000 J, must be done, because it is lifted twice as high.

BENCH TESTED

Building the Pyramids

Imagine moving 2.3 million blocks of limestone, each weighing more than 1,000 kg. That is exactly what the builders of the Great Pyramid at Giza did. Although no one knows for sure exactly how they did it, they probably pulled the blocks most of the way.

● Real-World Question

How is the force needed to lift a block related to the distance it travels?

Goals
■ **Compare** the force needed to lift a block with the force needed to pull it up a ramp.

Materials
wood block
tape
spring scale
ruler

thin notebooks
meterstick
several books

Safety Precautions 🥽 🖐

● Procedure

1. Stack several books together on a tabletop to model a half-completed pyramid. Measure the height of the books in centimeters. Record the height on the first row of the data table under *Distance*.

2. Use the wood block as a model for a block of stone. Use tape to attach the block to the spring scale.

3. Place the block on the table and lift it straight up the side of the stack of books until the top of the block is even with the top of the books. Record the force shown on the scale in the data table under *Force*.

Work Done Using Different Ramps		
Distance (cm)	Force (N)	Work (J)
	Answers will vary.	

4. **Arrange** a notebook so that one end is on the stack of books and the other end is on the table. Measure the length of the notebook and record this length as distance in the second row of the data table under *Distance*.

5. **Measure** the force needed to pull the block up the ramp. Record the force in the data table.

6. Repeat steps 4 and 5 using a longer notebook to make the ramp longer.

7. **Calculate** the work done in each row of the data table.

● Conclude and Apply

1. **Evaluate** how much work you did in each instance.

2. **Determine** what happened to the force needed as the length of the ramp increased.

3. **Infer** How could the builders of the pyramids have designed their task to use less force than they would lifting the blocks straight up? Draw a diagram to support your answer.

*C*ommunicating Your Data

Add your data to that found by other groups. **For more help, refer to the** Science Skill Handbook.

● Real-World Question

Purpose Students investigate the mechanical advantage of a ramp. L2 ELL COOP LEARN 𝕂 **Kinesthetic**

Process Skills observe, infer, compare and contrast, make and use tables, interpret data, make models, separate and control variables, work with numbers

Time Required 45 minutes

● Procedure

Teaching Strategy Have students determine the force used to pull the block while the block is moving at a constant speed.

Troubleshooting Zero the spring scales before use and secure the ramps so they do not move when a block is pulled along them.

● Conclude and Apply

1. Work should be similar in each instance.
2. It decreased.
3. They could have built ramps along the sides of the pyramids.

✔ Assessment

Content Have each student write a short essay explaining whether he or she thinks the hypothesis that the Egyptians used ramps to build the pyramids is feasible. Use **Performance Assessment in the Science Classroom,** p. 157.

*C*ommunicating Your Data

Encourage students to use a spreadsheet to display their data. If the groups use different ramp lengths, have students plot the results using the graphing feature of the spreadsheet program.

Bellringer

Section Focus Transparencies also are available on the Interactive Chalkboard CD-ROM.

L2 **ELL**

SECTION 2 Section Focus Transparency **The Puck Stops Here**

If you've ever tried to walk or run on ice, you know how difficult it can be. Because ice can be so slippery, hockey players on skates can move quickly, making hockey a fast and exciting sport.

1. Why do you sometimes slip when you step onto a patch of ice on the sidewalk?
2. Why can a hockey player move faster than a runner?
3. When a player takes a shot, is work being done on the puck? Explain.

L2

Work and Simple Machines

Tie to Prior Knowledge

Energy Law Review with students the law of conservation of energy, which states that energy cannot be created or destroyed but only transformed into different forms. Inform students that in this section they will explore how machines obey this law.

as you read

What You'll Learn

- **Explain** how a machine makes work easier.
- **Calculate** the mechanical advantages and efficiency of a machine.
- **Explain** how friction reduces efficiency.

Why It's Important

Machines can't change the amount of work you need to do, but they can make doing work easier.

Review Vocabulary

friction: force that opposes motion between two touching surfaces

New Vocabulary

- input force
- output force
- mechanical advantage
- efficiency

What is a machine?

Did you use a machine today? When you think of a machine you might think of a device, such as a car, with many moving parts powered by an engine or an electric motor. But if you used a pair of scissors or a broom, or cut your food with a knife, you used a machine. A machine is simply a device that makes doing work easier. Even a sloping surface can be a machine.

Mechanical Advantage

Even though machines make work easier, they don't decrease the amount of work you need to do. Instead, a machine changes the way in which you do work. When you use a machine, you exert a force over some distance. For example, you exert a force to move a rake or lift the handles of a wheelbarrow. The force that you apply on a machine is the **input force.** The work you do on the machine is equal to the input force times the distance over which your force moves the machine. The work that you do on the machine is the input work.

The machine also does work by exerting a force to move an object over some distance. A rake, for example, exerts a force to move leaves. Sometimes this force is called the resistance force because the machine is trying to overcome some resistance. The force that the machine applies is the **output force.** The work that the machine does is the output work. **Figure 4** shows how a machine transforms input work to output work.

When you use a machine, the output work can never be greater than the input work. So what is the advantage of using a machine? A machine makes work easier by changing the amount of force you need to exert, the distance over which the force is exerted, or the direction in which you exert your force.

Figure 4 No matter what type of machine is used, the output work is never greater than the input work.

Input work   **Machine**   Output work

Section 2 Resource Manager

Chapter *FAST FILE* Resources
- Transparency Activity, pp. 45, 47–48
- Directed Reading for Content Mastery, p. 21
- Enrichment, p. 31
- Reinforcement, p. 28

Reading and Writing Skill Activities, p. 35

Changing Force Some machines make doing work easier by reducing the force you have to apply to do work. This type of machine increases the input force, so that the output force is greater than the input force. The number of times a machine increases the input force is the **mechanical advantage** of the machine. The mechanical advantage of a machine is the ratio of the output force to the input force and can be calculated from this equation:

Mechanical Advantage Equation

$$\text{mechanical advantage} = \frac{\text{output force (in newtons)}}{\text{input force (in newtons)}}$$

$$MA = \frac{F_{out}}{F_{in}}$$

Mechanical advantage does not have any units, because it is the ratio of two numbers with the same units.

Science nline

Topic: Historical Tools

Visit bookm.msscience.com for Web links to information about early types of tools and how they took advantage of simple machines.

Activity Write a paragraph describing how simple machines were used to design early tools.

Applying Math **Solve a One-Step Equation**

CALCULATING MECHANICAL ADVANTAGE To pry the lid off a paint can, you apply a force of 50 N to the handle of the screwdriver. What is the mechanical advantage of the screwdriver if it applies a force of 500 N to the lid?

Solution

1 *This is what you know:*
- input force: $F_{in} = 50$ N
- output force: $F_{out} = 500$ N

2 *This is what you need to find out:*
mechanical advantage: $MA = ?$

3 *This is the procedure you need to use:*
Substitute the known values $F_{in} = 50$ N and $F_{out} = 500$ N into the mechanical advantage equation:

$$MA = \frac{F_{out}}{F_{in}} = \frac{500 \text{ N}}{50 \text{ N}} = 10$$

4 *Check your answer:*
Check your answer by multiplying the mechanical advantage you calculated by the input force given in the problem. The result should be the output force given in the problem.

Practice Problems

1. To open a bottle, you apply a force of 50 N to the bottle opener. The bottle opener applies a force of 775 N to the bottle cap. What is the mechanical advantage of the bottle opener?

2. To crack a pecan, you apply a force of 50 N to the nutcracker. The nutcracker applies a force of 750 N to the pecan. What is the mechanical advantage of the nutcracker?

Science nline

For more practice, visit bookm.msscience.com/math_practice

Discussion

Building Variations How is building skyscrapers today similar to and different from the building of the pyramids? Both are large construction projects in which tools are used. Pyramid construction relied largely on people power, but skyscrapers are built using machines with engines powered by fossil fuels.

Applying Math

National Math Standards

Correlation to Mathematics Objectives

1, 2, 9

Answers to Practice Problems

1. $MA = F_{out}/F_{in}$
   $= 775 \text{ N}/50 \text{ N} = 15.5$

2. $MA = F_{out}/F_{in}$
   $= 750 \text{ N}/50 \text{ N} = 15$

Activity

Problem-Solving Contest Give students practice solving problems from this section by having a contest. Divide the students into two groups. Have a member from each group go to the board and give them a problem to solve. The first one to solve the problem wins and the team gets one point. Allow each student on the team to have a turn. If the student at the board cannot solve the problem, let the team help them. The team with the most points wins.

Differentiated Instruction

Challenge In the late 1800s and early 1900s, many people tried to develop perpetual motion machines. Have interested students research perpetual motion machines and attempts to develop them. Ask students to prepare written reports explaining why these machines are impossible to develop. A perpetual motion machine is a device that can either deliver more work than is put into it or can continue to work with no energy input other than that which was used to start it. L3 IN **Linguistic**

Figure 5 Changing the direction or the distance that a force is applied can make a task easier.

Sometimes it is easier to exert your force in a certain direction. This boy would rather pull down on the rope to lift the flag than to climb to the top of the pole and pull up.

When you rake leaves, you move your hands a short distance, but the end of the rake moves over a longer distance.

Changing Distance Some machines allow you to exert your force over a shorter distance. In these machines, the output force is less than the input force. The rake in **Figure 5** is this type of machine. You move your hands a small distance at the top of the handle, but the bottom of the rake moves a greater distance as it moves the leaves. The mechanical advantage of this type of machine is less than one because the output force is less than the input force.

Changing Direction Sometimes it is easier to apply a force in a certain direction. For example, it is easier to pull down on the rope in **Figure 5** than to pull up on it. Some machines enable you to change the direction of the input force. In these machines neither the force nor the distance is changed. The mechanical advantage of this type of machine is equal to one because the output force is equal to the input force. The three ways machines make doing work easier are summarized in **Figure 6.**

Figure 6 Machines are useful because they can increase force, increase distance, or change the direction in which a force is applied.

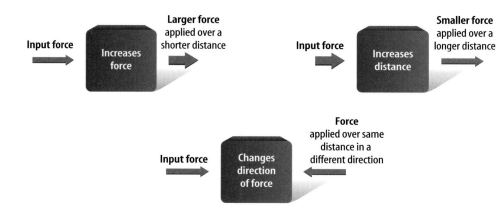

Efficiency

A machine doesn't increase the input work. For a real machine, the output work done by the machine is always less than the input work that is done on the machine. In a real machine, there is friction as parts of the machine move. Friction converts some of the input work into heat, so that the output work is reduced. The **efficiency** of a machine is the ratio of the output work to the input work, and can be calculated from this equation:

Efficiency Equation

$$\text{efficiency (in percent)} = \frac{\textbf{output work (in joules)}}{\textbf{input work (in joules)}} \times 100\%$$

$$eff = \frac{W_{\text{out}}}{W_{\text{in}}} \times 100\%$$

If the amount of friction in the machine is reduced, the efficiency of the machine increases.

INTEGRATE Life Science

Body Temperature
Chemical reactions that enable your muscles to move also produce heat that helps maintain your body temperature. When you shiver, rapid contraction and relaxation of muscle fibers produces a large amount of heat that helps raise your body temperature. This causes the efficiency of your muscles to decrease as more energy is converted into heat.

INTEGRATE Life Science

Body Temperature Each time a muscle contracts, molecules of adenosine triphosphate (ATP) react with water to form adenosine diphosphate (ADP) and release energy. Some of this energy is used by other chemical reactions and some is lost as heat.

Applying Math

National Math Standards
Correlation to Mathematics Objectives
1, 2, 9

Answers to Practice Problems
1. $Eff = (W_{out}/W_{in}) \times 100\% = (70\,\text{J}/100\,\text{J}) \times 100\% = 70\%$
2. $Eff = (W_{out}/W_{in}) \times 100\% = (105\,\text{J}/150\,\text{J}) \times 100\% = 70\%$

Applying Math Solve a One-Step Equation

CALCULATING EFFICIENCY Using a pulley system, a crew does 7,500 J of work to load a box that requires 4,500 J of work. What is the efficiency of the pulley system?

Solution

1️⃣ *This is what you know:*
- input work: $W_{\text{in}} = 7{,}500$ J
- output work: $W_{\text{out}} = 4{,}500$ J

2️⃣ *This is what you need to find out:*
efficiency: $eff = ?$ %

3️⃣ *This is the procedure you need to use:*
Substitute the known values $W_{\text{in}} = 7{,}500$ J and $W_{\text{out}} = 4{,}500$ J into the efficiency equation:
$$eff = \frac{W_{\text{out}}}{W_{\text{in}}} = \frac{4{,}500\,\text{J}}{7{,}500\,\text{J}} \times 100\% = 60\%$$

4️⃣ *Check your answer:*
Check your answer by dividing the efficiency by 100% and then multiplying your answer times the work input. The product should be the work output given in the problem.

Practice Problems

1. You do 100 J of work in pulling out a nail with a claw hammer. If the hammer does 70 J of work, what is the hammer's efficiency?

2. You do 150 J of work pushing a box up a ramp. If the ramp does 105 J of work, what is the efficiency of the ramp?

Science Online
For more practice, visit bookm.msscience.com/math_practice

Differentiated Instruction

Learning Disabled Have students show you how they would do the Applying Math example step-by-step. Answer any questions and correct any misconceptions they may have. Make sure they show all of their work. Check their practice problems to make sure they understand how to do the problems.

✔ Active Reading

Bubble Map In a bubble map, words are clustered to describe a topic or idea. A bubble map can be used for prewriting, to generate ideas before writing, or to review for a test. Have students design a bubble map to help them find the relationship between mechanical advantage and efficiency. L2 KS **Logical-Mathematical** P

Frictional Force The frictional force depends on the force pushing two surfaces together and not on the area of contact. This is because friction depends on the total contact area between microscopic bumps on the two surfaces. Making the surface area larger increases the number of microscopic bumps in contact. However, this also decreases the pressure pushing the bumps together, so the contact area between individual bumps decreases. As a result, the total microscopic contact area stays the same, and the frictional force is unchanged.

3 Assess

Check for Understanding

Visual-Spatial Have students investigate how a car jack works and explain the process in an illustrated drawing. L3 IS

Reteach

Efficiency Why is it impossible to have a machine that is perfectly efficient? There is always some amount of friction changing some of the work done by the machine into heat. L2

IS **Logical-Mathematical**

Surface
Oil
Surface

Figure 7 Lubrication can reduce the friction between two surfaces. Two surfaces in contact can stick together where the high spots on each surface come in contact. Adding oil or another lubricant separates the surface so that fewer high spots make contact.

Friction To help understand friction, imagine pushing a heavy box up a ramp. As the box begins to move, the bottom surface of the box slides across the top surface of the ramp. Neither surface is perfectly smooth—each has high spots and low spots, as shown in **Figure 7.**

As the two surfaces slide past each other, high spots on the two surfaces come in contact. At these contact points, shown in **Figure 7,** atoms and molecules can bond together. This makes the contact points stick together. The attractive forces between all the bonds in the contact points added together is the frictional force that tries to keep the two surfaces from sliding past each other.

To keep the box moving, a force must be applied to break the bonds between the contact points. Even after these bonds are broken and the box moves, new bonds form as different parts of the two surfaces come into contact.

Friction and Efficiency One way to reduce friction between two surfaces is to add oil. **Figure 7** shows how oil fills the gaps between the surfaces, and keeps many of the high spots from making contact. Because there are fewer contact points between the surfaces, the force of friction is reduced. More of the input work then is converted to output work by the machine.

---

section 2 review

Summary

What is a machine?
- A machine is a device that makes doing work easier.
- A machine can make doing work easier by reducing the force exerted, changing the distance over which the force is exerted, or changing the direction of the force.
- The output work done by a machine can never be greater than the input work done on the machine.

Mechanical Advantage and Efficiency
- The mechanical advantage of a machine is the number of times the machine increases the input force:
$$MA = \frac{F_{out}}{F_{in}}$$
- The efficiency of a machine is the ratio of the output work to the input work:
$$eff = \frac{W_{out}}{W_{in}} \times 100\%$$

Self Check

1. **Identify** three specific situations in which machines make work easier.
2. **Infer** why the output force exerted by a rake must be less than the input force.
3. **Explain** how the efficiency of an ideal machine compares with the efficiency of a real machine.
4. **Explain** how friction reduces the efficiency of machines.
5. **Think Critically** Can a machine be useful even if its mechanical advantage is less than one? Explain and give an example.

Applying Math

6. **Efficiency** Find the efficiency of a machine if the input work is 150 J and the output work is 90 J.
7. **Mechanical Advantage** To lift a crate, a pulley system exerts a force of 2,750 N. Find the mechanical advantage of the pulley system if the input force is 250 N.

Science Online bookm.msscience.com/self_check_quiz

✔ **Assessment**

Performance Have students suggest methods other than using oil for reducing friction in machines. Possible answers: Use another lubricant such as graphite; sand surfaces to make them as smooth as possible; use wheels or similar devices to slide one surface over another Use **PASC**, p. 93. L2

---

section 2 review

1. Possible answers: using ramps to move heavy furniture, using a screwdriver to turn a screw, using a wheelbarrow to move heavy loads
2. The output arm of the rake moves a greater distance than the input arm moves. Because the output work cannot be greater than the input

work, the output force must be less than the input force.
3. The efficiency of an ideal machine is 100%, but real machines always have an efficiency less than 100%.
4. Friction converts some of the input work into heat, so that the output

work is always less than the input work.
5. Yes. This type of machine increases the distance over which the output force is applied. An example is a rake or a baseball bat.
6. 60%
7. 11

Simple Machines

What is a simple machine?

What do you think of when you hear the word *machine?* Many people think of machines as complicated devices such as cars, elevators, or computers. However, some machines are as simple as a hammer, shovel, or ramp. A **simple machine** is a machine that does work with only one movement. The six simple machines are the inclined plane, lever, wheel and axle, screw, wedge, and pulley. A machine made up of a combination of simple machines is called a **compound machine.** A can opener is a compound machine. The bicycle in **Figure 8** is a familiar example of another compound machine.

Inclined Plane

Ramps might have enabled the ancient Egyptians to build their pyramids. To move limestone blocks weighing more than 1,000 kg each, archaeologists hypothesize that the Egyptians built enormous ramps. A ramp is a simple machine known as an inclined plane. An **inclined plane** is a flat, sloped surface. Less force is needed to move an object from one height to another using an inclined plane than is needed to lift the object. As the inclined plane becomes longer, the force needed to move the object becomes smaller.

What You'll Learn

- **Distinguish** among the different simple machines.
- **Describe** how to find the mechanical advantage of each simple machine.

Why It's Important

All machines, no matter how complicated, are made of simple machines.

⦿ Review Vocabulary
compound: made of separate pieces or parts

New Vocabulary
- simple machine
- compound machine
- inclined plane
- wedge
- screw
- lever
- wheel and axle
- pulley

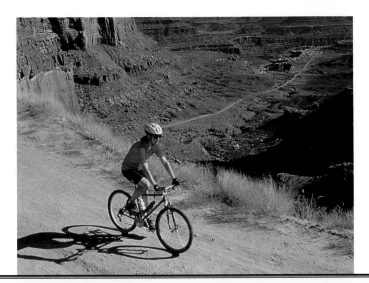

Figure 8 Devices that use combinations of simple machines, such as this bicycle, are called compound machines.

Bellringer

Section Focus Transparencies also are available on the Interactive Chalkboard CD-ROM.
L2 ELL

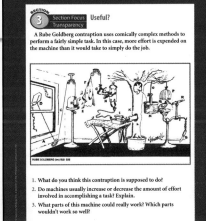

Tie to Prior Knowledge

Mechanical Advantage and Efficiency
Remind students of the definition of mechanical advantage and the concept of efficiency as you prepare them to explore the different types of simple machines.

Section 3 Resource Manager

Chapter *FAST FILE* Resources
Transparency Activity, p. 46
Directed Reading for Content Mastery, pp. 21–22
Enrichment, p. 32
Reinforcement, p. 29
MiniLAB, p. 4

Lab Activity, pp. 13–16
Lab Worksheets, pp. 7–8
Lab Management and Safety, p. 39
Physical Science Critical Thinking/Problem Solving, p. 7
Performance Assessment in the Science Classroom, p. 37

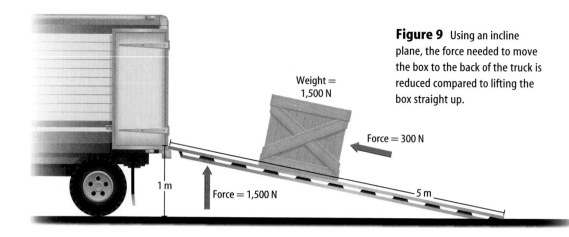

Figure 9 Using an incline plane, the force needed to move the box to the back of the truck is reduced compared to lifting the box straight up.

Weight = 1,500 N

Force = 300 N

1 m

Force = 1,500 N

5 m

IDENTIFYING
Misconceptions

Machines v. Tools Many people refer to simple devices such as knives or screwdrivers as tools. Students may think that a machine must be a more complicated device, such as an electric drill. In science, however, there is no distinction between machines and tools. A machine is any device that is used to multiply or change the direction of a force. Thus, a hammer or a knife is as much a machine as is a lathe or an electric drill.

Inquiry Lab

Tools and Gadgets

Purpose To invent a new gadget using simple machines

Possible Materials wood, plastic, cardboard, rubber hose, recycled materials, rope

Estimated Time one week outside class time

Teaching Strategies

• Challenge students to invent a new gadget using simple machines.
• Have students construct their gadget from inexpensive materials.
• Students should present their new gadget to the class. Students should identify the simple machines they used to construct the gadget.

For additional inquiry activities, see *Science Inquiry Labs*.

Using Inclined Planes Imagine having to lift a box weighing 1,500 N to the back of a truck that is 1 m off the ground. You would have to exert a force of 1,500 N, the weight of the box, over a distance of 1 m, which equals 1,500 J of work. Now suppose that instead you use a 5-m-long ramp, as shown in **Figure 9.** The amount of work you need to do does not change. You still need to do 1,500 J of work. However, the distance over which you exert your force becomes 5 m. You can calculate the force you need to exert by dividing both sides of the equation for work by distance.

$$\text{Force} = \frac{\text{work}}{\text{distance}}$$

If you do 1,500 J of work by exerting a force over 5 m, the force is only 300 N. Because you exert the input force over a distance that is five times as long, you can exert a force that is five times less.

The mechanical advantage of an inclined plane is the length of the inclined plane divided by its height. In this example, the ramp has a mechanical advantage of 5.

Wedge An inclined plane that moves is called a **wedge.** A wedge can have one or two sloping sides. The knife shown in **Figure 10** is an example of a wedge. An axe and certain types of doorstops are also wedges. Just as for an inclined plane, the mechanical advantage of a wedge increases as it becomes longer and thinner.

Figure 10 This chef's knife is a wedge that slices through food.

110 ◆ **M CHAPTER 4** Work and Simple Machines

Science Journal

Inclined Planes Ask students to note all the inclined planes they see in a two-day period. Have them list each one in their Science Journals and describe how it is used. [L2] [IS] **Visual-Spatial**

Differentiated Instruction

Challenge Encourage students with a strong interest in nature to look for examples of the use of simple machines by animals. Examples include the way a parrot uses its powerful bill to crack nuts and the use of sticks by chimpanzees to obtain food that is hard to reach. Ask students to prepare a poster with examples to share with the class. [L3] [IS] **Naturalist** [P]

Figure 11 Wedge-shaped
teeth help tear food.

Your front
teeth help
tear an apple
apart.

The wedge-shaped teeth of this *Tyrannosaurus rex* show that it was a carnivore.

Wedges in Your Body You have wedges in your body. The bite marks on the apple in **Figure 11** show how your front teeth are wedge shaped. A wedge changes the direction of the applied effort force. As you push your front teeth into the apple, the downward effort force is changed by your teeth into a sideways force that pushes the skin of the apple apart.

The teeth of meat eaters, or carnivores, are more wedge shaped than the teeth of plant eaters, or herbivores. The teeth of carnivores are used to cut and rip meat, while herbivores' teeth are used for grinding plant material. By examining the teeth of ancient animals, such as the dinosaur in **Figure 11,** scientists can determine what the animal ate when it was living.

The Screw Another form of the inclined plane is a screw. A **screw** is an inclined plane wrapped around a cylinder or post. The inclined plane on a screw forms the screw threads. Just like a wedge changes the direction of the effort force applied to it, a screw also changes the direction of the applied force. When you turn a screw, the force applied is changed by the threads to a force that pulls the screw into the material. Friction between the threads and the material holds the screw tightly in place. The mechanical advantage of the screw is the length of the inclined plane wrapped around the screw divided by the length of the screw. The more tightly wrapped the threads are, the easier it is to turn the screw. Examples of screws are shown in **Figure 12.**

Reading Check *How are screws related to the inclined plane?*

Figure 12 The thread around a screw is an inclined plane. Many familiar devices use screws to make work easier.

Discussion
Saber-Toothed Tiger The saber-toothed tiger, or smilodon (knife-tooth), which became extinct 10,000 years ago, was a ferocious predator that used its 20-cm-long serrated canines for puncturing the thick hides of mastodons and other large animals. It was slightly smaller than today's lion. Its mouth could open to a 120° angle, allowing it to grab and pierce at the same time. What simple machines are involved in this animal's assault? wedges in the teeth and lever in the jaw

Activity
Screw Types Bring in a piece of wood, a screwdriver, and several screws with different numbers of threads. Allow students to experiment to determine how the distance between threads per centimeter of screw length affects the mechanical advantage of the screw. The more threads per centimeter of screw length, the greater its mechanical advantage. L2 ELL
LS **Kinesthetic**

Teacher FYI

Tool Materials The materials used to make simple machines must be strong enough to support the weight of the objects they move. For example, a piece of cardboard won't work as an inclined plane to move a refrigerator.

Reading Check

Answer A screw is an inclined plane wrapped around a shaft.

Cultural Diversity

Pyramid Construction Until the early part of the twentieth century, the Great Pyramid of Khufu in Egypt was the world's largest building, standing more than 145 m tall, covering an area of seven city blocks and weighing 6.5 million tons. Archaeologists believe the ancient Egyptians constructed enormous ramps to move more than 2 million 1,000-kg limestone blocks into place. A ramp with a length that would enable about ten people to drag one of these blocks would require more material than the pyramid itself! Archaeologists discovered that the Egyptians used a type of clay called tafla that is strong and becomes slippery when wet. Tests indicate that if the Egyptians used tafla as a lubricant on the ramps, they could have made steeper ramps, which would have required much less material.

Make a Model

First-Class Levers Have students use a pencil, a ruler, and books to model a first-class lever. Have students experiment to find out how changing the distance between the fulcrum (pencil) and the resistance (books) changes the amount of force that must be exerted to lift the books. L2

Caption Answer

Figure 14 *by making the radius of the wheel larger or the radius of the axle smaller*

Teacher FYI

Inventing the Wheel The wheel was invented about the time of the building of the pyramids (3600 B.C.). It was used initially not for transporting heavy loads but to turn a potter's table. A heavy, round stone was attached to a shaft under the potter's table. With a small kick of the foot, the potter could keep the table turning while shaping the clay.

Figure 13 The mechanical advantage of a lever changes as the position of the fulcrum changes. The mechanical advantage increases as the fulcrum is moved closer to the output force.

Figure 14 A faucet handle is a wheel and axle. A wheel and axle is similar to a circular lever. The center is the fulcrum, and the wheel and axle turn around it. **Explain** *how you can increase the mechanical advantage of a wheel and axle.*

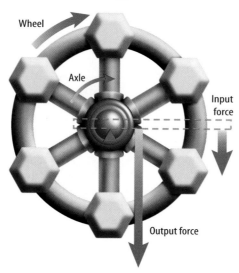

Lever

You step up to the plate. The pitcher throws the ball and you swing your lever to hit the ball? That's right! A baseball bat is a type of simple machine called a lever. A **lever** is any rigid rod or plank that pivots, or rotates, about a point. The point about which the lever pivots is called a fulcrum.

The mechanical advantage of a lever is found by dividing the distance from the fulcrum to the input force by the distance from the fulcrum to the output force, as shown in **Figure 13.** When the fulcrum is closer to the output force than the input force, the mechanical advantage is greater than one.

Levers are divided into three classes according to the position of the fulcrum with respect to the input force and output force. **Figure 15** shows examples of three classes of levers.

Wheel and Axle

Do you think you could turn a doorknob easily if it were a narrow rod the size of a pencil? It might be possible, but it would be difficult. A doorknob makes it easier for you to open a door because it is a simple machine called a wheel and axle. A **wheel and axle** consists of two circular objects of different sizes that are attached in such a way that they rotate together. As you can see in **Figure 14,** the larger object is the wheel and the smaller object is the axle.

The mechanical advantage of a wheel and axle is usually greater than one. It is found by dividing the radius of the wheel by the radius of the axle. For example, if the radius of the wheel is 12 cm and the radius of the axle is 4 cm, the mechanical advantage is 3.

112 ◆ **M** CHAPTER 4 Work and Simple Machines

LAB DEMONSTRATION

Purpose to demonstrate the mechanical advantage of a wheel and axle

Materials wheel and axle, rod, 2 strings, 500-g mass

Preparation Mount the wheel and axle on the support rod.

Procedure Wrap one string clockwise around the axle and the other counterclockwise around the wheel. Hang the 500-g mass from the end of the wheel string. Have student volunteers pull down on the axle string until the mass is lifted about 10 cm.

Expected Outcome The force used is large, and the distance moved is small.

Assessment

Ask students to explain the results, using the concept of mechanical advantage. The mechanical advantage is less than one, because a large input force over a small distance produced a smaller output force over a larger distance. L2

NATIONAL GEOGRAPHIC VISUALIZING LEVERS

Figure 15

Levers are among the simplest of machines, and you probably use them often in everyday life without even realizing it. A lever is a bar that pivots around a fixed point called a fulcrum. As shown here, there are three types of levers—first class, second class, and third class. They differ in where two forces—an input force and an output force—are located in relation to the fulcrum.

▲ Fulcrum
▼ Input force
▲ Output force

In a first-class lever, the fulcrum is between the input force and the output force. First-class levers, such as scissors and pliers, multiply force or distance depending on where the fulcrum is placed. They always change the direction of the input force, too.

First-class lever

In a second-class lever, such as a wheelbarrow, the output force is between the input force and the fulcrum. Second-class levers always multiply the input force but don't change its direction.

Second-class lever

Third-class lever

In a third-class lever, such as a baseball bat, the input force is between the output force and the fulcrum. For a third-class lever, the output force is less than the input force, but is in the same direction.

SECTION 3 Simple Machines **M** ◆ 113

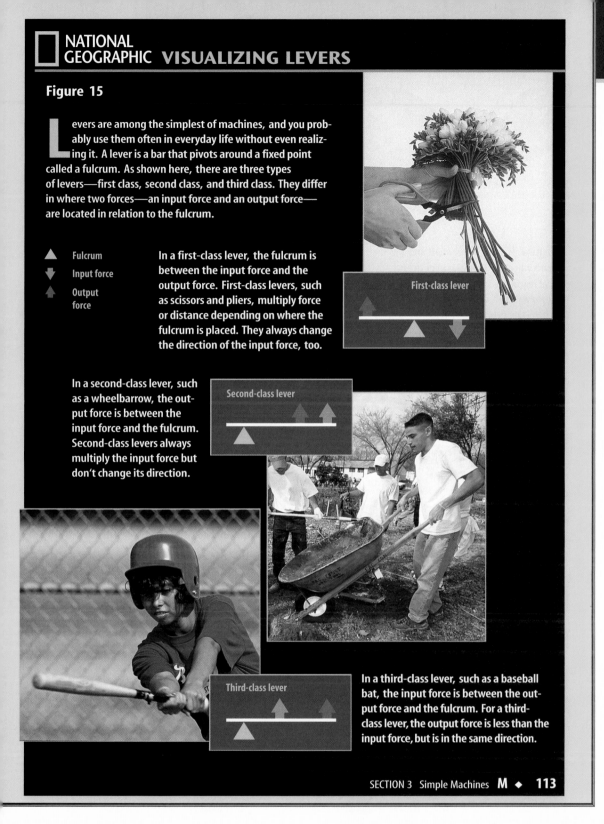

NATIONAL GEOGRAPHIC

Visualizing Levers

Have students examine the pictures and read the captions. Then ask the following questions.

What are the fundamental differences between 1st-, 2nd-, and 3rd-class levers? They differ in the locations of the input force, output force, and fulcrum.

What are other examples of 1st-class levers? Answers will vary. Possible answers include crowbar, teeter totter or see-saw, and laboratory balances.

What are other examples of 2nd-class levers? Answers will vary. Possible answers include nutcrackers, bottle openers, and doors.

What are other examples of 3rd-class levers? Answers will vary. Possible answers include hammers, tweezers, shovels, rakes, and fishing poles.

Activity

Collecting Levers Have students assemble collections of the three types of levers. Encourage students to find examples that are not listed in this text. [L2] [IS] **Kinesthetic**

Fun Fact

The ancient Greek mathematician Archimedes was the first to understand the full potential of the lever. According to legend, when he announced his discovery to the king, he said, "Give me a place to stand, and I will move the Earth!" He then proceeded to move a grounded ship with an enormous lever.

Differentiated Instruction

English-Language Learners Have students find photos of levers in magazines, catalogues, or other sources. Have students make a poster using their examples. Students should identify which class of lever each example represents. [L2]

Mini LAB

Purpose Students observe different pulley systems. L2 ELL

COOP LEARN IS **Kinesthetic**

Materials 2 broomsticks, 3-m rope

Teaching Strategy Have two students hold the broomsticks in place while a third pulls on the rope for the first trial.

Analysis

1. The rope is harder to pull with two turns than with four turns.
2. It would be easier to pull the sticks together with ten turns of rope.

Assessment

Content Ask students to draw diagrams illustrating how a pulley system reduces the amount of effort needed to overcome a resistance force. The pulley multiplies the distance through which the force moves. Use **Performance Assessment in the Science Classroom,** p. 127.

☑ **Reading Check**

Answer It canges the direction of the force.

Quick Demo

Pulleys

Materials ringstand, fixed pulley, moveable pulley, and a pulley system

Estimated Time 10 minutes

Procedure Set up each type of pulley for the students to see. Use a small weight to show students how they work.

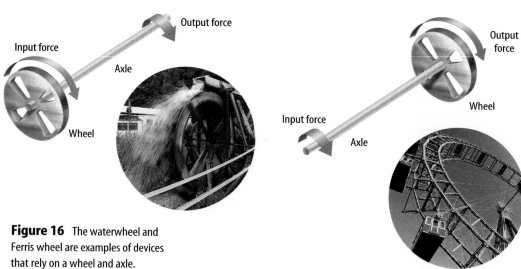

Figure 16 The waterwheel and Ferris wheel are examples of devices that rely on a wheel and axle. **Compare and contrast** waterwheels and Ferris wheels in terms of wheels and axles.

Mini LAB

Observing Pulleys

Procedure

1. Obtain two **broomsticks.** Tie a 3-m-long **rope** to the middle of one stick. Wrap the rope around both sticks four times.
2. Have two students pull the broomsticks apart while a third pulls on the rope.
3. Repeat with two wraps of rope.

Analysis

1. Compare the results.
2. Predict whether it will be easier to pull the broomsticks together with ten wraps of rope.

Using Wheels and Axles In some devices, the input force is used to turn the wheel and the output force is exerted by the axle. Because the wheel is larger than the axle, the mechanical advantage is greater than one. So the output force is greater than the input force. A doorknob, a steering wheel, and a screwdriver are examples of this type of wheel and axle.

In other devices, the input force is applied to turn the axle and the output force is exerted by the wheel. Then the mechanical advantage is less than one and the output force is less than the input force. A fan and a ferris wheel are examples of this type of wheel and axle. **Figure 16** shows an example of each type of wheel and axle.

Pulley

To raise a sail, a sailor pulls down on a rope. The rope uses a simple machine called a pulley to change the direction of the force needed. A **pulley** consists of a grooved wheel with a rope or cable wrapped over it.

Fixed Pulleys Some pulleys, such as the one on a sail, a window blind, or a flagpole, are attached to a structure above your head. When you pull down on the rope, you pull something up. This type of pulley, called a fixed pulley, does not change the force you exert or the distance over which you exert it. Instead, it changes the direction in which you exert your force, as shown in **Figure 17.** The mechanical advantage of a fixed pulley is 1.

☑ **Reading Check** *How does a fixed pulley affect the input force?*

Visual Learning

Figure 17 Encourage students to use their fingers to trace the movement of both the input force and the output force in each pulley diagram. Have students use their observations to describe how each pulley works. A single pulley changes the direction of the force; a movable pulley allows a smaller force to be exerted over a longer distance; systems of pulleys can multiply force and change its direction. L2

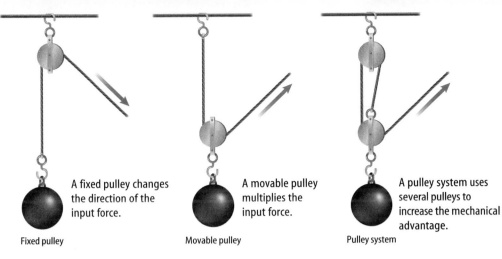

A fixed pulley changes the direction of the input force.

Fixed pulley

A movable pulley multiplies the input force.

Movable pulley

A pulley system uses several pulleys to increase the mechanical advantage.

Pulley system

Movable Pulleys Another way to use a pulley is to attach it to the object you are lifting, as shown in **Figure 17.** This type of pulley, called a movable pulley, allows you to exert a smaller force to lift the object. The mechanical advantage of a movable pulley is always 2.

More often you will see combinations of fixed and movable pulleys. Such a combination is called a pulley system. The mechanical advantage of a pulley system is equal to the number of sections of rope pulling up on the object. For the pulley system shown in **Figure 17** the mechanical advantage is 3.

Figure 17 Pulleys can change force and direction.

3 Assess

DAILY INTERVENTION

Check for Understanding

Linguistic Organize the class into groups, and give each group a machine to present to the class. Group members should describe the features, mechanical advantage, and efficiency of the group's machine and give an example of how it is used. [L2]

Reteach

Compound Machines Ask each student to bring in a compound machine or a picture of a compound machine. Have them identify the simple machines that make up the machine they selected and explain how they work together to perform the machine's intended function. [L2]
ELL **IS** **Visual-Spatial**

---

section 3 review

Summary

Simple and Compound Machines
- A simple machine is a machine that does work with only one movement.
- A compound machine is made from a combination of simple machines.

Types of Simple Machines
- An inclined plane is a flat, sloped surface.
- A wedge is an inclined plane that moves.
- A screw is an inclined plane that is wrapped around a cylinder or post.
- A lever is a rigid rod that pivots around a fixed point called the fulcrum.
- A wheel and axle consists of two circular objects of different sizes that rotate together.
- A pulley is a grooved wheel with a rope or cable wrapped over it.

Self Check

1. **Determine** how the mechanical advantage of a ramp changes as the ramp becomes longer.
2. **Explain** how a wedge changes an input force.
3. **Identify** the class of lever for which the fulcrum is between the input force and the output force.
4. **Explain** how the mechanical advantage of a wheel and axle change as the size of the wheel increases.
5. **Think Critically** How are a lever and a wheel and axle similar?

Applying Math

6. **Calculate Length** The Great Pyramid is 146 m high. How long is a ramp from the top of the pyramid to the ground that has a mechanical advantage of 4?
7. **Calculate Force** Find the output force exerted by a moveable pulley if the input force is 50 N.

Assessment

Performance Build a pulley system, and ask students to determine the mechanical advantage of the system. Use **Performance Assessment in the Science Classroom,** p. 89. [L2]

---

section 3 review

1. The mechanical advantage of a ramp increases as the ramp becomes longer if the height remains the same.
2. A wedge changes the direction of the input force.
3. first class lever
4. As the size of the wheel increases, so does the mechanical advantage.
5. The point that the wheel and axle rotate around would be the fulcrum. The radius of the axle would be the output arm, and the radius of the wheel would be the input arm. The wheel and axle would make a second-class lever.
6. 4×146 m $= 584$ m
7. 2×50 N $= 100$ N

Real-World Question

Purpose Students will experiment with multiple pulley systems and use the results to design a pulley system that can lift a heavy load. L2 ELL LS
Kinesthetic

Process Skills observe, infer, compare and contrast, design an experiment to test a hypothesis, interpret data, separate and control variables, predict, use numbers

Time Required 90 minutes

Possible Materials A block and tackle is a good multiple pulley system. The upper set of pulleys is attached to a support, and the lower set is attached to the load.

Safety Precautions Remind students to be careful when raising the weight.

Form a Hypothesis

Possible Hypothesis As the number of pulleys increases, the amount of rope needed (distance) increases and the force needed decreases.

Test Your Hypothesis

Possible Procedures Attach several pulleys to the load and an equal number to a support. Weigh the load, and then run a rope through the pulley system, attach a spring scale to the rope, and measure the force needed to lift the load.

Design Your Own

Pulley Power

Goals
- **Design** a pulley system.
- **Measure** the mechanical advantage and efficiency of the pulley system.

Possible Materials
single- and multiple-pulley systems
nylon rope
steel bar to support the pulley system
meterstick
*metric tape measure
variety of weights to test pulleys
force spring scale
brick
*heavy book
balance
*scale
*Alternate materials

Safety Precautions
WARNING: *The brick could be dangerous if it falls. Keep your hands and feet clear of it.*

Real-World Question

Imagine how long it might have taken to build the Sears Tower in Chicago without the aid of a pulley system attached to a crane. Hoisting the 1-ton I beams to a maximum height of 110 stories required large lifting forces and precise control of the beam's movement.

Construction workers also use smaller pulleys that are not attached to cranes to lift supplies to where they are needed. Pulleys are not limited to construction sites. They also are used to lift automobile engines out of cars, to help load and unload heavy objects on ships, and to lift heavy appliances and furniture. How can you use a pulley system to reduce the force needed to lift a load?

Form a Hypothesis

Write a hypothesis about how pulleys can be combined to make a system of pulleys to lift a heavy load, such as a brick. Consider the efficiency of your system.

Test Your Hypothesis

Make a Plan

1. Decide how you are going to support your pulley system. What materials will you use?

2. How will you measure the effort force and the resistance force? How will you determine the mechanical advantage? How will you measure efficiency?

3. **Experiment** by lifting small weights with a single pulley, double pulley, and so on. How efficient are the pulleys? In what ways can you increase the efficiency of your setup?

Alternative Inquiry Lab

Real-World Connection To make this Lab an Inquiry Lab, give the students more personal investment into the problem by connecting it to the real world. Tell the students that they are construction engineers. They must design a pulley system that will lift the construction materials for their construction project. Have students brainstorm how they can design their system so that it can be used on a multiple-story building. The same pulley system should be used throughout the construction project with slight modifications to allow for the increased height of the building. L2

4. Use the results of step 3 to design a pulley system to lift the brick. Draw a diagram of your design. Label the different parts of the pulley system and use arrows to indicate the direction of movement for each section of rope.

Follow Your Plan

1. Make sure your teacher approves your plan before you start.

2. Assemble the pulley system you designed. You might want to test it with a smaller weight before attaching the brick.

3. **Measure** the force needed to lift the brick. How much rope must you pull to raise the brick 10 cm?

◉ *Analyze Your Data*

1. **Calculate** the ideal mechanical advantage of your design.

2. **Calculate** the actual mechanical advantage of the pulley system you built.

3. **Calculate** the efficiency of your pulley system.

4. How did the mechanical advantage of your pulley system compare with those of your classmates?

◉ *Conclude and Apply*

1. **Explain** how increasing the number of pulleys increases the mechanical advantage.

2. **Infer** How could you modify the pulley system to lift a weight twice as heavy with the same effort force used here?

3. **Compare** this real machine with an ideal machine.

*C*ommunicating
Your Data

Show your design diagram to the class. Review the design and point out good and bad characteristics of your pulley system. **For more help, refer to the** Science Skill Handbook.

LAB M ◆ 117

Teaching Strategy Point out that every time a pulley is added to the system, it introduces more weight and friction. This lowers the efficiency of the pulley system.

Troubleshooting You may want to divide the class into groups to tackle different parts of the problem during the design phase.

Expected Outcome A multiple-pulley system can use a small force to raise a heavy load.

◉ *Analyze Your Data*

Answers to Questions

1. (length of rope pulled)/(distance load is raised) $= MA$

2. (weight of load)/(input force) $= MA$

3. $(W_{out}/W_{in})(100\%) = E$, where $W_{out} =$ (weight)(distance raised) and $W_{in} =$ (input force)(length of rope pulled)

4. Answers will depend on the number of pulleys used and the efficiencies of the pulley systems.

Error Analysis Have students compare their results and their hypotheses and explain any differences in their results.

◉ *Conclude and Apply*

1. Each pulley added increases the mechanical advantage by one.

2. Double the number of pulleys in the system.

3. An ideal pulley system would have an efficiency of 100%. The real system has noticeable loss of efficiency because of friction.

☑ Assessment

Oral How much work would it take for a simple pulley to lift a 910-kg I-beam 460 m? Does the weight of the cable affect the efficiency of the crane as it lifts an I-beam? 4,100,000 J; Yes; the cable is heavy and the crane must lift the cable as well as the I-beam. Use **Performance Assessment in the Science Classroom**, p. 101. L2

*C*ommunicating
Your Data

Have each student write a paragraph using information learned in the lab to explain how to design a pulley system with which one person could lift a building stone into position on a wall. L2

Content Background

By using sensors that stimulate nerve cells to send signals to the brain, it is possible to restore some function in senses damaged by injury or disease. For example, researchers are currently developing a retinal implant that will help transmit light messages from the eye to the brain. It is called an Artificial Retina Component Chip. Designed to be implanted near the vision center of the retina, the device transmits messages to the brain via a silicon microchip that is embedded with photosensor cells and electrodes. The photosensor converts patterns of light and dark into electric impulses, stimulating nerves behind the retina that send the information to the brain.

A device called a cochlear implant has enabled many deaf and hearing-impaired individuals to significantly increase their hearing. A cochlear implant is a device implanted in the ear that replaces the function of the cochlea, the organ that translates sound energy into nerve impulses and then sends the impulses to the brain. The device includes a transmitter implanted in the temporal bone and electrodes threaded through the cochlea that help stimulate the nerve fibers. Cochlear implants are no longer considered experimental and are used by thousands worldwide.

Discussion

Reasons What are some reasons people need the prosthetic devices discussed in the article? Possible answers include because of loss of the use of limbs due to accidents, birth defects, or disease. **L1** **IS** **Logical-Mathematical**

Bionic People

Artificial limbs can help people lead normal lives

People in need of transplants usually receive human organs. But many people's medical problems can only be solved by receiving artificial body parts. These synthetic devices, called prostheses, are used to replace anything from a heart valve to a knee joint. Bionics is the science of creating

artificial body parts. A major focus of bionics is the replacement of lost limbs. Through accident, birth defect, or disease, people sometimes lack hands or feet, or even whole arms or legs.

For centuries, people have used prostheses to replace limbs. In the past, physically challenged people used devices like peg legs or artificial arms that ended in a pair of hooks. These prostheses didn't do much to replace lost functions of arms and legs.

The knowledge that muscles respond to electricity has helped create more effective prostheses. One such prostheses is the myoelectric arm. This battery-powered device connects muscle nerves in an amputated arm to a sensor.

The sensor detects when the arm tenses, then transmits the signal to an artificial hand, which opens or closes. New prosthetic hands even give a sense of touch, as well as cold and heat.

Myoelectric arms make life easier for people who have them.

Research Use your school's media center to find other aspects of robotics such as walking machines or robots that perform planetary exploration. What are they used for? How do they work? You could take it one step further and learn about cyborgs. Report to the class.

Science Online
For more information, visit bookm.msscience.com/time

Research Visit bookm.msscience.com for information and illustrations on the use of robots for space exploration. Ask students to include information on the success and failure rates of robotics in space. Encourage them to find out why some designs were used more than once and why some were discarded after one excursion.

Resources for Teachers and Students

Spare Parts, by Wendy Murphy. 21st Century Books, 2001

Orthotics and Prosthetics in Rehabilitation, by editors Michelle M. Lusardi and Caroline Nielsen, Butterworth and Heinemann Medical, 2000

Reviewing Main Ideas

Section 1 Work and Power

1. Work is done when a force exerted on an object causes the object to move.

2. A force can do work only when it is exerted in the same direction as the object moves.

3. Work is equal to force times distance, and the unit of work is the joule.

4. Power is the rate at which work is done, and the unit of power is the watt.

Section 2 Using Machines

1. A machine can change the size or direction of an input force or the distance over which it is exerted.

2. The mechanical advantage of a machine is its output force divided by its input force.

Section 3 Simple Machines

1. A machine that does work with only one movement is a simple machine. A compound machine is a combination of simple machines.

2. Simple machines include the inclined plane, lever, wheel and axle, screw, wedge, and pulley.

3. Wedges and screws are inclined planes.

4. Pulleys can be used to multiply force and change direction.

Visualizing Main Ideas

Copy and complete the following concept map on simple machines.

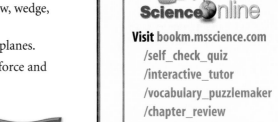

Reviewing Main Ideas

Summary statements can be used by students to review the major concepts of the chapter.

Visualizing Main Ideas

See student page.

Science Online

Visit bookm.msscience.com
/self_check_quiz
/interactive_tutor
/vocabulary_puzzlemaker
/chapter_review
/standardized_test

Assessment Transparency

For additional assessment questions, use the *Assessment Transparency* located in the transparency book.

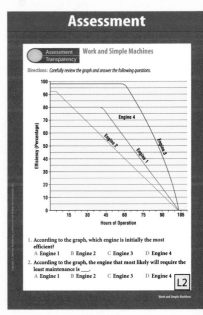

Using Vocabulary

1. efficiency
2. input force
3. output force
4. wheel and axle
5. mechanical advantage
6. simple machine
7. wedge
8. lever
9. inclined plane
10. power

Checking Concepts

11. C	16. C
12. D	17. B
13. B	18. B
14. A	19. B
15. B	

Thinking Critically

20. No; it would need to be at least 3 m from the fulcrum.

21. When work is done on the machine, energy is transferred to the machine. When work is done by the machine, the machine transfers energy to another object. According to the law of conservation of energy, energy cannot be created or destroyed. Therefore, the machine cannot create energy, so the energy transferred from the machine cannot be greater than the energy transferred to the machine.

22. The radius of the knob is greater than the radius of the axle. This means that when a force is applied to the knob, the knob moves a greater distance than the axle. The knob and the axle do the same amount of work. Therefore, the axle must multiply the force.

Using Vocabulary

chapter **4** Review

compound machine p. 109	output force p. 104
efficiency p. 107	power p. 101
inclined plane p. 109	pulley p. 114
input force p. 104	screw p. 111
lever p. 112	simple machine p. 109
mechanical advantage p. 105	wedge p. 110
	wheel and axle p. 112
	work p. 98

Each phrase below describes a vocabulary word. Write the vocabulary word that matches the phrase describing it.

1. percentage of work in to work out
2. force put into a machine
3. force exerted by a machine
4. two rigidly attached wheels
5. input force divided by output force
6. a machine with only one movement
7. an inclined plane that moves
8. a rigid rod that rotates about a fulcrum
9. a flat, sloped surface
10. amount of work divided by time

Checking Concepts

Choose the word or phrase that best answers the question.

11. Which of the following is a requirement for work to be done?
    A) Force is exerted.
    B) Object is carried.
    C) Force moves an object.
    D) Machine is used.

12. How much work is done when a force of 30 N moves an object a distance of 3 m?
    A) 3 J   C) 30 J
    B) 10 J   D) 90 J

Science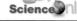nline bookm.msscience.com/vocabulary_puzzlemaker

13. How much power is used when 600 J of work are done in 10 s?
    A) 6 W   C) 600 W
    B) 60 W   D) 610 W

14. Which is a simple machine?
    A) baseball bat   C) can opener
    B) bicycle   D) car

15. Mechanical advantage can be calculated by which of the following expressions?
    A) input force/output force
    B) output force/input force
    C) input work/output work
    D) output work/input work

16. What is the ideal mechanical advantage of a machine that changes only the direction of the input force?
    A) less than 1   C) 1
    B) zero   D) greater than 1

Use the illustration below to answer question 17.

17. What is the output force if the input force on the wheel is 100 N?
    A) 5 N   C) 500 N
    B) 200 N   D) 2,000 N

18. Which of the following is a form of the inclined plane?
    A) pulley   C) wheel and axle
    B) screw   D) lever

19. For a given input force, a ramp increases which of the following?
    A) height   C) output work
    B) output force   D) efficiency

Use the ExamView® Pro Testmaker CD-ROM to:

• create multiple versions of tests
• create modified tests with one mouse click for inclusion students
• edit existing questions and add your own questions
• build tests aligned with state standards using built-in State Curriculum Tags
• change English tests to Spanish with one mouse click and vice versa

Thinking Critically

Use the illustration below to answer question 20.

9 N

3 m

20. Evaluate Would a 9-N force applied 2 m from the fulcrum lift the weight? Explain.

21. Explain why the output work for any machine can't be greater than the input work.

22. Explain A doorknob is an example of a wheel and axle. Explain why turning the knob is easier than turning the axle.

23. Infer On the Moon, the force of gravity is less than on Earth. Infer how the mechanical advantage of an inclined plane would change if it were on the Moon, instead of on Earth.

24. Make and Use Graphs A pulley system has a mechanical advantage of 5. Make a graph with the input force on the *x*-axis and the output force on the *y*-axis. Choose five different values of the input force, and plot the resulting output force on your graph.

Use the diagram below to answer question 25.

Total force = 50 N

Vertical part = 30

Horizontal part = 40 N

25. Work The diagram above shows a force exerted at an angle to pull a sled. How much work is done if the sled moves 10 m horizontally?

Performance Activities

26. Identify You have levers in your body. Your muscles and tendons provide the input force. Your joints act as fulcrums. The output force is used to move everything from your head to your hands. Describe and draw any human levers you can identify.

27. Display Make a display of everyday devices that are simple and compound machines. For devices that are simple machines, identify which simple machine it is. For compound machines, identify the simple machines that compose it.

Applying Math

28. Mechanical Advantage What is the mechanical advantage of a 6-m long ramp that extends from a ground-level sidewalk to a 2-m high porch?

29. Input Force How much input force is required to lift an 11,000-N beam using a pulley system with a mechanical advantage of 20?

30. Efficiency The input work done on a pulley system is 450 J. What is the efficiency of the pulley system if the output work is 375 J?

Use the table below to answer question 31.

Output Force Exerted by Machines

Machine	Input Force (N)	Output Force (N)
A	500	750
B	300	200
C	225	225
D	800	1,100
E	75	110

31. Mechanical Advantage According to the table above, which of the machines listed has the largest mechanical advantage?

23. The mechanical advantage of an inclined plane would be the same on Earth as on the Moon. The mechanical advantage of an inclined plane depends only on its length and height.

24. Check students' graphs.

25. work = force in direction of motion × distance moved by this force = 40 N × 10 m = 400 J

Performance Activities

26. Arms and legs are examples of levers. The elbows and knees are the fulcrums. Forces are exerted by muscles.

27. Check students' displays.

Applying Math

National Math Standards

1, 2, 5, 9

28. $MA = 6/2 = 3$

29. $MA = F_{out}/F_{in}$; $F_{in} = F_{out}/MA = 11,000 \text{ N}/20 = 550 \text{ N}$

30. $eff = \dfrac{W_{out}}{W_{in}} \times 100\% = \dfrac{375 \text{ J}}{450 \text{ J}} \times 100\% = 83\%$

31. Using the equation $MA = F_{out}/F_{in}$ shows that machine *A* has the largest mechanical advantage.

✔ Assessment   Resources

Reproducible Masters

Chapter *Fast File* Resources
Chapter Review, pp. 37–38
Chapter Tests, pp. 39–42
Assessment Transparency Activity, p. 49

Glencoe Science Web site
Chapter Review Test
Standardized Test Practice

Glencoe Technology

- Assessment Transparency
- Exam*View*® Pro Testmaker
- MindJogger Videoquiz
- Interactive Chalkboard

FAST FILE

Answer Sheet A practice answer sheet can be found at bookm.msscience.com/answer_sheet.

S A M P L E

Part 1 | Multiple Choice

1. B	5. C	9. C
2. A	6. B	
3. C	7. C	
4. D	8. C	

Part 2 | Short Response

10. fulcrum

11. The mechanical advantage of a pulley or pulley system is the number of sections of rope pulling up on the object supported by the pulleys.

12. The tip of the dart is a wedge. The feathers function as wedges as they push the air aside while the dart flies toward its target.

13. Yes, the mechanical advantage of the tip would increase.

14. $W = P \times t = 75 \text{ W} \times 15 \text{ s} = 1,125$ J

15. $MA = 2 \text{ m}/1 \text{ m} = 2$

16. Possible answers: wedge—teeth; forearm—lever

17. The efficiency of the machine increases because the lubricant decreases friction and less work is converted to thermal energy.

Part 1 | Multiple Choice

Record your answers on the answer sheet provided by your teacher or on a sheet of paper.

1. The work done by a boy pulling a snow sled up a hill is 425 J. What is the power expended by the boy if he pulls on the sled for 10.5 s?
   - **A.** 24.7 W
   - **B.** 40.5 W
   - **C.** 247 W
   - **D.** 4460 W

Use the illustration below to answer questions 2 and 3.

Input force	Output force
20 cm	120 cm

2. What is the mechanical advantage of the lever shown above?
   - **A.** $\frac{1}{5}$
   - **B.** $\frac{1}{2}$
   - **C.** 2
   - **D.** 5

3. What would the mechanical advantage of the lever be if the triangular block were moved to a position 40 cm from the edge of the output force side of the plank?
   - **A.** $\frac{1}{4}$
   - **B.** $\frac{1}{2}$
   - **C.** 2
   - **D.** 4

4. Which of the following causes the efficiency of a machine to be less than 100%?
   - **A.** work
   - **B.** power
   - **C.** mechanical advantage
   - **D.** friction

Test-Taking Tip

Simplify Diagrams Write directly on complex charts, such as a Punnett square.

Use the illustration below to answer questions 5 and 6.

5. The pulley system in the illustration above uses several pulleys to increase the mechanical advantage. What is the mechanical advantage of this system?
   - **A.** 1
   - **B.** 2
   - **C.** 3
   - **D.** 4

6. Suppose the lower pulley was removed so that the object was supported only by the upper pulley. What would the mechanical advantage be?
   - **A.** 0
   - **B.** 1
   - **C.** 2
   - **D.** 3

7. You push a shopping cart with a force of 12 N for a distance of 1.5 m. You stop pushing the cart, but it continues to roll for 1.1 m. How much work did you do?
   - **A.** 8.0 J
   - **B.** 13 J
   - **C.** 18 J
   - **D.** 31 J

8. What is the mechanical advantage of a wheel with a radius of 8.0 cm connected to an axle with a radius of 2.5 cm?
   - **A.** 0.31
   - **B.** 2.5
   - **C.** 3.2
   - **D.** 20

9. You push a 5-kg box across the floor with a force of 25 N. How far do you have to push the box to do 63 J of work?
   - **A.** 0.40 m
   - **B.** 1.6 m
   - **C.** 2.5 m
   - **D.** 13 m

Part 3 | Open Ended

18. In a real machine, the output work is always less than the input work because some of the work is converted into heat by friction. Energy is conserved in the machine because input work = output work + thermal energy.

19. changing the amount of force exerted; examples: scissors or pliers; changing the distance over which the force is exerted; examples: inclined plane or ramp; changing the direction in which the force is exerted; example: a fixed pulley

20. For some systems, the F_{in} is used to turn the wheel, and the F_{out} is exerted by the axle. The MA is greater than one. Examples: doorknob, a steering wheel, and a screwdriver. In other systems, the F_{in} is applied to turn the axle, and

Part 2 | Short Response/Grid In

*Record your answers on the answer sheet
provided by your teacher or on a sheet of paper.*

10. What is the name of the center point
about which a lever rotates?

11. Describe how you can determine the
mechanical advantage of a pulley or a
pulley system.

Use the figure below to answer questions 12 and 13.

12. What type of simple machine is the tip of
the dart in the photo above?

13. Would the mechanical advantage of the
dart tip change if the tip were longer and
thinner? Explain.

14. How much energy is used by a 75-W
lightbulb in 15 s?

15. A lever has a total length of 3 m. If the
distance from the fulcrum to the output
force is 1 m, what is the lever's mechanical
advantage?

16. Your body contains simple machines.
Name one part that is a wedge and one
part that is a lever.

17. Explain why applying a lubricant, such as
oil, to the surfaces of a machine causes the
efficiency of the machine to increase.

18. Apply the law of conservation of energy to
explain why the output work done by a
real machine is always less than the input
work done on the machine.

Part 3 | Open Ended

Record your answers on a sheet of paper.

19. The output work of a machine can never
be greater than the input work. However,
the advantage of using a machine is that it
makes work easier. Describe and give an
example of the three ways a machine can
make work easier.

20. A wheel and axle may have a mechanical
advantage that is either greater than 1 or
less than 1. Describe both types and give
some examples of each.

21. Draw a sketch showing the cause of friction as two surfaces slide past each other.
Explain your sketch, and describe how
lubrication can reduce the friction
between the two surfaces.

22. Draw the two types of simple pulleys and
an example of a combination pulley. Draw
arrows to show the direction of force on
your sketches.

Use the figure below to answer question 23.

23. Identify two simple machines in the photo
above and describe how they make riding
a bicycle easier.

24. Explain why the mechanical advantage of
an inclined plane can never be less than 1.

lever, and the pedal crank is a
wheel and axle.

24. For the mechanical advantage of an
inclined plane to be less than one, the
height must be greater than the
length of the plane. This is impossible.

Rubrics

For more help evaluating open-
ended assessment questions, see
the rubric on p. 10T.

the F_{out} is exerted by the wheel.
The *MA* is less than one. Examples:
fan and Ferris wheel

21. Sketches should show contact
points between two irregular surfaces. Applying a lubricant such as
oil to the surfaces fills in the gaps

between the surfaces, reducing the
friction between the surfaces.

22. (1) a fixed pulley supporting an
object; (2) rope tied to an upper
support and a movable pulley on
the rope supporting an object;
(3) a pulley system consisting of a

fixed pulley and one or more movable pulleys. In each sketch, the F_{in}
should be along the rope away
from the last pulley in the system.

23. Possible answers: the brakes on
the handlebars are levers, the
gearshift on the handlebar is a

Section/Objectives	Standards		Labs/Features
	National	**State/Local**	
Chapter Opener	See pp. 9T–10T for a Key to Standards.		**Launch Lab:** Marbles and Energy, p. 125 **Foldables,** p. 125
Section 1 What is energy? 🕐 3 sessions 📦 1.5 blocks 1. **Explain** what energy is. 2. **Distinguish** between kinetic energy and potential energy. 3. **Identify** the various forms of energy.	National Content Standards: UCP.1, UCP.2, UCP.3, UCP.5, A.1, A.2, B.1, B.2, B.3, G.2, G.3		
Section 2 Energy Transformations 🕐 3 sessions 📦 1.5 blocks 4. **Apply** the law of conservation of energy to energy transformations. 5. **Identify** how energy changes form. 6. **Describe** how electric power plants produce energy.	National Content Standards: UCP.1, UCP.2, UCP.3, UCP.5, A.1, A.2, B.1, B.2, B.3		**Science Online,** p. 132 **MiniLAB:** Analyzing Energy Transformations, p. 133 **Visualizing Energy Transformations,** p. 134 **Integrate Life Science,** p. 135 **Lab:** Hearing with Your Jaw, p. 138
Section 3 Sources of Energy 🕐 4 sessions 📦 2 blocks 7. **Explain** what renewable, nonrenewable, and alternative resources are. 8. **Describe** the advantages and disadvantages of using various energy sources.	National Content Standards: UCP.1, UCP.2, UCP.3, UCP.5, A.1, A.2, B.3, F.2, F.4		**Integrate Earth Science,** p. 140 **Science Online,** p. 142 **Applying Science:** Is energy consumption outpacing production?, p. 142 **MiniLAB:** Building a Solar Collector, p. 143 **Lab:** Energy to Power Your Life, p. 148 **Science Stats:** Energy to Burn, p. 150

Glencoe Exclusive!
TeacherWorks™
All-In-One Planner and Resource Center

Lab Materials	Reproducible Resources	Section Assessment	Technology
Launch Lab: book, glass marble, steel marbles, 3 metersticks	**Chapter FAST FILE Resources** Foldables Worksheet, p. 15 Directed Reading Overview, p. 17 Note-taking Worksheets, pp. 31–32	**GLENCOE'S ASSESSMENT ADVANTAGE**	**TeacherWorks** includes: • Interactive Teacher Edition • Lesson Planner with calendar • Access to all program blacklines • Correlations to standards • Web links ▣ Video Lab
Need materials? Contact Science Kit at 1-800-828-7777 or www.sciencekit.com on the Internet.	**Chapter FAST FILE Resources** Transparency Activity, p. 42 Enrichment, p. 28 Reinforcement, p. 25 Directed Reading, p. 18 **Reading and Writing Skill Activities,** p. 35	**Portfolio** Curriculum Connection, p. 127 **Performance** Applying Skills, p. 130 **Content** Section Review, p. 130	⌖ Section Focus Transparency ◉ Virtual Labs CD-ROM ∩ Guided Reading Audio Program ◉ Interactive Chalkboard CD-ROM
MiniLAB: soft clay, golf ball, steel ball, rubber ball, table-tennis ball, metric ruler **Lab:** radio or CD player, small electrical motor, headphone jack	**Chapter FAST FILE Resources** Transparency Activity, p. 43 MiniLAB, p. 3 Enrichment, p. 29 Reinforcement, p. 26 Directed Reading, p. 19 Lab Activity, pp. 9–10 Lab Worksheet, pp. 5–6	**Portfolio** Curriculum Connection, p. 136 **Performance** MiniLAB, p. 133 Applying Skills, p. 137 **Content** Section Review, p. 137	⌖ Section Focus Transparency ∩ Guided Reading Audio Program ◉ Interactive Chalkboard CD-ROM
MiniLAB: black plastic garbage bag, scissors, large pot, water, clear plastic wrap, tape, computer temperature probe or thermometer, watch **Lab:** Internet and other resources on energy	**Chapter FAST FILE Resources** Transparency Activity, p. 44 MiniLAB, p. 4 Enrichment, p. 30 Reinforcement, p. 27 Directed Reading, pp. 19, 20 Lab Activity, pp. 11–13 Lab Worksheet, pp. 7–8 Transparency Activity, pp. 45–46 **Lab Management and Safety,** p. 37	**Portfolio** Activity, p. 145 **Performance** Applying Science, p. 142 MiniLAB, p. 143 Applying Math, p. 147 **Content** Section Review, p. 147	⌖ Section Focus Transparency ⌖ Teaching Transparency ∩ Guided Reading Audio Program ◉ Interactive Chalkboard CD-ROM

End of Chapter Assessment

GLENCOE'S ASSESSMENT ADVANTAGE

Blackline Masters	Technology	Professional Series
Chapter FAST FILE Resources Chapter Review, pp. 35–36 Chapter Tests, pp. 37–40 **Standardized Test Practice,** pp. 23–26	▣ MindJogger Videoquiz ◉ Virtual Labs CD-ROM ◉ ExamView® Pro Testmaker ◉ TeacherWorks CD-ROM ◉ Interactive Chalkboard CD-ROM	**Performance Assessment in the Science Classroom (PASC)**

Transparencies

Section Focus

Section Focus Transparency 1 — Zot!

Lightning is a natural electrical spark. Sometimes the lightning we see goes from the clouds to the ground, but lightning also travels within a single cloud and between two clouds.

1. When do you most often see lightning?
2. Since lightning is a form of electricity, do you think it could be used by people to run appliances? Why or why not?

L2

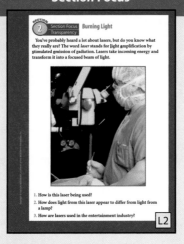

Section Focus Transparency 2 — Burning Light

You've probably heard a lot about lasers, but do you know what they really are? The word *laser* stands for *light amplification by stimulated emission of radiation*. Lasers take incoming energy and transform it into a focused beam of light.

1. How is this laser being used?
2. How does light from this laser appear to differ from light from a lamp?
3. How are lasers used in the entertainment industry?

L2

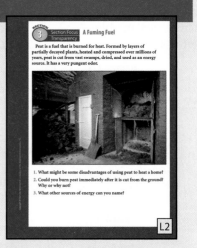

Section Focus Transparency 3 — A Fuming Fuel

Peat is a fuel that is burned for heat. Formed by layers of partially decayed plants, heated and compressed over millions of years, peat is cut from vast swamps, dried, and used as an energy source. It has a very pungent odor.

1. What might be some disadvantages of using peat to heat a home?
2. Could you burn peat immediately after it is cut from the ground? Why or why not?
3. What other sources of energy can you name?

L2

This is a representation of key blackline masters available in the Teacher Classroom Resources. See Resource Manager boxes within the chapter for additional information.

Key to Teaching Strategies

The following designations will help you decide which activities are appropriate for your students.

L1 Level 1 activities should be appropriate for students with learning difficulties.

L2 Level 2 activities should be within the ability range of all students.

L3 Level 3 activities are designed for above-average students.

ELL ELL activities should be within the ability range of English-Language Learners.

COOP LEARN Cooperative Learning activities are designed for small group work.

LS Multiple Learning Styles logos, as described on page 6T, are used throughout to indicate strategies that address different learning styles.

P These strategies represent student products that can be placed into a best-work portfolio.

PBL Problem-Based Learning activities apply real-world situations to learning.

Assessment

Assessment Transparency — Energy

Directions: Carefully review the diagrams and answer the following questions.

Ramp 1   Ramp 2

1. In the diagram of Ramp 1, at which spot does the car have the most potential energy?
   A A
   B B
   C C
   D D
2. The energy transformation that is occurring as the car rolls down Ramp 1 is ___.
   F kinetic energy to potential energy
   G chemical energy to kinetic energy
   H potential energy to kinetic energy
   J electrical energy to potential energy
3. The diagram shows a second ramp next to Ramp 2. If the car is allowed to roll down from the top of Ramp 2 it will probably ___.
   A roll further away from Ramp 2 than it did from Ramp 1
   B stop at the bottom of Ramp 2
   C have no kinetic energy at the bottom of Ramp 2
   D stop in the middle of Ramp 2

L2

Teaching

Teaching Transparency — Energy Transformations

5. Electrical energy out of generator
4. Kinetic energy of turbine
3. Kinetic energy of steam
2. Thermal energy of water
1. Nuclear energy of atoms

L2

Hands-on Activities

Student Text Lab Worksheet

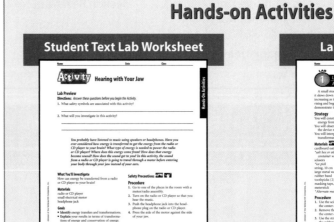

Activity — Hearing with Your Jaw

Lab Preview

Directions: Answer these questions before you begin the Activity.

1. What safety symbols are associated with this activity?

2. What will you investigate in this activity?

You probably have listened to music using speakers or headphones. Have you ever considered how energy is transferred to get the energy from the radio or CD player to your brain? What type of energy is needed to power the radio or CD player? Where does this energy come from? How does that energy become sound? How does the sound get to you? In this activity, the sound from a radio or CD player is going to travel through a motor before entering your body through your jaw instead of your ears.

What You'll Investigate
How can energy be transferred from a radio or CD player to your brain?

Materials
radio or CD player
small electrical motor
headphone jack

Goals
- Identify energy transfers and transformations.
- Explain energy transfers in terms of transformations of energy and conservation of energy.

Safety Precautions

Procedure
1. Go to one of the places in the room with a motor/radio assembly.
2. Turn on the radio or CD player so that you hear the music.
3. Push the headphone jack into the headphone plug on the radio or CD player.
4. Press the axle of the motor against the side of your jaw.

Conclude and Apply
1. Describe what you heard.

2. What type of energy did you have in the beginning? In the end?

L2

Laboratory Activities

Laboratory Activity 1 — Energy Transformations

A small stone thrown up into the air has kinetic energy because it is moving. As it rises higher, it slows down and its kinetic energy decreases. At the same time, however, its potential energy is increasing as its position above Earth's surface increases. When gravity causes the stone to stop rising and begin falling, its potential energy decreases as its kinetic energy increases. How can you demonstrate that potential energy can be converted to kinetic energy and vice versa?

Strategy
You will construct a device that changes energy from one kind to another.
You will observe and measure the distances the device moves.
You will interpret data in terms of energy transformations.

Materials
cardboard oatmeal box, with lid
*salt box or other round cardboard container with lid
scissors
*ice pick
string, 10 cm
large metal washer
rubber band
toothpicks (2)
masking tape, 1 m
*Alternate materials

Procedure
1. Use the scissors to punch a small hole in the center of the bottom of the box.
2. Remove the lid and punch another hole in the center of the lid.
3. Use the string to tie the metal washer to the rubber band. Cut off the excess string.
4. From the inside of the box, push part of the rubber band through the hole in the bottom. Put a toothpick through the loop in the rubber band, as shown in Figure 1. Pull any excess rubber band back into the box.
5. While a partner holds the lid close to the top of the box, stretch the rubber band and push the other end through the hole in the lid. Put a toothpick through the loop to hold the rubber band in place on the lid. Your device should look like Figure 2.

6. Put the lid on the box.
7. Place the strip of masking tape on the floor or a table. Place the box on its side at one end of the tape.
8. Push the box gently, so it rolls along the tape strip. Ask your partner to mark how far the box rolls before it stops and begins rolling back to you. Measure and record this distance in the table.
9. Repeat step 8 two more times, pushing the box with a little more force each time.

Figure 1

Loop of rubber band
Box bottom
Toothpick
Oatmeal box

Figure 2

Loop of rubber band
Box lid
Oatmeal box
Toothpick
Washer tied to rubber band

L2

Meeting Different Ability Levels

Content Outline

L2

Reinforcement

L2

Enrichment
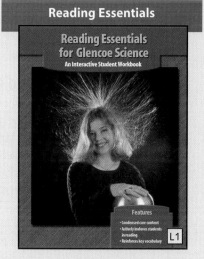

L3

Directed Reading (English/Spanish)

L1

Study Guide

L2

Reading Essentials
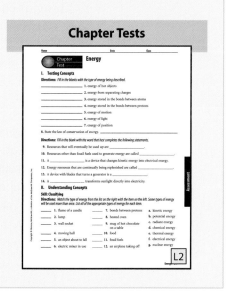

L1

Assessment

Test Practice Workbook

L2

Chapter Review

L2

Chapter Tests

L2

Science Content Background

section 1 · What is energy?

The Nature of Energy

Energy is not matter. Some forms of energy, such as light, can exist independent of matter. Other forms, such as chemical and kinetic energy, only can exist with matter.

section 2 · Energy Transformations

Changing Forms of Energy

In our common experience on Earth, energy is neither created nor destroyed, just transformed from one form into another. Heat often is produced from energy transformations.

The Law of Conservation of Energy

The law of conservation of energy states that energy is neither created nor destroyed, only converted from one form into another. Sometimes energy may appear to be lost. For example, when a moving object slows down kinetic energy appears to be lost. However, friction converts kinetic energy into thermal energy so that the sum of the kinetic energy and thermal energy stays constant.

In processes involving nuclear fission or nuclear fusion matter can be changed to energy. Energy also can be changed to matter. According to Einstein's equation $E = mc^2$, a small amount of mass can be converted into an enormous amount of energy. However, even when nuclear reactions are involved the law of conservation of energy still is true.

section 3 · Sources of Energy

Fossil Fuels

Fossil fuels were once living organisms that obtained energy from the Sun, and could thus be considered a type of solar energy. Unlike more direct forms of solar energy, burning fossil fuels produces carbon dioxide gas and other pollutants.

Geothermal Energy

You don't need to live near a volcano to use geothermal energy. Geothermal heat pumps, in use in 400,000 homes in the United States alone, take advantage of fairly constant below-ground temperatures. The temperature range in the first ten feet of soil is 10°C to 15.5°C (50°F to 60°F). This usually means the soil is warmer than the winter air and cooler than the summer air. In a heat pump, air gains or loses heat to the ground before entering a heating or cooling unit.

Iceland leads the world in its use of geothermal energy for heating. Almost 50% of its buildings are warmed using water heated by hot magma below Earth's surface. The Philippines is a leader in the use of geothermal energy to produce electricity. Approximately 22% of its electricity is produced with geothermal energy.

chapter content resources

Internet Resources

For additional content background, visit
bookm.msscience.com to:

- access your book online
- find references to related articles in popular science magazines
- access Web links with related content background
- access current events with science journal topics

Print Resources

Renewable Energy, Sorensen, Brent, Academic Press, 2000

The Feynman Lectures on Physics: Feynman on Fundamentals, Feynman, Richard P., Perseus Publishing, 1999

The Energy of Nature, Pielou, E.C., University of Chicago Press, 2001

IDENTIFYING Misconceptions

Find Out What Students Think

Students may think that . . .

Energy is something that is used and then disappears.

Students may have this misconception because people commonly talk about energy as though we use it and then it's gone. An athlete may say, "I ran out of energy." A parent may say, "Turn off the lights. You're wasting energy." An environmentalist may caution that the world is running out of energy. Another problem is that energy can seem abstract. Perhaps it is easy to understand that food contains energy. But energy contained by a book sitting on a desk is more difficult to comprehend.

Demonstration and Discussion

Hold up a windup toy. As you wind it, explain that your actions take energy. Release the toy and allow it to move until it winds down. Ask students to explain what has happened to the energy that you put into the toy. If students say that the toy used it up, ask them to explain what they mean. Did it disappear or become something else? Have students share their ideas.

Promote Understanding

Activity

Use books and tag board to make a U-shaped ramp. Students may have observed similar ramps used in skateboarding and bicycle stunt competitions.

- Hold a marble on top of one side of the ramp. Explain that the marble has potential energy due to its position. Gravity is pulling down on it.

- Release the marble. Explain that as the marble falls, its potential energy is converted to kinetic energy. Then, as the marble rises up the other side of the ramp, the kinetic energy is converted into potential energy.

- Now have students release the marble. Direct them to observe how high the marble rises up on each side of the ramp. Have them mark the heights achieved on each side of the ramp. Have students repeat this process at least five times.

- How does the maximum height reached by the marble change throughout each trial? Why does the marble go a little less high each time? How do we know the marble will eventually stop rolling? Help students realize that in this energy transformation between potential energy and kinetic energy, some energy is lost due to friction. This converts some kinetic energy of the marble into heat energy. Have the students rub their hands together to experience friction producing heat energy.

Assess

After completing the chapter, see *Identifying Misconceptions* in the Study Guide at the end of the chapter.

Chapter Vocabulary

energy, p. 126
kinetic energy, p. 127
potential energy, p. 128
thermal energy, p. 128
chemical energy, p. 129
radiant energy, p. 129
electrical energy, p. 130
nuclear energy, p. 130
law of conservation of energy,
    p. 132
generator, p. 136
turbine, p. 136
nonrenewable resource, p. 140
renewable resource, p. 142
alternative resource, p. 143
inexhaustible resource, p. 143
photovoltaic, p. 144

Science Journal Possible answers: hair dryer produces heat and blows air, toaster produces heat, TV produces sound and images, CD player produces sound

PowerPoint® Presentations

This CD-ROM is an editable Microsoft® PowerPoint® presentation that includes:
• a pre-made presentation for every chapter
• interactive graphics
• animations
• audio clips
• image bank
• all new section and chapter questions
• Standardized Test Practice
• transparencies
• pre-lab questions for all labs
• Foldables directions
• links to bookm.msscience.com

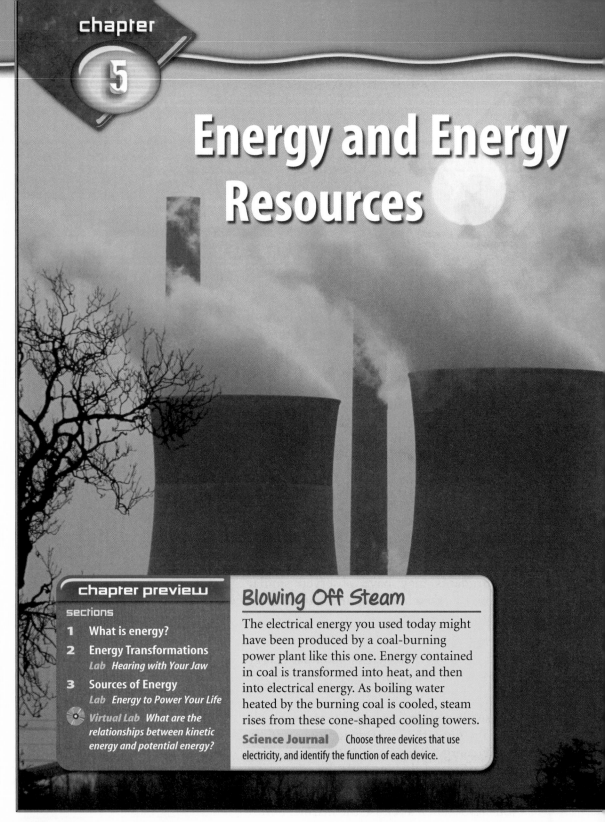

Energy and Energy Resources

chapter preview
sections
1 **What is energy?**
2 **Energy Transformations**
    Lab Hearing with Your Jaw
3 **Sources of Energy**
    Lab Energy to Power Your Life
    Virtual Lab What are the relationships between kinetic energy and potential energy?

Blowing Off Steam
The electrical energy you used today might have been produced by a coal-burning power plant like this one. Energy contained in coal is transformed into heat, and then into electrical energy. As boiling water heated by the burning coal is cooled, steam rises from these cone-shaped cooling towers.

Science Journal   Choose three devices that use electricity, and identify the function of each device.

Theme Connection

Systems and Interactions This chapter explores the various forms of energy, the interactions among them, and how they are harnessed for use in various systems.

About the Photo

Running on Steam In fossil-fuel-burning power plants and nuclear power plants, water is heated to produce steam. The steam drives turbines that are connected to electric generators. After the steam passes through the turbine, it is condensed by passing the steam over pipes containing cold water. This water then is cooled in the cooling towers.

Start-Up Activities

Marbles and Energy

What's the difference between a moving marble and one at rest? A moving marble can hit something and cause a change to occur. How can a marble acquire energy—the ability to cause change?

1. Make a track on a table by slightly separating two metersticks placed side by side.

2. Using a book, raise one end of the track slightly and measure the height.

3. Roll a marble down the track. Measure the distance from its starting point to where it hits the floor. Repeat. Calculate the average of the two measurements.

4. Repeat steps 2 and 3 for three different heights. Predict what will happen if you use a heavier marble. Test your prediction and record your observations.

5. **Think Critically** In your Science Journal, describe how the distance traveled by the marble is related to the height of the ramp. How is the motion of the marble related to the ramp height?

Energy Make the following Foldable to help identify what you already know, what you want to know, and what you learned about energy.

STEP 1 Fold a vertical sheet of paper from side to side. Make the front edge about 1 cm shorter than the back edge.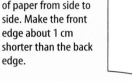

STEP 2 Turn lengthwise and **fold** into thirds

STEP 3 Unfold, cut, and label each tab for only the top layer along both folds to make three tabs.

| Know? | Like to know? | Learned? |

Identify Questions Before you read the chapter, write what you know and what you want to know about the types, sources, and transformation of energy under the appropriate tabs. As you read the chapter, correct what you have written and add more questions under the *Learned* tab.

 Science Online Preview this chapter's content and activities at bookm.msscience.com

---

Purpose Use the Launch Lab to help students see how the height from which an object is released on a ramp affects the distance it will roll. L2 ELL COOP LEARN IS Kinesthetic

Materials book, glass marble, steel marble, 3 metersticks

Teaching Strategy Make sure students always release the marble at the same point on the ramp, and be sure there isn't a significant bump where the ramp contacts the table. An index card can be used to smooth out the bump.

Think Critically

The higher the ramp, the farther from the table the marble hits the floor. The more massive marble lands the same distance from the table because it has the same horizontal velocity when it leaves the table as the less massive marble has.

Assessment

Performance Have students redesign the experiment to explore how changes in the mass of the marble affect an object it strikes. Use **Performance Assessment in the Science Classroom**, p. 105.

FOLDABLES Study Organizer **Dinah Zike Study Fold**

Student preparation materials for this Foldable are available in the Chapter *FAST FILE* Resources.

1 Motivate

Bellringer

INTERACTIVE CHALKBOARD
PowerPoint® Presentations

Section Focus Transparencies also are available on the Interactive Chalkboard CD-ROM.

L2 ELL

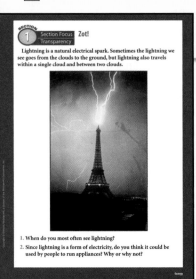

Tie to Prior Knowledge

Changes in Surroundings Ask students to name changes they have observed going on around them since they got up this morning. Possible answers include lights going on or off, changes in the positions of objects and of themselves, changes in temperature, and so on. Tell students that in this section they will learn about some of the causes of these changes.

Text Question Answer

Students' answers will vary. Possible answers: sunlight coming through window and heating room or students moving paper.

Caption Answer

Figure 1 The pizza can provide energy to its consumer, the candle flame can warm and burn objects, and the car can move itself and everything in it.

What is energy?

as you read

What **You'll Learn**

- **Explain** what energy is.
- **Distinguish** between kinetic energy and potential energy.
- **Identify** the various forms of energy.

Why **It's Important**

Energy is involved whenever a change occurs.

⊙ Review Vocabulary
mass: a measure of the amount of matter in an object

New Vocabulary
- energy
- kinetic energy
- potential energy
- thermal energy
- chemical energy
- radiant energy
- electrical energy
- nuclear energy

The Nature of Energy

What comes to mind when you hear the word *energy*? Do you picture running, leaping, and spinning like a dancer or a gymnast? How would you define energy? When an object has energy, it can make things happen. In other words, **energy** is the ability to cause change. What do the items shown in **Figure 1** have in common?

Look around and notice the changes that are occurring—someone walking by or a ray of sunshine that is streaming through the window and warming your desk. Maybe you can see the wind moving the leaves on a tree. What changes are occurring?

Transferring Energy You might not realize it, but you have a large amount of energy. In fact, everything around you has energy, but you notice it only when a change takes place. Anytime a change occurs, energy is transferred from one object to another. You hear a footstep because energy is transferred from a foot hitting the ground to your ears. Leaves are put into motion when energy in the moving wind is transferred to them. The spot on the desktop becomes warmer when energy is transferred to it from the sunlight. In fact, all objects, including leaves and desktops, have energy.

Figure 1 Energy is the ability to cause change.
Explain *how these objects cause change.*

Section 1 Resource Manager

Chapter FAST FILE Resources
Transparency Activity, p. 42
Directed Reading for Content Mastery, pp. 17, 18
Note-taking Worksheets, pp. 31–32

Enrichment, p. 28
Reinforcement, p. 25
Reading and Writing Skill Activities, p. 35

Energy of Motion

Things that move can cause change. A bowling ball rolls down the alley and knocks down some pins, as in **Figure 2A.** Is energy involved? A change occurs when the pins fall over. The bowling ball causes this change, so the bowling ball has energy. The energy in the motion of the bowling ball causes the pins to fall. As the ball moves, it has a form of energy called kinetic energy. **Kinetic energy** is the energy an object has due to its motion. If an object isn't moving, it doesn't have kinetic energy.

Kinetic Energy and Speed If you roll the bowling ball so it moves faster, what happens when it hits the pins? It might knock down more pins, or it might cause the pins to go flying farther. A faster ball causes more change to occur than a ball that is moving slowly. Look at **Figure 2B.** The professional bowler rolls a fast-moving bowling ball. When her ball hits the pins, pins go flying faster and farther than for a slower-moving ball. All that action signals that her ball has more energy. The faster the ball goes, the more kinetic energy it has. This is true for all moving objects. Kinetic energy increases as an object moves faster.

Reading Check *How does kinetic energy depend on speed?*

Kinetic Energy and Mass Suppose, as shown in **Figure 2C,** you roll a volleyball down the alley instead of a bowling ball. If the volleyball travels at the same speed as a bowling ball, do you think it will send pins flying as far? The answer is no. The volleyball might not knock down any pins. Does the volleyball have less energy than the bowling ball even though they are traveling at the same speed?

An important difference between the volleyball and the bowling ball is that the volleyball has less mass. Even though the volleyball is moving at the same speed as the bowling ball, the volleyball has less kinetic energy because it has less mass. Kinetic energy also depends on the mass of a moving object. Kinetic energy increases as the mass of the object increases.

Figure 2 The kinetic energy of an object depends on the mass and speed of the object.

A This ball has kinetic energy because it is rolling down the alley.

B This ball has more kinetic energy because it has more speed.

C This ball has less kinetic energy because it has less mass.

SECTION 1 What is energy? **M** ◆ 127

Curriculum Connection

Art Kinetic sculptures move using motors, pendulum action, or slight breezes that act upon sails. Among the most famous are the mobiles of artist Alexander Calder, who invented the art form in the 1920s. Have students research kinetic sculpture and build a sculpture of their own that models this art form. L2 **S** **Kinesthetic** P

2 Teach

Text Question Answer
They can cause change.

Text Question Answer
The person is changing position, the sun is warming up the desk, and the leaves are changing position.

Inquiry Lab

Observing Kinetic Energy

Purpose To explore and observe kinetic energy, have the students shoot rubber bands of various length and width and measure the distance of their flight.

Materials rubber bands of varying lengths and widths, tape measure

Estimated Time ½ class session

Teaching Strategies
• Students can predict the distance based on the length and width of the rubber bands. Have them write their hypothesis down and then test it by charting their data.
• Allow students to explore how stretching the rubber bands various lengths will affect the distance.
• Allow students to explore how shooting multiple rubber bands at once affects the flight distance of each rubber band.

For additional inquiry activities, see Science Inquiry Labs.

Reading Check

Answer Kinetic energy increases as speed increases.

Text Question Answer

The object on the higher level with the most mass has the most potential energy.

Caption Answer

Figure 3 If the two vases have the same mass, the higher vase has more potential energy because it has farther to fall.

Use Science Words

Word Origin The word *kinetic* comes from the Greek word *kinein*, meaning "to move," and *potential* comes from the Latin root *potens*, meaning "powerful." Have students explain how potential energy and kinetic energy are related to the meanings of their roots. Kinetic energy is the energy an object has because of its motion. Potential energy is energy stored in an object because of its position. An object's potential energy makes it powerful. L2 IS **Linguistic**

Activity

Thermal Energy Have students measure the temperature of a sample of hot water and of a sample of cold water. Have them mix the samples together and measure the temperature of the mixture every minute for ten minutes. Ask students to make time-temperature graphs of their results. What happens to the thermal energy of the water? Thermal energy is transferred from the hot water to the cold water until all the water is at the same temperature. L2 IS **Kinesthetic**

Virtual Labs

Energy *What are the relationships between kinetic energy and potential energy?*

Figure 3 The potential energy of an object depends on its mass and height above the ground.
Determine *which vase has more potential energy, the red one or the blue one.*

Energy of Position

An object can have energy even though it is not moving. For example, a glass of water sitting on the kitchen table doesn't have any kinetic energy because it isn't moving. If you accidentally nudge the glass and it falls on the floor, changes occur. Gravity pulls the glass downward, and the glass has energy of motion as it falls. Where did this energy come from?

When the glass was sitting on the table, it had potential (puh TEN chul) energy. **Potential energy** is the energy stored in an object because of its position. In this case, the position is the height of the glass above the floor. The potential energy of the glass changes to kinetic energy as the glass falls. The potential energy of the glass is greater if it is higher above the floor. Potential energy also depends on mass. The more mass an object has, the more potential energy it has. Which object in **Figure 3** has the most potential energy?

Forms of Energy

Food, sunlight, and wind have energy, yet they seem different because they contain different forms of energy. Food and sunlight contain forms of energy different from the kinetic energy in the motion of the wind. The warmth you feel from sunlight is another type of energy that is different from the energy of motion or position.

Thermal Energy The feeling of warmth from sunlight signals that your body is acquiring more thermal energy. All objects have **thermal energy** that increases as its temperature increases. A cup of hot chocolate has more thermal energy than a cup of cold water, as shown in **Figure 4.** Similarly, the cup of water has more thermal energy than a block of ice of the same mass. Your body continually produces thermal energy. Many chemical reactions that take place inside your cells produce thermal energy. Where does this energy come from? Thermal energy released by chemical reactions comes from another form of energy called chemical energy.

Figure 4 The hotter an object is, the more thermal energy it has. A cup of hot chocolate has more thermal energy than a cup of water, which has more thermal energy than a block of ice with the same mass.

Teacher FYI

Flow of Energy Heat is the flow of energy from a hot system to a cold system. Objects do not contain heat, only thermal energy.

Visual Learning

Figure 4 Point out that if the temperature remains the same, as the mass of a substance increases, the amount of thermal energy it has also increases. When could a sample of warm water have more thermal energy than a sample of warmer water? If the cooler sample has more mass than the warmer sample, it might have more thermal energy. L2 IS **Logical-Mathematical**

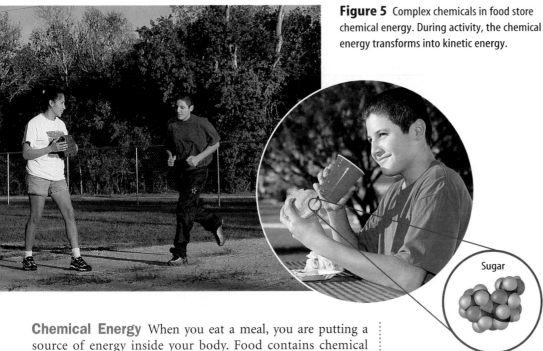

Figure 5 Complex chemicals in food store chemical energy. During activity, the chemical energy transforms into kinetic energy.

Sugar

Reading Check

Answer when chemicals are broken apart and new chemicals are formed

Discussion

Chemical Energy Tell your class that chemical energy is a very important form of energy. It includes burning gasoline in cars among other things. Ask your students what some other examples of chemical engery might be. Answers could include burning natural gas or oil for heat, burning logs, body metabolism, burning natural gas in electricity generators, natural gas stoves, natural gas clothes dryers, and battery-operated things.

Chemical Energy When you eat a meal, you are putting a source of energy inside your body. Food contains chemical energy that your body uses to provide energy for your brain, to power your movements, and to fuel your growth. As in **Figure 5,** food contains chemicals, such as sugar, which can be broken down in your body. These chemicals are made of atoms that are bonded together, and energy is stored in the bonds between atoms. **Chemical energy** is the energy stored in chemical bonds. When chemicals are broken apart and new chemicals are formed, some of this energy is released. The flame of a candle is the result of chemical energy stored in the wax. When the wax burns, chemical energy is transformed into thermal energy and light energy.

Reading Check *When is chemical energy released?*

Light Energy Light from the candle flame travels through the air at an incredibly fast speed of 300,000 km/s. This is fast enough to circle Earth almost eight times in 1 s. When light strikes something, it can be absorbed, transmitted, or reflected. When the light is absorbed by an object, the object can become warmer. The object absorbs energy from the light and this energy is transformed into thermal energy. Then energy carried by light is called **radiant energy. Figure 6** shows a coil of wire that produces radiant energy when it is heated. To heat the metal, another type of energy can be used—electrical energy.

Differentiated Instruction

Learning Disabled Light a candle and explain that the flame is a chemical reaction between the carbon compounds in the candle and the oxygen in the air. The flame gives off heat and light.

Figure 6 Electrical energy is transformed into thermal energy in the metal heating coil. As the metal becomes hotter, it emits more radiant energy.

Science Journal

Chemical Energy Have students list all the chemical energy transformations they encounter in a day. For each item have them list how the chemical energy was transformed or from what it was obtained. Possible answers include combustion of fuel in a car, digestion of food, use of oxygen by the body, photosynthesis in plants, use of battery-powered toys or appliances. L2 IS **Visual-Spatial**

Differentiated Instruction

Challenge In living things, the chemical energy in food is released through the process of respiration. Have students research and report on the chemical changes that occur in this process. During respiration, oxygen joins with glucose to release energy that is then used by the cells. Carbon dioxide and water are released as waste products. L3 IS **Linguistic**

Check For Understanding

Interpersonal Have students discuss why bat speed is the key factor in hitting homeruns in baseball. When a bat hits a ball, some of the kinetic energy of the bat is transferred to the ball. The more kinetic energy that is transferred to the ball, the farther it will travel. More kinetic energy can be transferred to the ball by increasing the bat's kinetic energy. The kinetic energy of an object is given by the equation $KE = \frac{1}{2}mv^2$. Because the velocity is squared in this equation, a fractional increase in the speed of the bat will have a greater effect on the bat's kinetic energy than the same fractional increase in the mass of the bat.

Reteach

Energy Types Have students identify the different types of energy that they rely upon. Discuss the specific tasks each type of energy is used to perform. L1 LS
Logical-Mathematical

✔ Assessment

Oral During the Explore Activity, the more massive marble had the same speed as the less massive marble. What conclusion can you draw about the energy of the two marbles? Explain. The more massive marble had more kinetic energy than the less massive marble. Use **Performance Assessment in the Science Classroom**, p. 89.

Figure 7 Complex power plants are required to obtain useful energy from the nucleus of an atom.

Electrical Energy Electrical lighting is one of the many ways electrical energy is used. Look around at all the devices that use electrical energy. The electric current that comes out of batteries and wall sockets carries **electrical energy.** The amount of electrical energy depends on the voltage. The current out of a 120-V wall socket can carry more energy than the current out of a 1.5-V battery. To produce the enormous quantities of electrical energy consumed each day, large power plants are needed. In the United States, about 20 percent of the electrical energy that is generated comes from nuclear power plants.

Nuclear Energy Nuclear power plants use the energy stored in the nucleus of an atom to generate electricity. Every atomic nucleus contains energy—**nuclear energy**—that can be transformed into other forms of energy. However, releasing the nuclear energy is a difficult process. It involves the construction of complex power plants, shown in **Figure 7.** In contrast, all that is needed to release chemical energy from wood is a lighted match.

section 1 review

Summary

The Nature of Energy

- Energy is the ability to cause change.
- Kinetic energy is the energy an object has due to its motion. Kinetic energy depends on an object's speed and mass.
- Potential energy is the energy an object has due to its position. Potential energy depends on an object's height and mass.

Forces of Energy

- Thermal energy increases as temperature increases.
- Chemical energy is the energy stored in chemical bonds in molecules.
- Light energy, also called radiant energy, is the energy contained in light.
- Electrical energy is the energy carried by electric current.
- Nuclear energy is the energy contained in the nucleus of an atom.

Self Check

1. **Explain** why a high-speed collision between two cars would cause more damage than a low-speed collision between the same two cars.
2. **Describe** the energy transformations that occur when a piece of wood is burned.
3. **Identify** the form of energy that is converted into thermal energy by your body.
4. **Explain** how, if two vases are side by side on a shelf, one could have more potential energy.
5. **Think Critically** A golf ball and a bowling ball are moving and both have the same kinetic energy. Which one is moving faster? If they move at the same speed, which one has more kinetic energy?

Applying Skills

6. **Communicate** In your Science Journal, record different ways the word *energy* is used. Which ways of using the word *energy* are closest to the definition of energy given in this section?

 Science Online bookm.msscience.com/self_check_quiz

section 1 review

1. At high speed, both cars have more kinetic energy. This greater kinetic energy will result in more damage occurring when the cars collide.
2. Chemical energy in the wood is transformed into thermal energy and radiant energy.

3. chemical energy
4. The vase with the larger mass would have more potential energy.

5. The golf ball has less mass so it must be moving faster. If they move at the same speed, the bowling ball has more kinetic energy.
6. Answers will vary.

Energy Transformations

Changing Forms of Energy

Chemical, thermal, radiant, and electrical are some of the forms that energy can have. In the world around you, energy is transforming continually between one form and another. You observe some of these transformations by noticing a change in your environment. Forest fires are a dramatic example of an environmental change that can occur naturally as a result of lightning strikes. A number of changes occur that involve energy as the mountain biker in **Figure 8** pedals up a hill. What energy transformations cause these changes to occur?

Tracking Energy Transformations As the mountain biker pedals, his leg muscles transform chemical energy into kinetic energy. The kinetic energy of his leg muscles transforms into kinetic energy of the bicycle as he pedals. Some of this energy transforms into potential energy as he moves up the hill. Also, some energy is transformed into thermal energy. His body is warmer because chemical energy is being released. Because of friction, the mechanical parts of the bicycle are warmer, too. Energy in the form of heat is almost always one of the products of an energy transformation. The energy transformations that occur when people exercise, when cars run, when living things grow and even when stars explode, all produce heat.

as you read

What **You'll Learn**

- **Apply** the law of conservation of energy to energy transformations.
- **Identify** how energy changes form.
- **Describe** how electric power plants produce energy.

Why **It's Important**

Changing energy from one form to another is what makes cars run, furnaces heat, telephones work, and plants grow.

🔎 **Review Vocabulary**
transformation: a change in composition or structure

New Vocabulary
- law of conservation of energy
- generator
- turbine

Figure 8 The ability to transform energy allows the biker to climb the hill.
Identify *all the forms of energy that are represented in the photograph.*

M ◆ 131

1 Motivate

Bellringer

Section Focus Transparencies also are available on the Interactive Chalkboard CD-ROM.
L2 ELL

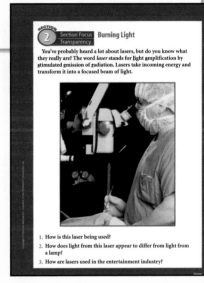

Tie to Prior Knowledge

Changing Energy Ask students to give examples of energy they used to get ready for school. Possible answers: thermal energy to dry hair, electricity to run appliances. Point out that energy changes from one form to another. For example, electrical energy was transformed to thermal energy by a hairdryer.

Caption Answer

Figure 8 kinetic energy of the bike and rider, potential energy of the bike and rider due to the height of the hill, and chemical energy in the rider's muscles

---

Section 2 Resource Manager

Chapter *FAST FILE* **Resources**
Transparency Activity, p. 43
Directed Reading for Content Mastery, p. 19
MiniLAB, p. 3
Lab Activity, pp. 9–10
Enrichment, p. 29

Reinforcement, p. 26
Lab Worksheet, pp. 5–6
Physical Science Critical Thinking/Problem Solving, p. 17

IDENTIFYING Misconceptions

Where Energy Goes Students may think that energy is something that is used and then disappears. See page F at the beginning of this chapter for teacher strategies that address this misconception.

Science Online

Topic: Energy Transformations

Visit bookm.msscience.com for Web links to information about energy transformations the occur during different activities and processes.

Activity Choose an activity or process and make a graph showing how the kinetic and potential energy change during it.

The Law of Conservation of Energy

It can be a challenge to track energy as it moves from object to object. However, one extremely important principle can serve as a guide as you trace the flow of energy. According to the **law of conservation of energy,** energy is never created or destroyed. The only thing that changes is the form in which energy appears. When the biker is resting at the summit, all his original energy is still around. Some of the energy is in the form of potential energy, which he will use as he coasts down the hill. Some of this energy was changed to thermal energy by friction in the bike. Chemical energy was also changed to thermal energy in the biker's muscles, making him feel hot. As he rests, this thermal energy moves from his body to the air around him. No energy is missing—it can all be accounted for.

✔ Reading Check *Can energy ever be lost? Why or why not?*

Changing Kinetic and Potential Energy

The law of conservation of energy can be used to identify the energy changes in a system, especially if the system is not too complicated. For example, tossing a ball into the air and catching it is a simple system. As shown in **Figure 9,** as the ball leaves your hand, most of its energy is kinetic. As the ball rises, it slows and loses kinetic energy. But, the total energy of the ball hasn't changed. The loss of kinetic energy equals the gain of potential energy as the ball flies higher in the air. The total amount of energy always remains constant. Energy moves from place to place and changes form, but it never is created or destroyed.

Figure 9 During the flight of the baseball, energy is transforming between kinetic and potential energy.
Determine *where the ball has the most kinetic energy. Where does the ball have the most total energy?*

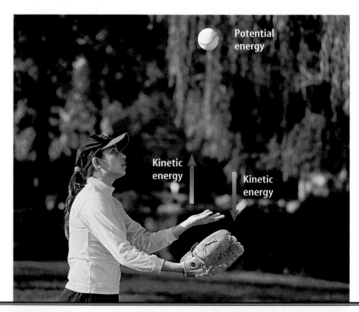

Potential energy

Kinetic energy

Kinetic energy

LAB DEMONSTRATION

Purpose to observe the exchange of potential and kinetic energy

Materials 1.0-kg mass attached to a 2-m string

Procedure Hang the pendulum so the bob just misses the floor at its lowest point. Release the bob at different heights, and measure the height to which it rises at the other end of its swing.

Expected Outcome The pendulum will swing up to nearly the original height from which it was released. The final height will be slightly lower due to the effects of air resistance and friction.

Assessment

Where does the bob have the greatest potential energy? just before it is released The greatest kinetic energy? at the bottom of its swing How does the height at which the bob is released affect the energy? Greater height means more total energy.

Figure 10 Hybrid cars that use an electric motor and a gasoline engine for power are now available. Hybrid cars make energy transformations more efficient.

Battery

Gasoline engine

Generator

Electric motor

Energy Changes Form

Energy transformations occur constantly all around you. Many machines are devices that transform energy from one form to another. For example, an automobile engine transforms the chemical energy in gasoline into energy of motion. However, not all of the chemical energy is converted into kinetic energy. Instead, some of the chemical energy is converted into thermal energy, and the engine becomes hot. An engine that converts chemical energy into more kinetic energy is a more efficient engine. New types of cars, like the one shown in **Figure 10,** use an electric motor along with a gasoline engine. These engines are more efficient so the car can travel farther on a gallon of gas.

INTEGRATE Life Science

Transforming Chemical Energy Inside your body, chemical energy also is transformed into kinetic energy. Look at **Figure 11.** The transformation of chemical to kinetic energy occurs in muscle cells. There, chemical reactions take place that cause certain molecules to change shape. Your muscle contracts when many of these changes occur, and a part of your body moves.

The matter contained in living organisms, also called biomass, contains chemical energy. When organisms die, chemical compounds in their biomass break down. Bacteria, fungi, and other organisms help convert these chemical compounds to simpler chemicals that can be used by other living things.

Thermal energy also is released as these changes occur. For example, a compost pile can contain plant matter, such as grass clippings and leaves. As the compost pile decomposes, chemical energy is converted into thermal energy. This can cause the temperature of a compost pile to reach 60°C.

Mini LAB

Analyzing Energy Transformations

Procedure
1. Place soft **clay** on the floor and smooth out its surface.
2. Hold a **marble** 1.5 m above the clay and drop it. Measure the depth of the crater made by the marble.
3. Repeat this procedure using a **golf ball** and a **plastic golf ball.**

Analysis
1. Compare the depths of the craters to determine which ball had the most kinetic energy as it hit the clay. Why did this ball have the most kinetic energy?
2. Explain how potential energy was transformed into kinetic energy during your activity.

Try at Home

Visualizing Energy Transformations

Have students examine the pictures and read the captions. Then ask the following questions.

Why is it necessary for skeletal muscles in the arm to be arranged in pairs? This is necessary so that the arm can move in more than one direction. For instance, when the arm is raised by the biceps, as shown in the art drawing, the triceps are needed to lower it.

What is the source of chemical energy for the muscles? Chemical energy is provided by breaking the chemical bonds in the foods we eat.

Activity

Leg Muscles Have your students research the major muscles in the human leg. Have students make drawings in their Science Journals of their leg muscles. Encourage them to make their drawings similar to those shown for the arm in **Figure 11.** L2
LS Visual-Spatial

NATIONAL GEOGRAPHIC VISUALIZING ENERGY TRANSFORMATIONS

Figure 11

Paddling a raft, throwing a baseball, playing the violin — your skeletal muscles make these and countless other body movements possible. Muscles work by pulling, or contracting. At the cellular level, muscle contractions are powered by reactions that transform chemical energy into kinetic energy.

▶ Energy transformations taking place in your muscles provide the power to move.

Biceps

Triceps

▲ Many skeletal muscles are arranged in pairs that work in opposition to each other. When you bend your arm, the biceps muscle contracts, while the triceps relaxes. When you extend your arm the triceps contracts, and the biceps relaxes.

Skeletal muscle

Muscle fiber

Bundle of muscle fibers

Filament bundle

Nerve fiber

Muscle fibers

Muscle filaments

▲ Skeletal muscles are made up of bundles of muscle cells, or fibers. Each fiber is composed of many bundles of muscle filaments.

▲ A signal from a nerve fiber starts a chemical reaction in the muscle filament. This causes molecules in the muscle filament to gain energy and move. Many filaments moving together cause the muscle to contract.

134 ◆ **M CHAPTER 5**

Differentiated Instruction

Challenge Have students research how electrical stimulation is being used to help paraplegics walk again. Encourage students to report their findings to the class. L2

Figure 12 The simple act of listening to a radio involves many energy transformations. A few are diagrammed here.

Electrical energy of radio signal → Kinetic energy of speaker → Sound energy of air → Kinetic energy of eardrum and fluid → Electrical energy of brain and nerve cells

Transforming Electrical Energy Every day you use electrical energy. When you flip a light switch, or turn on a radio or television, or use a hair drier, you are transforming electrical energy to other forms of energy. Every time you plug something into a wall outlet, or use a battery, you are using electrical energy. **Figure 12** shows how electrical energy is transformed into other forms of energy when you listen to a radio. A loudspeaker in the radio converts electrical energy into sound waves that travel to your ear—energy in motion. The energy that is carried by the sound waves causes parts of the ear to move also. This energy of motion is transformed again into chemical and electrical energy in nerve cells, which send the energy to your brain. After your brain interprets this energy as a voice or music, where does the energy go? The energy finally is transformed into thermal energy.

Transforming Thermal Energy Different forms of energy can be transformed into thermal energy. For example, chemical energy changes into thermal energy when something burns. Electrical energy changes into thermal energy when a wire that is carrying an electric current gets hot. Thermal energy can be used to heat buildings and keep you warm. Thermal energy also can be used to heat water. If water is heated to its boiling point, it changes to steam. This steam can be used to produce kinetic energy by steam engines, like the steam locomotives that used to pull trains. Thermal energy also can be transformed into radiant energy. For example, when a bar of metal is heated to a high temperature, it glows and gives off light.

INTEGRATE Life Science

Controlling Body Temperature Most organisms have some adaptation for controlling the amount of thermal energy in their bodies. Some living in cooler climates have thick fur coats that help prevent thermal energy from escaping, and some living in desert regions have skin that helps keep thermal energy out. Research some of the adaptations different organisms have for controlling the thermal energy in their bodies.

Discussion

Using Electrical Energy Discuss with students the activities in their lives that depend on electrical energy. Possible answers: operating blow-dryers, listening to radios, watching television Where does the electrical energy for these appliances come from? Possible answers: from batteries or from power plants that generate electrical energy. L2

IS **Logical-Mathematical**

Activity

Using a Generator Have students turn a hand-held generator when it is not hooked up to a light bulb and then again when it is. Try different wattage light bulbs. Why was no electrical energy generated when the light bulb was not connected? There was no circuit in which the current could flow. L2 **IS** **Kinesthetic**

Reading Check

Answer A generator converts the kinetic energy of a spinning turbine into electrical energy.

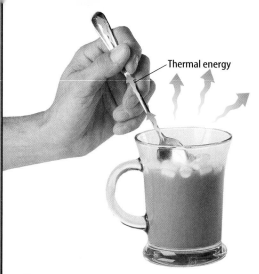

Figure 13 Thermal energy moves from the hot chocolate to the cooler surroundings.
Explain *what happens to the hot chocolate as it loses thermal energy.*

Figure 14 A coal-burning power plant transforms the chemical energy in coal into electrical energy.
List *some of the other energy sources that power plants use.*

How Thermal Energy Moves Thermal energy can move from one place to another. Look at **Figure 13.** The hot chocolate has thermal energy that moves from the cup to the cooler air around it, and to the cooler spoon. Thermal energy only moves from something at a higher temperature to something at a lower temperature.

Generating Electrical Energy

The enormous amount of electrical energy that is used every day is too large to be stored in batteries. The electrical energy that is available for use at any wall socket must be generated continually by power plants. Every power plant works on the same principle—energy is used to turn a large generator. A **generator** is a device that transforms kinetic energy into electrical energy. In fossil fuel power plants, coal, oil, or natural gas is burned to boil water. As the hot water boils, the steam rushes through a **turbine,** which contains a set of narrowly spaced fan blades. The steam pushes on the blades and turns the turbine, which in turn rotates a shaft in the generator to produce the electrical energy, as shown in **Figure 14.**

Reading Check *What does a generator do?*

Chemical energy in coal → Thermal energy in water → Kinetic energy of steam → Kinetic energy of turbine → Electrical energy out of generator

Stack

Steam line   Turbine   Generator

Transformer that increases voltage

Coal supply

Conveyor belt

Boiler

River or reservoir

Cooling water

Curriculum Connection

History The invention of the AC electric generator by Nikola Tesla in 1882 sometimes is described as the beginning of the second Industrial Revolution. Have students research and write reports about Tesla's life or his research on electricity. Tesla immigrated to the United States from Croatia. Thomas Edison advocated the use of DC electricity, and fought hard to prevent the adoption of Tesla's AC generator. L2 **IS** **Linguistic** P

Power Plants Almost 90 percent of the electrical energy generated in the United States is produced by nuclear and fossil fuel power plants, as shown in **Figure 15.** Other types of power plants include hydroelectric (hi droh ih LEK trihk) and wind. Hydroelectric power plants transform the kinetic energy of moving water into electrical energy. Wind power plants transform the kinetic energy of moving air into electrical energy. In these power plants, a generator converts the kinetic energy of moving water or wind to electrical energy.

To analyze the energy transformations in a power plant, you can diagram the energy changes using arrows. A coal-burning power plant generates electrical energy through the following series of energy transformations.

chemical energy of coal	→	thermal energy of water	→	kinetic energy of steam	→	kinetic energy of turbine	→	electrical energy out of generator

Nuclear power plants use a similar series of transformations. Hydroelectric plants, however, skip the steps that change water into steam because the water strikes the turbine directly.

Figure 15 The graph shows sources of electrical energy in the United States.
Name the energy source that you think is being used to provide the electricity for the lights overhead.

3 Assess

DAILY INTERVENTION

Check For Understanding
Linguistic Have students write in their Science Journals, using **Figure 12,** how the electrical energy of a radio signal is transformed into electrical energy in the brain and nerve cells. The energy in radio waves is transformed by the radio into kinetic energy in the form of sound waves. The sound waves strike the eardrum and are transformed from kinetic energy to electrical energy in the cochlea, which is then transmitted through nerve tissue to the brain.

Reteach
Energy Type Have volunteers explain each type of energy discussed in this section. As each energy type is discussed, challenge students to explain how this form of energy is used in their daily lives. **L2** **IS** **Linguistic**

☑ Assessment

Performance Have students make posters illustrating the energy transformations that occur when oil is used to generate electricity. Chemical energy of oil → thermal energy of water → kinetic energy of steam → kinetic energy of turbine → electrical energy out of generator Use **Performance Assessment in the Science Classroom,** p. 145.

---

section 2 review

Summary

Changing Forms of Energy
- Heat usually is one of the forms of energy produced in energy transformations.
- The law of conversation of energy states that energy cannot be created or destroyed; it can only change form.
- The total energy doesn't change when an energy transformation occurs.
- As an object rises and falls, kinetic and potential energy are transformed into each other, but the total energy doesn't change.

Generating Electrical Energy
- A generator converts kinetic energy into electrical energy.
- Burning fossil fuels produce thermal energy that is used to boil water and produce steam.
- In a power plant, steam is used to spin a turbine which then spins an electric generator.

Self Check

1. **Describe** the conversions between potential and kinetic energy that occur when you shoot a basketball at a basket.
2. **Explain** whether your body gains or loses thermal energy if your body temperature is 37°C and the temperature around you is 25°C.
3. **Describe** a process that converts chemical energy to thermal energy.
4. **Think Critically** A lightbulb converts 10 percent of the electrical energy it uses into radiant energy. Make a hypothesis about the other form of energy produced.

Applying Math
5. **Use a Ratio** How many times greater is the amount of electrical energy produced in the United States by coal-burning power plants than the amount produced by nuclear power plants?

---

section 2 review

1. Ball has kinetic energy when it leaves your hand; kinetic energy is converted to potential energy as ball rises; potential energy is converted to kinetic energy as ball falls
2. Your temperature is higher than your surroundings, so thermal energy is transferred from you to your surroundings.
3. Possible answer: burning of wood
4. The other 90 percent is converted into thermal energy.
5. (51%)/(20%) = 2.5 times greater

BENCH TESTED

▶ Real-World Question

Purpose Students track energy conversions from electrical energy to vibrations to sound.
L2 IS **Auditory-Musical**

Process Skills observing, inferring, predicting

Time Required 20 minutes

▶ Procedure

Teaching Strategy Have reference books about sound and electricity available.

Troubleshooting Make sure the wiring is securely connected. The motor will not turn even though students will be able to "hear" the music when they press the axle against their jaws.

▶ Conclude and Apply

1. Students should hear the sound of the radio or disc.
2. sound energy
3. Transformation should start with electrical energy (from a wall outlet or from a battery), change to mechanical energy, and end with sound energy. If a CD player is used, students also might include light energy.
4. The motor will probably get warmer as it runs. Some of the energy changes to heat because of friction.
5. All of the energy put into the system can be accounted for as motion, heat, light, or sound.

✔ Assessment

Content Have students work in groups to write a song or poem or make a picture about transfers of energy. Use **Performance Assessment in the Science Classroom,** p. 151.

Hearing with Your Jaw

You probably have listened to music using speakers or headphones. Have you ever considered how energy is transferred to get the energy from the radio or CD player to your brain? What type of energy is needed to power the radio or CD player? Where does this energy come from? How does that energy become sound? How does the sound get to you? In this activity, the sound from a radio or CD player is going to travel through a motor before entering your body through your jaw instead of your ears.

▶ Real-World Question
How can energy be transferred from a radio or CD player to your brain?

Goals
■ **Identify** energy transfers and transformations.
■ **Explain** your observations using the law of conservation of energy.

Materials
radio or CD player
small electrical motor
headphone jack

▶ Procedure
1. Go to one of the places in the room with a motor/radio assembly.
2. Turn on the radio or CD player so that you hear the music.
3. Push the headphone jack into the headphone plug on the radio or CD player.
4. Press the axle of the motor against the side of your jaw.

▶ Conclude and Apply
1. **Describe** what you heard in your Science Journal.
2. **Identify** the form of energy produced by the radio or CD player.
3. **Draw** a diagram to show all of the energy transformations taking place.
4. **Evaluate** Did anything get hotter as a result of this activity? Explain.
5. **Explain** your observations using the law of conservation of energy.

Communicating Your Data
Compare your conclusions with those of other students in your class. **For more help, refer to the** Science Skill Handbook.

Communicating Your Data
Students could use an electronic presentation program to present their picture and/or events chain to the rest of the class.

Sources of Energy

Using Energy

Every day, energy is used to provide light and to heat and cool homes, schools, and workplaces. According to the law of conservation of energy, energy can't be created or destroyed. Energy only can change form. If a car or refrigerator can't create the energy they use, then where does this energy come from?

Energy Resources

Energy cannot be made, but must come from the natural world. As you can see in **Figure 16,** the surface of Earth receives energy from two sources—the Sun and radioactive atoms in Earth's interior. The amount of energy Earth receives from the Sun is far greater than the amount generated in Earth's interior. Nearly all the energy you used today can be traced to the Sun, even the gasoline used to power the car or school bus you came to school in.

as you read

What You'll Learn
- **Explain** what renewable, non-renewable, and alternative resources are.
- **Describe** the advantages and disadvantages of using various energy sources.

Why It's Important
Energy is vital for survival and making life comfortable. Developing new energy sources will improve modern standards of living.

Review Vocabulary
resource: a source of something that is needed

New Vocabulary
- nonrenewable resource
- renewable resource
- alternative resource
- inexhaustible resource
- photovoltaic

Bellringer

Section Focus Transparencies also are available on the Interactive Chalkboard CD-ROM.

L2 ELL

A Fuming Fuel

Peat is a fuel that is burned for heat. Formed by layers of partially decayed plants, heated and compressed over millions of years, peat is cut from vast swamps, dried, and used as an energy source. It has a very pungent odor.

1. What might be some disadvantages of using peat to heat a home?
2. Could you burn peat immediately after it is cut from the ground? Why or why not?
3. What other sources of energy can you name?

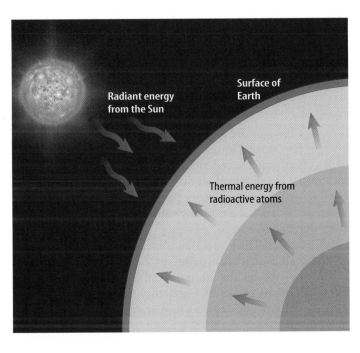

Radiant energy from the Sun

Surface of Earth

Thermal energy from radioactive atoms

Figure 16 All the energy you use can be traced to one of two sources—the Sun or radioactive atoms in Earth's interior.

Tie to Prior Knowledge

Energy Sources Ask students how their homes are heated. Possible answers: by burning oil or natural gas, or using electricity. Have them recall the sources of energy, such as fossil fuels, used to produce electricity in some power plants, and the energy transformations involved. Explain that they learn about other energy sources in this section.

SECTION 3 Sources of Energy **M** ◆ **139**

Section 3 Resource Manager

Chapter *FAST FILE* Resources
　Transparency Activity, pp. 44, 45–46
　Directed Reading for Content Mastery,
　　pp. 19, 20
　MiniLAB, p. 4
　Lab Activity, pp. 11–13
　Enrichment, p. 30

　Reinforcement, p. 27
　Lab Worksheet, pp. 7–8
Cultural Diversity, p. 45
Home and Community Involvement, p. 26
Lab Management and Safety, p. 73

Use an Analogy

Building Energy In fossil fuels, the chemical energy between the carbon atoms and the other atoms of the original organic matter has been concentrated. Burning fossil fuel yields a high amount of energy for a period of time that is fleeting compared with the time it took to transform the organic material into fossil fuel. In the same way, professional musicians and players of professional sports spend years learning to concentrate their energy and perfecting techniques that may take mere seconds to perform.

INTEGRATE Earth Science

Energy Source Origins Coal was formed from the remains of partially decomposed plants that had accumulated hundreds of millions of years ago. Coal formation gradually occurred after the plant debris had been covered and compressed by rocks, soil, and water and then subjected to great pressure and heat over long periods of time. Oil and natural gas formed from the remains of marine life and plants that had been rapidly buried in fine-grained sediment. This rapid burial prevented these organic debris from completely decomposing; and, along with increases in temperature and pressure, oil and natural gas deposits gradually formed.

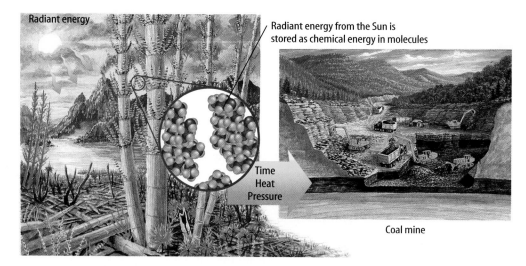

Radiant energy

Radiant energy from the Sun is stored as chemical energy in molecules

Time Heat Pressure

Coal mine

Figure 17 Coal is formed after the molecules in ancient plants are heated under pressure for millions of years. The energy stored by the molecules in coal originally came from the Sun.

INTEGRATE Earth Science

Energy Source Origins The kinds of fossil fuels found in the ground depend on the kinds of organisms (animal or plant) that died and were buried in that spot. Research coal, oil, and natural gas to find out what types of organisms were primarily responsible for producing each.

Fossil Fuels

Fossil fuels are coal, oil, and natural gas. Oil and natural gas were made from the remains of microscopic organisms that lived in Earth's oceans millions of years ago. Heat and pressure gradually turned these ancient organisms into oil and natural gas. Coal was formed by similar process from the remains of ancient plants that once lived on land, as shown in **Figure 17.**

Through the process of photosynthesis, ancient plants converted the radiant energy in sunlight to chemical energy stored in various types of molecules. Heat and pressure changed these molecules into other types of molecules as fossil fuels formed. Chemical energy stored in these molecules is released when fossil fuels are burned.

Using Fossil Fuels The energy used when you ride in a car, turn on a light, or use an electric appliance usually comes from burning fossil fuels. However, it takes millions of years to replace each drop of gasoline and each lump of coal that is burned. This means that the supply of oil on Earth will continue to decrease as oil is used. An energy source that is used up much faster than it can be replaced is a **nonrenewable resource.** Fossil fuels are nonrenewable resources.

Burning fossil fuels to produce energy also generates chemical compounds that cause pollution. Each year billions of kilograms of air pollutants are produced by burning fossil fuels. These pollutants can cause respiratory illnesses and acid rain. Also, the carbon dioxide gas formed when fossil fuels are burned might cause Earth's climate to warm.

140 ◆ **M CHAPTER 5** Energy and Energy Resources

Science Journal

Energy Matters Some people believe the demand for energy in the world will quadruple in the next fifty years. Have students write paragraphs in their Science Journals speculating how people will meet the demands for more energy. L2 LS
Intrapersonal P

Nuclear Energy

Can you imagine running an automobile on 1 kg of fuel that releases almost 3 million times more energy than 1 L of gas? What could supply so much energy from so little mass? The answer is the nuclei of uranium atoms. Some of these nuclei are unstable and break apart, releasing enormous amounts of energy in the process. This energy can be used to generate electricity by heating water to produce steam that spins an electric generator, as shown in **Figure 18.** Because no fossil fuels are burned, generating electricity using nuclear energy helps make the supply of fossil fuels last longer. Also, unlike fossil fuel power plants, nuclear power plants produce almost no air pollution. In one year, a typical nuclear power plant generates enough energy to supply 600,000 homes with power and produces only 1 m^3 of waste.

Nuclear Wastes Like all energy sources, nuclear energy has its advantages and disadvantages. One disadvantage is the amount of uranium in Earth's crust is nonrenewable. Another is that the waste produced by nuclear power plants is radioactive and can be dangerous to living things. Some of the materials in the nuclear waste will remain radioactive for many thousands of years. As a result the waste must be stored so no radioactivity is released into the environment for a long time. One method is to seal the waste in a ceramic material, place the ceramic in protective containers, and then bury the containers far underground. However, the burial site would have to be chosen carefully so underground water supplies aren't contaminated. Also, the site would have to be safe from earthquakes and other natural disasters that might cause radioactive material to be released.

Figure 18 To obtain electrical energy from nuclear energy, a series of energy transformations must occur.

1. Nuclear energy of atoms
2. Thermal energy of water
3. Kinetic energy of steam
4. Kinetic energy of turbine
5. Electrical energy out of generator
Generator

Quick Demo
Chain Reaction

Materials many mousetraps, large box with short walls

Estimated Time 2–5 minutes

Procedure To model the chain reaction that can occur in nuclear fission, place many set mousetraps into a large box with fairly short walls. **Warning:** *Keep fingers clear of trap area.* The traps should be fairly close together for a good response. Drop a table-tennis ball into the box and have students observe what happens. Explain that the ball represents a loose neutron that initiates the fission process while the mousetraps model uranium-235 nuclei.

Differentiated Instruction

Challenge The first human use of nuclear fission was in atomic weapons. Have students research the development of these weapons and give speeches describing their findings. During World War II, Albert Einstein twice wrote to President Franklin Delano Roosevelt to warn him that the technology needed to build nuclear weapons existed and that such weapons might be developed by Germany, which could lead to a global disaster. Einstein's warnings led to the formation of the Manhattan Project, which led to development of the world's first atomic weapons. L2 IS **Linguistic**

Active Reading

Four-Corner Discussion This strategy encourages the class to debate a complex issue. Make four signs: Strongly Agree, Agree, Disagree, and Strongly Disagree. Place one sign in each corner of the room. Write on the chalkboard a statement that will elicit reactions from students. Have the students respond on paper to the statement. After several minutes, direct them to move to the corner with the sign that most closely reflects their opinions. In the corners, students share responses. Each group then selects a spokesperson to report the opinions of the group. After all groups have reported, open the floor for debate. Allow students who have changed their opinions to change corners. Have students conduct a Four-Corner Discussion about the use of nuclear energy.

Make a Model

Pinwheel Have students make a pinwheel by folding each corner of a large index card into the center and attaching it to a pencil eraser with a pin. Have students place their pinwheels under a stream of water running from a faucet to observe that the kinetic energy of moving water can be transferred to the blades of a turbine. L1 LS **Kinesthetic**

Applying Science

Answers to Practice Problems

1. 1949 = ~30 quadrillion Btu;
   1999 = ~70 quadrillion Btu;
   Production has more than doubled.

2. 1949 = ~30 quadrillion Btu;
   1999 = ~95 quadrillion Btu;
   Consumption has more than tripled.

3. Additional energy comes from imports.

Science Online

Topic: Hydroelectricity
Visit bookm.msscience.com for Web links to information about the use of hydroelectricity in various parts of the world.

Activity On a map of the world, show where the use of hydroelectricity is the greatest.

Hydroelectricity

Currently, transforming the potential energy of water that is trapped behind dams supplies the world with almost 20 percent of its electrical energy. Hydroelectricity is the largest renewable source of energy. A **renewable resource** is an energy source that is replenished continually. As long as enough rain and snow fall to keep rivers flowing, hydroelectric power plants can generate electrical energy, as shown in **Figure 19.**

Although production of hydroelectricity is largely pollution free, it has one major problem. It disrupts the life cycle of aquatic animals, especially fish. This is particularly true in the Northwest where salmon spawn and run. Because salmon return to the spot where they were hatched to lay their eggs, the development of dams has hindered a large fraction of salmon from reproducing. This has greatly reduced the salmon population. Efforts to correct the problem have resulted in plans to remove a number of dams. In an attempt to help fish bypass some dams, fish ladders are being installed. Like most energy sources, hydroelectricity has advantages and disadvantages.

Applying Science

Is energy consumption outpacing production?

You use energy every day—to get to school, to watch TV, and to heat or cool your home. The amount of energy consumed by an average person has increased over time. Consequently, more energy must be produced.

U.S. Energy Overview, 1949–1999

Identifying the Problem

The graph above shows the energy produced and consumed in the United States from 1949 to 1999. How does energy that is consumed by Americans compare with energy that is produced in the United States?

Solving the Problem

1. Determine the approximate amount of energy produced in 1949 and in 1999

and how much it has increased in 50 years. Has it doubled or tripled?

2. Do the same for consumption. Has it doubled or tripled?

3. Using your answers for steps 1 and 2 and the graph, where does the additional energy that is needed come from? Give some examples.

142 ◆ **M CHAPTER 5** Energy and Energy Resources

Differentiated Instruction

Challenge Have groups of students build solar-powered toy cars. The cars should be built from scratch with parts from other toys. Upon completion, students should make diagrams describing how the cars work. L3 **ELL** COOP LEARN
LS **Kinesthetic**

Cultural Diversity

Three Gorges Dam The largest hydroelectric dam in the world, Three Gorges Dam, is under construction in China. Have students find out more about this dam and present their findings to the class. The dam will produce 18,200 megawatts of electricity and is to be completed in 2009. It will submerge 13 cities, 140 towns, and 1,352 villages. L2 LS **Linguistic**

1. Potential energy of water → 2. Kinetic energy of water

3. Kinetic energy of turbine

4. Electrical energy out of generator

Long-distance power lines

Figure 19 The potential energy of water behind a dam supplies the energy to turn the turbine. **Explain** *why hydroelectric power is a renewable energy source.*

Alternative Sources of Energy

Electrical energy can be generated in several ways. However, each has disadvantages that can affect the environment and the quality of life for humans. Research is being done to develop new sources of energy that are safer and cause less harm to the environment. These sources often are called **alternative resources.** These alternative resources include solar energy, wind, and geothermal energy.

Solar Energy

The Sun is the origin of almost all the energy that is used on Earth. Because the Sun will go on producing an enormous amount of energy for billions of years, the Sun is an inexhaustible source of energy. An **inexhaustible resource** is an energy source that can't be used up by humans.

Each day, on average, the amount of solar energy that strikes the United States is more than the total amount of energy used by the entire country in a year. However, less than 0.1 percent of the energy used in the United States comes directly from the Sun. One reason is that solar energy is more expensive to use than fossil fuels. However, as the supply of fossil fuels decreases, the cost of finding and mining these fuels might increase. Then, it may be cheaper to use solar energy or other energy sources to generate electricity and heat buildings than to use fossil fuels.

Reading Check *What is an inexhaustible energy source?*

Building a Solar Collector

Procedure
1. Line a **large pot** with **black plastic** and fill with **water.**
2. Stretch **clear-plastic wrap** over the pot and tape it taut.
3. Make a slit in the top and slide a **thermometer** or a **computer probe** into the water.
4. Place your solar collector in direct sunlight and monitor the temperature change every 3 min for 15 min.
5. Repeat your experiment without using any black plastic.

Analysis
1. Graph the temperature changes in both setups.
2. Explain how your solar collector works.

Visual Learning

Figure 19 Ask students to study the diagram of a hydroelectric plant and then explain why hydroelectric power is more efficient than fossil fuel or nuclear power. Hydroelectric power does not use heat, which is easily transferred to the surroundings, to generate electrical energy. In hydroelectric power, the energy of falling water is directly transferred to the turbine blades. L2
IS Visual-Spatial

Purpose to construct a simple solar collector L2 IS **Kinetic**

Materials black plastic garbage bag, scissors, large pot, water, clear plastic wrap, tape, thermometer, watch

Teaching Strategies Explain that black materials absorb more radiant energy from the Sun than shiny materials do.

Analysis
1. The temperature increases faster in the setup with the plastic.
2. The black plastic absorbs heat from the Sun, and the clear plastic traps the heat. This heat is transferred to the water.

Assessment

Process Have students make time/temperature graphs of their data for both collectors. Use **Performance Assessment in the Science Classroom,** p. 111.

Reading Check

Answer an energy source that can't be used up by humans

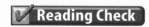
Teacher FYI

Geothermal Energy Geothermal energy can be used for heating in the winter and cooling in the summer. A loop of pipe with water running through it is inserted below the frost line where the ground stays at a constant temperature of about 10°C to 20°C, as in a cave. In summer, when the house air is warmer than this underground temperature, water in the pipe carries underground heat out of the house and underground, where the water is cooled. The water then returns above ground to collect more heat. In the winter, the reverse takes place. This method of heating and cooling is more efficient than many other methods and has recently become cost effective. Also, this method does not depend on thermal vents, which occur in only a few isolated regions of the world, and it can be used nearly everywhere.

Discussion

Advantages of Geothermal Energy What advantages does geothermal energy have over burning fossil fuels or using nuclear energy? Possible answers: Geothermal energy is a renewable resource. Using it instead of a nonrenewable resource such as coal or petroleum reserves fossil fuels for other uses, produces less air pollution, and eliminates waste disposal problems associated with nuclear power.

Figure 20 Solar energy can be collected and utilized by individuals using thermal collectors or photovoltaic collectors.

Collecting the Sun's Energy Two types of collectors capture the Sun's rays. If you look around your neighborhood, you might see large, rectangular panels attached to the roofs of buildings or houses. If, as in **Figure 20,** pipes come out of the panel, it is a thermal collector. Using a black surface, a thermal collector heats water by directly absorbing the Sun's radiant energy. Water circulating in this system can be heated to about 70°C. The hot water can be pumped through the house to provide heat. Also, the hot water can be used for washing and bathing. If the panel has no pipes, it is a photovoltaic (foh toh vol TAY ihk) collector, like the one pictured in **Figure 20.** A **photovoltaic** is a device that transforms radiant energy directly into electrical energy. Photovoltaics are used to power calculators and satellites, including the *International Space Station.*

Reading Check *What does a photovoltaic do?*

Geothermal Energy

Imagine you could take a journey to the center of Earth—down to about 6,400 km below the surface. As you went deeper and deeper, you would find the temperature increasing. In fact, after going only about 3 km, the temperature could have increased enough to boil water. At a depth of 100 km, the temperature could be over 900°C. The heat generated inside Earth is called geothermal energy. Some of this heat is produced when unstable radioactive atoms inside Earth decay, converting nuclear energy to thermal energy.

At some places deep within Earth the temperature is hot enough to melt rock. This molten rock, or magma, can rise up close to the surface through cracks in the crust. During a volcanic eruption, magma reaches the surface. In other places, magma gets close to the surface and heats the rock around it.

Geothermal Reservoirs In some regions where magma is close to the surface, rainwater and water from melted snow can seep down to the hot rock through cracks and other openings in Earth's surface. The water then becomes hot and sometimes can form steam. The hot water and steam can be trapped under high pressure in cracks and pockets called geothermal reservoirs. In some places, the hot water and steam are close enough to the surface to form hot springs and geysers.

Differentiated Instruction

Learning Disabled Light from different sources, most notably the sun, can be transformed directly into electricity. Have a light-powered calculator available to demonstrate this. When the photovoltaic cell is in the light the light energy turns into electricity which runs the calculator. Cover the cell and the source of electricity is gone. The calculator runs out of energy and goes off.

Cultural Diversity

Geothermal Iceland Iceland gets 50% of its energy from geothermal sources. Fossil fuels are only used to power automobiles, ships, and airplanes. About 86% of all space heating in Iceland is provided by geothermal energy and about 16% of Iceland's electricity is generated using geothermal energy. Geothermal energy is also used to heat outdoor pools, where people swim year round.

Geothermal Power Plants In places where the geothermal reservoirs are less than several kilometers deep, wells can be drilled to reach them. The hot water and steam produced by geothermal energy then can be used by geothermal power plants, like the one in **Figure 21,** to generate electricity.

Most geothermal reservoirs contain hot water under high pressure. **Figure 22** shows how these reservoirs can be used to generate electricity. While geothermal power is an inexhaustible source of energy, geothermal power plants can be built only in regions where geothermal reservoirs are close to the surface, such as in the western United States.

Heat Pumps Geothermal heat helps keep the temperature of the ground at a depth of several meters at a nearly constant temperature of about 10° to 20°C. This constant temperature can be used to cool and heat buildings by using a heat pump.

A heat pump contains a water-filled loop of pipe that is buried to a depth where the temperature is nearly constant. In summer the air is warmer than this underground temperature. Warm water from the building is pumped through the pipe down into the ground. The water cools and then is pumped back to the house where it absorbs more heat, and the cycle is repeated. During the winter, the air is cooler than the ground below. Then, cool water absorbs heat from the ground and releases it into the house.

Figure 21 This geothermal power plant in Nevada produces enough electricity to power about 50,000 homes.

Figure 22 The hot water in a geothermal reservoir is used to generate electricity in a geothermal power plant.

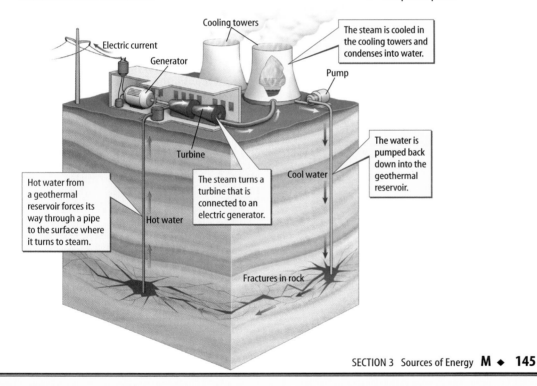

Cooling towers

Electric current

Generator

The steam is cooled in the cooling towers and condenses into water.

Pump

Turbine

The water is pumped back down into the geothermal reservoir.

Cool water

Hot water from a geothermal reservoir forces its way through a pipe to the surface where it turns to steam.

The steam turns a turbine that is connected to an electric generator.

Hot water

Fractures in rock

Differentiated Instruction

Learning Disabled Have another student use a poster that was made in the activity above to explain each step in the heat pump process. Have learning disabled students define any unfamiliar words in their science journals for future reference. [LS] **Interpersonal**

Science Journal

Geothermal Heat Pumps Have students make a chart in their Science Journals listing advantages and disadvantages of installing a geothermal heat pump in their home. [LS] **Logical-Mathematical**

Water Energy What produces the mechanical energy used in a tidal power plant? The flow of water through a turbine, which causes the turbine to spin; in this way mechanical energy can be changed to electrical energy. Why is this system available in only a few locations around the world? There are only a few locations that have a large enough difference between the height of high and low tides.

Make a Model

Tidal Energy Have groups of students make simple models demonstrating how tidal energy can be used to generate electricity. Instruct students to use their models to explain this process to a group of younger students or another class. **LS Interpersonal**

Activity

Venn Diagram Have students make a Venn diagram to compare and contrast hydroelectric and tidal power. **LS Visual-Spatial**

Figure 23 This tidal power plant in Annapolis Royal, Nova Scotia, is the only operating tidal power plant in North America.

Figure 24 A tidal power plant can generate electricity when the tide is coming in and going out.

Energy from the Oceans

The ocean is in constant motion. If you've been to the seashore you've seen waves roll in. You may have seen the level of the ocean rise and fall over a period of about a half day. This rise and fall in the ocean level is called a tide. The constant movement of the ocean is an inexhaustible source of mechanical energy that can be converted into electric energy. While methods are still being developed to convert the motion in ocean waves to electric energy, several electric power plants using tidal motion have been built.

Using Tidal Energy A high tide and a low tide each occur about twice a day. In most places the level of the ocean changes by less than a few meters. However, in some places the change is much greater. In the Bay of Fundy in Eastern Canada, the ocean level changes by 16 m between high tide and low tide. Almost 14 trillion kg of water move into or out of the bay between high and low tide.

Figure 23 shows an electric power plant that has been built along the Bay of Fundy. This power plant generates enough electric energy to power about 12,000 homes. The power plant is constructed so that as the tide rises, water flows through a turbine that causes a electric generator to spin, as shown in **Figure 24A.** The water is then trapped behind a dam. When the tide goes out, the trapped water behind the dam is released through the turbine to generate more electricity, as shown in **Figure 24B.** Each day electric power is generated for about ten hours when the tide is rising and falling.

While tidal energy is a nonpolluting, inexhaustible energy source, its use is limited. Only in a few places is the difference between high and low tide large enough to enable a large electric power plant to be built.

A As the tide comes in, it turns a turbine connected to a generator. When high tide occurs, gates are closed that trap water behind a dam.

B As the tide goes out and the ocean level drops, the gates are opened and water from behind the dam flows through the turbine, causing it to spin and turn a generator.

146 ◆ M CHAPTER 5 Energy and Energy Resources

Curriculum Connection

Geography The first large-scale tidal plant was constructed on the Rance River in Saint-Malo, France. Have students locate this area on a map. **LS Visual-Spatial**

Wind

Wind is another inexhaustible supply of energy. Modern windmills, like the ones in **Figure 25,** convert the kinetic energy of the wind to electrical energy. The propeller is connected to a generator so that electrical energy is generated when wind spins the propeller. These windmills produce almost no pollution. Some disadvantages are that windmills produce noise and that large areas of land are needed. Also, studies have shown that birds sometimes are killed by windmills.

Conserving Energy

Fossil fuels are a valuable resource. Not only are they burned to provide energy, but oil and coal also are used to make plastics and other materials. One way to make the supply of fossil fuels last longer is to use less energy. Reducing the use of energy is called conserving energy.

You can conserve energy and also save money by turning off lights and appliances such as televisions when you are not using them. Also keep doors and windows closed tightly when it's cold or hot to keep heat from leaking out of or into your house. Energy could also be conserved if buildings are properly insulated, especially around windows. The use of oil could be reduced if cars were used less and made more efficient, so they went farther on a liter of gas. Recycling materials such as aluminum cans and glass also helps conserve energy.

Figure 25 Windmills work on the same basic principles as a power plant. Instead of steam turning a turbine, wind turns the rotors. **Describe** *some of the advantages and disadvantages of using windmills.*

3 Assess

DAILY INTERVENTION

Check for Understanding

Linguistic Have students answer the following questions in their Science Journals: "What kind of energy source is ethanol derived from corn, and why does adding it to gasoline prolong the supply of oil?" Ethanol derived from corn is a renewable source of energy. As long as corn keeps being planted and grown, there will be a source for ethanol to burn in cars. Adding ethanol to gasoline allows us to reduce our usage of gasoline, slowing down the rate at which we are using that non-renewable source of energy.

Reteach

Sources of Energy Have each student make a list of all of the sources of energy discussed in this section. Ask students to explain how each energy source releases its energy and classify each source as renewable or nonrenewable. L2 IS **Linguistic**

---

section 3 review

Summary

Nonrenewable Resources

- All energy resources have advantages and disadvantages.
- Nonrenewable energy resources are used faster than they are replaced.
- Fossil fuels include oil, coal, and natural gas and are nonrenewable resources. Nuclear energy is a non-renewable resource.

Renewable and Alternative Resources

- Renewable energy resources, such as hydroelectricity, are resources that are replenished continually.
- Alternative energy sources include solar energy, wind energy, and geothermal energy.

Self Check

1. **Diagram** the energy conversions that occur when coal is formed, and then burned to produce thermal energy.
2. **Explain** why solar energy is considered an inexhaustible source of energy.
3. **Explain** how a heat pump is used to both heat and cool a building.
4. **Think Critically** Identify advantages and disadvantages of using fossil fuels, hydroelectricity, and solar energy as energy sources.

Applying Math

5. **Use a Ratio** Earth's temperature increases with depth. Suppose the temperature increase inside Earth is 500°C at a depth of 50 km. What is the temperature increase at a depth of 10 km?

Science Online bookm.msscience.com/self_check_quiz

SECTION 3 Sources of Energy **M ◆ 147**

Assessment

Oral Where does all the electrical energy produced in power plants end up? It is converted into energy forms such as thermal, radiant, or sound energy.

---

section 3 review

1. Radiant energy from the Sun is converted into chemical energy when coal is formed; chemical energy in coal is converted into thermal energy and radiant energy when coal is burned.
2. The Sun's energy cannot be used up by humans because the Sun will produce an enormous amount of energy for billions of years and humans can use only a small amount of the energy the Sun produces.
3. The ground at several meters' depth is cooler than the outside air in summer and warmer than the outside air in winter. Heat can be transferred from the building to the ground in summer, and from the ground to the building in winter.
4. fossil fuels: cheap, plentiful, but nonrenewable and produces pollution; hydroelectricity: nonpolluting, renewable, but can alter local ecosystems and available only in certain areas; solar energy: inexhaustible, but expensive
5. 100°C

Real-World Question

Purpose Students will investigate the types of energy they use in everyday activities.

Process Skills Locate and evaluate sources of information on the Internet, in books, and in periodicals.

Time Required about two days

Internet Students use Internet sites that can be accessed through bookm.msscience.com/internet_lab.

They will investigate the types of energy they use in everyday activities. L2

IS **Logical-Mathematical**

Non-Internet Sources Identify different science books to research energy sources.

Make a Plan

Preparation

Internet To run through the steps that the students will follow, visit bookm.msscience.com/internet_lab.

Non-Internet Sources Collect books and materials that contain information about energy sources such as gasoline, coal, and solar energy.

Follow Your Plan

Teaching Strategy Ahead of time, do some Internet searches to locate and evaluate several Web sites noting their strengths and weaknesses. This will help you guide your students as they research Internet sites. Also, ask your librarian to give a short presentation on using library materials as part of their research.

LAB **Use the Internet**

Energy to Power Your Life

Goals
- **Identify** how energy you use is produced and delivered.
- **Investigate** alternative sources for the energy you use.
- **Outline** a plan for how these alternative sources of energy could be used.

Data Source

Science Online

Visit bookm.msscience.com/internet_lab for more information about sources of energy and for data collected by other students.

Real-World Question

Over the past 100 years, the amount of energy used in the United States and elsewhere has greatly increased. Today, a number of energy sources are available, such as coal, oil, natural gas, nuclear energy, hydroelectric power, wind, and solar energy. Some of these energy sources are being used up and are nonrenewable, but others are replaced as fast as they are used and, therefore, are renewable. Some energy sources are so vast that human usage has almost no effect on the amount available. These energy sources are inexhaustible.

Think about the types of energy you use at home and school every day. In this lab, you will investigate how and where energy is produced, and how it gets to you. You will also investigate alternative ways energy can be produced, and whether these sources are renewable, nonrenewable, or inexhaustible. What are the sources of the energy you use every day?

Local Energy Information	
Energy Type	
Where is that energy produced?	
How is that energy produced?	
How is that energy delivered to you?	Answers will
Is the energy source renewable, nonrenewable, or inexhaustible?	vary.
What type of alternative energy source could you use instead?	

Form a Hypothesis

When you wake up in the morning and turn on a light, you use electrical energy. When you ride to school in a car or bus, its engine consumes chemical energy. What other types of energy do you use? Where is that energy produced? Which energy sources are nonrenewable, which are renewable, and which are inexhaustible? What are other sources of energy that you could use instead?

148 ◆ M CHAPTER 5 Energy and Energy Resources

Alternative Inquiry Lab

Energy Types and Sources Every energy source has its pros and cons. Have the students choose from a list of sources including, but not limited to, coal, gasoline, natural gas, heating oil, nuclear power, ethanol, hydrogen power, solar power, and wind power. They should summarize what the pros and cons are for that particular energy source, and take a position on the advisability of staying with or changing to that source of energy. This lab will challenge students to use critical thinking and higher order thinking skills.

▶ Test Your Hypothesis

Make a Plan

1. Think about the activities you do every day and the things you use. When you watch television, listen to the radio, ride in a car, use a hair drier, or turn on the air conditioning, you use energy. Select one activity or appliance that uses energy.

2. **Identify** the type of energy that is used.

3. **Investigate** how that energy is produced and delivered to you.

4. **Determine** if the energy source is renewable, nonrenewable, or inexhaustible.

5. If your energy source is nonrenewable, describe how the energy you use could be produced by renewable sources.

Follow Your Plan

1. Make sure your teacher approves your plan before you start.

2. Organize your findings in a data table, similar to the one that is shown.

▶ Analyze Your Data

1. **Describe** the process for producing and delivering the energy source you researched. How is it created, and how does it get to you?

2. How much energy is produced by the energy source you investigated?

3. Is the energy source you researched renewable, nonrenewable, or inexhaustible? Why?

▶ Conclude and Apply

1. **Describe** If the energy source you investigated is nonrenewable, how the use of this energy source be reduced?

2. **Organize** What alternative sources of energy could you use for everyday energy needs? On the computer, create a plan for using renewable or inexhaustible sources.

Find this lab using the link below. Post your data in the table that is provided. **Compare** your data to those of other students. **Combine** your data with those of other students and make inferences using the combined data.

ScienceOnline

bookm.msscience.com/internet_lab

▶ Analyze Your Data

1. Answers may vary. One example would be the process for producing gasoline, which involves drilling crude oil from wells, and the process involved in refining the crude oil into the product that we pump at the gas station.

2. If students investigated gasoline, they may discover that it is a small part of their daily energy use.

3. Gasoline is an example of a non-renewable energy source, because it is a fossil fuel.

▶ Conclude and Apply

1. Answers will vary.

2. One strategy may be to replace a calculator that runs on nonrechargeable batteries with one that is powered by solar cells.

Assessment

Process Have students make displays that show their research about an activity or appliance and its energy source. They should include pictures and descriptions of how the energy source used is produced and delivered so it can be used. Use **Performance Assessment in the Science Classroom,** p.135.

Communicating
Your Data

Have students make a chart that compares the energy source they investigated with other energy sources that could be used, including alternative or renewable energy sources. Students should also compare costs and environmental impacts.

SCIENCE Stats

Content Background

Solar, wind, and geothermal are inexhaustible energy sources, and biomass and hydroelectric powered systems are considered renewable energy sources. Not all sources can be used to produce a continuous supply of energy in all areas. Also, the technology needed to store and supply this energy on demand is insufficient and often far too costly to use. As technology improves, these alternative sources will supplement and possibly even replace fossil fuels.

Discussion

Energy Sources What are some possible explanations for why only 18 percent of the energy used worldwide is from renewable and inexhaustible resources? Answers will vary. Currently the technology does not exist to supply energy from these sources on demand and at an affordable price.

Activity

Alternatives Have students research alternative energy sources available in their area. Students should make posters showing how energy is obtained from these sources. L2 IS **Visual-Spatial**

Applying Math

Answer 320 calories

Find Out About It

Solar collectors would do well in the southwestern United States because it is sunny there for most of the year.

SCIENCE Stats

Energy to Burn

Did you know...

... The energy released by the average hurricane is equal to about 200 times the total energy produced by all of the world's power plants. Almost all of this energy is released as heat when raindrops form.

... The energy Earth gets each half hour from the Sun is enough to meet the world's demands for a year. Renewable and inexhaustible resources, including the Sun, account for only 18 percent of the energy that is used worldwide.

... The Calories in one medium apple will give you enough energy to walk for about 15 min, swim for about 10 min, or jog for about 9 min.

Applying Math
If walking for 15 min requires 80 Calories of fuel (from food), how many Calories would someone need to consume to walk for 1 h?

Write About It
Where would you place solar collectors in the United States? Why? For more information on solar energy, go to bookm.msscience.com/science_stats.

Reviewing Main Ideas

Section 1 What is energy?

1. Energy is the ability to cause change.

2. A moving object has kinetic energy that depends on the object's mass and speed.

3. Potential energy is energy due to position and depends on an object's mass and height.

4. Light carries radiant energy, electric current carries electrical energy, and atomic nuclei contain nuclear energy.

Section 2 Energy Transformations

1. Energy can be transformed from one form to another. Thermal energy is usually produced when energy transformations occur.

2. The law of conservation of energy states that energy cannot be created or destroyed.

3. Electric power plants convert a source of energy into electrical energy. Steam spins a turbine which spins an electric generator.

Section 3 Sources of Energy

1. The use of an energy source has advantages and disadvantages.

2. Fossil fuels and nuclear energy are nonrenewable energy sources that are consumed faster than they can be replaced.

3. Hydroelectricity is a renewable energy source that is continually being replaced.

4. Alternative energy sources include solar, wind, and geothermal energy. Solar energy is an inexhaustible energy source.

Visualizing Main Ideas

Copy and complete the concept map using the following terms: fossil fuels, hydroelectric, solar, wind, oil, coal, photovoltaic, *and* nonrenewable resources.

 bookm.msscience.com/interactive_tutor

STUDY GUIDE **M** ◆ **151**

Reviewing Main Ideas

Summary statements can be used by students to review the major concepts of the chapter.

Visualizing Main Ideas

See student page.

Visit bookm.msscience.com
/self_check_quiz
/interactive_tutor
/vocabulary_puzzlemaker
/chapter_review
/standardized_test
/field_guide

Assessment Transparency

For additional assessment questions, use the *Assessment Transparency* located in the transparency book.

Assessment

Identifying Misconceptions   Assess

Use the assessment as follow-up to page F at the beginning of the chapter.

Activity Display examples of the work of the famous cartoonist Rube Goldberg. Have students draw their own Rube Goldberg style invention that includes four energy transformations. Direct students to draw red arrows to indicate areas where heat loss would occur.

Expected Outcome Students recognize that energy is transferred from one form into another.

Reinforcement Have students exchange drawings and describe the energy transformations depicted.

Using Vocabulary

1. Nuclear energy is sometimes used to generate electrical energy.

2. A rotating turbine helps produce electrical energy by causing a generator to spin.

3. A photovoltaic collector changes radiant energy from the Sun directly into electrical energy.

4. Inexhaustible resources are resources that can't be used up by humans. Renewable resources are replenished by nature. Neither source gets used up.

5. Potential energy due to gravity changes to kinetic energy as an object falls.

6. In an electrical generator, kinetic energy is changed into electrical energy.

7. Thermal energy and radiant energy are two forms of energy that can be converted into each other or other forms of energy.

8. The law of conservation of energy states that in energy transformations, energy can be neither created nor destroyed. It only can change from one form to another.

9. Some sources of chemical energy, such as fossil fuels, are nonrenewable. Some, such as biomass, are renewable.

Checking Concepts

10. C	14. A	18. D
11. D	15. A	19. B
12. D	16. B	
13. C	17. A	

Thinking Critically

20. When the swing is pulled back, its potential energy increases. When the swing is released, potential energy is converted into kinetic energy as it moves downward. As it moves upward, kinetic energy is converted into potential energy.

Using Vocabulary

alternative resource p. 143	nonrenewable
chemical energy p. 129	resource p. 140
electrical energy p. 130	nuclear energy p. 130
energy p. 126	photovoltaic p. 144
generator p. 136	potential energy p. 128
inexhaustible	radiant energy p. 129
resource p. 143	renewable resource p. 142
kinetic energy p. 127	thermal energy p. 128
law of conservation	turbine p. 136
of energy p. 132	

For each of the terms below, explain the relationship that exists.

1. electrical energy—nuclear energy

2. turbine—generator

3. photovoltaic—radiant energy—electrical energy

4. renewable resource—inexhaustible resource

5. potential energy—kinetic energy

6. kinetic energy—electrical energy—generator

7. thermal energy—radiant energy

8. law of conservation of energy—energy transformations

9. nonrenewable resource—chemical energy

Checking Concepts

Choose the word or phrase that best answers the question.

10. Objects that are able to fall have what type of energy?
    A) kinetic   C) potential
    B) radiant   D) electrical

11. Which form of energy does light have?
    A) electrical   C) kinetic
    B) nuclear   D) radiant

 Science Online bookm.msscience.com/vocabulary_puzzlemaker

---

12. Muscles perform what type of energy transformation?
    A) kinetic to potential
    B) kinetic to electrical
    C) thermal to radiant
    D) chemical to kinetic

13. Photovoltaics perform what type of energy transformation?
    A) thermal to radiant
    B) kinetic to electrical
    C) radiant to electrical
    D) electrical to thermal

14. The form of energy that food contains is which of the following?
    A) chemical   C) radiant
    B) potential   D) electrical

15. Solar energy, wind, and geothermal are what type of energy resource?
    A) inexhaustible C) nonrenewable
    B) inexpensive   D) chemical

16. Which of the following is a nonrenewable source of energy?
    A) hydroelectricity
    B) nuclear
    C) wind
    D) solar

17. A generator is NOT required to generate electrical energy when which of the following energy sources is used?
    A) solar   C) hydroelectric
    B) wind   D) nuclear

18. Which of the following are fossil fuels?
    A) gas   C) oil
    B) coal   D) all of these

19. Almost all of the energy that is used on Earth's surface comes from which of the following energy sources?
    A) radioactivity C) chemicals
    B) the Sun   D) wind

Use the Exam*View*® Pro Testmaker CD-ROM to:

- create multiple versions of tests
- create modified tests with one mouse click for inclusion students
- edit existing questions and add your own questions
- build tests aligned with state standards using built-in State Curriculum Tags
- change English tests to Spanish with one mouse click and vice versa

Thinking Critically

20. **Explain** how the motion of a swing illustrates the transformation between potential and kinetic energy.

21. **Explain** what happens to the kinetic energy of a skateboard that is coasting along a flat surface, slows down, and comes to a stop.

22. **Describe** the energy transformations that occur in the process of toasting a bagel in an electric toaster.

23. **Compare and contrast** the formation of coal and the formation of oil and natural gas.

24. **Explain** the difference between the law of conservation of energy and conserving energy. How can conserving energy help prevent energy shortages?

25. **Make a Hypothesis** about how spacecraft that travel through the solar system obtain the energy they need to operate. Do research to verify your hypothesis.

26. **Concept Map** Copy and complete this concept map about energy.

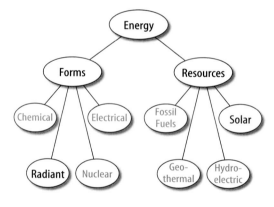

27. **Diagram** the energy transformations that occur when you rub sandpaper on a piece of wood and the wood becomes warm.

 bookm.msscience.com/chapter_review

Performance Activities

28. **Multimedia Presentation** Alternative sources of energy that weren't discussed include biomass energy, wave energy, and hydrogen fuel cells. Research an alternative energy source and then prepare a digital slide show about the information you found. Use the concepts you learned from this chapter to inform your classmates about the future prospects of using such an energy source on a large scale.

Applying Math

29. **Calculate Number of Power Plants** A certain type of power plant is designed to provide energy for 10,000 homes. How many of these power plants would be needed to provide energy for 300,000 homes?

Use the table below to answer questions 30 and 31.

Energy Sources Used in the United States	
Energy Source	**Percent of Energy Used**
Coal	23%
Oil	39%
Natural gas	23%
Nuclear	8%
Hydroelectric	4%
Other	3%

30. **Use Percentages** According to the data in the table above, what percentage of the energy used in the United States comes from fossil fuels?

31. **Calculate a Ratio** How many times greater is the amount of energy that comes from fossil fuels than the amount of energy from all other energy sources?

Thinking Critically

21. The kinetic energy of the skate is converted into thermal energy by friction.

22. In the toaster, electrical energy is converted into thermal energy. Thermal energy is converted into chemical energy in the bagel, causing it to become toasted.

23. Both formed over millions of years. Coal formed from the effects of heat and pressure on buried vegetation. Oil and natural gas formed from the effects of heat and pressure on the buried remains of microscopic organisms on the ocean floor.

24. Law of conservation of energy states that energy cannot be created or destroyed. Conserving energy means reducing energy usage, which can prevent energy shortages by reducing the consumption of nonrenewable energy sources.

25. Possible answers: spacecrafts use solar cells, spacecrafts use batteries

26. See student page.

27. chemical energy in muscles → kinetic energy of sandpaper → thermal energy of wood

Performance Activities

28. Check students' work. Use **Performance Assessment in the Science Classroom,** p. 149.

Applying Math

National Math Standards
1, 2, 9
29. 30
30. 85%
31. 5.7 times greater

 Assessment **Resources**

📁 Reproducible Masters
Chapter *Fast File* Resources
  Chapter Review, pp. 35–36
  Chapter Tests, pp. 37–40
  Assessment Transparency Activity, p. 47
Glencoe Science Web site
  Chapter Review Test
  Standardized Test Practice

Glencoe Technology
  🖌 Assessment Transparency
  💿 Exam*View*® Pro Testmaker
  📼 MindJogger Videoquiz
  💿 Interactive Chalkboard

FAST FILE

Answer Sheet A practice answer sheet can be found at bookm.msscience.com/answer_sheet.

S A M P L E

Part 1 **Multiple Choice**

1. B
2. B
3. D
4. D
5. C
6. C
7. A
8. B

Part 1 **Multiple Choice**

Record your answers on the answer sheet provided by your teacher or on a sheet of paper.

1. The kinetic energy of a moving object increases if which of the following occurs?
A. Its mass decreases.
B. Its speed increases.
C. Its height above the ground increases.
D. Its temperature increases

Use the figure below to answer questions 2–4.

Global Oil Production

2. According to the graph above, in which year will global oil production be at a maximum?
A. 1974 **C.** 2010
B. 2002 **D.** 2050

3. Approximately how many times greater was oil production in 1970 than oil production in 1950?
A. 2 times **C.** 6 times
B. 10 times **D.** 3 times

4. In which year will the production of oil be equal to the oil production in 1970?
A. 2010 **C.** 2022
B. 2015 **D.** 2028

5. Which of the following energy sources is being used faster than it can be replaced?
A. tidal **C.** fossil fuels
B. wind **D.** hydroelectric

Use the graph below to answer question 6.

6. The graph shows the sources of electrical energy in the United States. In 2002, the total amount of electrical energy produced in the United States was 38.2 quads. How much electrical energy was produced by using nuclear energy?
A. 3.0 quads **C.** 3.8 quads
B. 305.6 quads **D.** 35.1 quads

7. When chemical energy is converted into thermal energy, which of the following must be true?
A. The total amount of thermal energy plus chemical energy changes.
B. Only the amount of chemical energy changes.
C. Only the amount of thermal energy changes.
D. The total amount of thermal energy plus chemical energy doesn't change.

8. A softball player hits a fly ball. Which of the following describes the energy conversion that occurs as it falls from its highest point?
A. kinetic to potential
B. potential to kinetic
C. thermal to potential
D. thermal to kinetic

154 ◆ **M** STANDARDIZED TEST PRACTICE

Part 2 **Short Response/Grid In**

9. The law of conservation of energy would prevent such a machine from being built.

10. The kinetic energy is the same.

11. The basketball dropped from a height of 4 m.

12. about two times

13. 1970–1975

Part 2 | Short Response/Grid In

Record your answers on the answer sheet provided by your teacher or on a sheet of paper.

9. Why is it impossible to build a machine that produces more energy than it uses?

10. You toss a ball upward and then catch it on the way down. The height of the ball above the ground when it leaves your hand on the way up and when you catch it is the same. Compare the ball's kinetic energy when it leaves your hand and just before you catch it?

11. A basket ball is dropped from a height of 2 m and another identical basketball is dropped from a height of 4 m. Which ball has more kinetic energy just before it hits the ground?

Use the graph below to answer questions 12 and 13.

Global Energy Use 1970–2000

12. According to the graph above, by about how many times did the global use of energy increase from 1970 to 2000?

13. Over which five-year time period was the increase in global energy use the largest?

Test-Taking Tip

Do Your Studying Regularly Do not "cram" the night before the test. It can hamper your memory and make you tired.

Part 3 | Open Ended

Record your answers on a sheet of paper.

14. When you drop a tennis ball, it hits the floor and bounces back up. But it does not reach the same height as released, and each successive upward bounce is smaller than the one previous. However, you notice the tennis ball is slightly warmer after it finishes bouncing. Explain how the law of conservation of energy is obeyed.

Use the graph below to answer questions 15–17.

Potential Energy of Batted Ball

15. The graph shows how the potential energy of a batted ball the distance from the batter increases. At what distances is the kinetic energy of the ball the greatest?

16. At what distance from the batter is the height of the ball the greatest?

17. How much less is the kinetic energy of the ball at a distance of 20 m from the batter than at a distance of 0 m?

18. List advantages and disadvantages of the following energy sources: fossil fuels, nuclear energy, and geothermal energy.

Rubrics

The following rubrics are sample scoring devices for short response and open-ended questions.

Short Response

Points	Description
2	The student demonstrates a thorough understanding of the science of the task. The response may contain minor flaws that do not detract from the demonstration of a thorough understanding.
1	The student has provided a response that is only partially correct.
0	The student has provided a completely incorrect solution or no response at all.

Open Ended

Points	Description
4	The student demonstrates a thorough understanding of the science of the task. The response may contain minor flaws that do not detract from the demonstration of a thorough understanding.
3	The student demonstrates an understanding of the science of the task. The response is essentially correct and demonstrates an essential but less than thorough understanding of the science.
2	The student demonstrates only a partial understanding of the science of the task. Although the student may have used the correct approach to a solution or may have provided a correct solution, the work lacks an essential understanding of the underlying science concepts.
1	The student demonstrates a very limited understanding of the science of the task. The response is incomplete and exhibits many flaws.
0	The student provides a completely incorrect solution or no response at all.

Part 3 | Open Ended

14. During each bounce, some of the kinetic energy of the ball is converted into thermal energy. As a result, energy is not created or destroyed, but only changes form, so that the law of conservation of energy is obeyed.

15. The kinetic energy of the ball is greatest at the distances where the potential energy is smallest. This is at distances of 0 m and 40 m.

16. The height of the ball is greatest where the ball's potential energy is greatest. This is at a distance of 20 m.

17. In moving from 0 m to 20 m, the increase in potential energy of the ball equals the decrease in the ball's kinetic energy. The ball's potential energy increases by 15 J, so its kinetic energy decreases by 15 J.

18. fossil fuels: currently cheap and plentiful, but nonrenewable and produces pollution; nuclear energy: does not produce pollution, cheap, but produces nuclear waste and is nonrenewable; geothermal energy: inexhaustible, but only available in a few places

Section/Objectives	Standards		Labs/Features
Chapter Opener	**National**	**State/Local**	**Launch Lab:** Measuring Temperature, p. 157 **Foldables**, p. 157
	See pp. 9T–10T for a Key to Standards.		A data-collection lab using Probeware technology can be found in the **Probeware Lab Manual,** pp. 49–52
Section 1 **Temperature and Thermal Energy** 🕐 3 sessions 📦 1.5 blocks 1. **Explain** how temperature is related to kinetic energy. 2. **Describe** three scales used for measuring temperature. 3. **Define** thermal energy.	National Content Standards: UCP.1, UCP.2, UCP.3, UCP.5, A.1, A.2, B.1, B.3		**Applying Math:** Converting to Celsius, p. 160
Section 2 **Heat** 🕐 3 sessions 📦 1.5 blocks 4. **Explain** the difference between thermal energy and heat. 5. **Describe** three ways heat is transferred. 6. **Identify** materials that are insulators or conductors.	National Content Standards: UCP.1, UCP.2, UCP.3, UCP.5, A.1, A.2, B.1, B.2, B.3		**MiniLAB:** Comparing Rates of Melting, p. 164 **MiniLAB:** Observing Convection, p. 165 **Integrate Life Science,** p. 166 **Lab:** Heating Up and Cooling Down, p. 168
Section 3 **Engines and Refrigerators** 🕐 4 sessions 📦 2 blocks 7. **Identify** what a heat engine does. 8. **Explain** that energy can exist in different forms, but is never created or destroyed. 9. **Describe** how an internal combustion engine works. 10. **Explain** how refrigerators move heat.	National Content Standards: UCP.1, UCP.2, UCP.3, UCP.5, A.1, A.2, B.2, B.3		**Science Online,** p. 170 **Visualizing the Four-Stroke Cycle,** p. 171 **Integrate Career,** p. 172 **Lab:** Comparing Thermal Insulators, p. 174 **Science and Society:** The Heat is On, p. 176

Lab Materials	Reproducible Resources	Section Assessment	Technology
Launch Lab: water, ice, three pans, refrigerator	**Chapter *FAST FILE* Resources** Foldables Worksheet, p. 17 Directed Reading Overview, p. 19 Note-taking Worksheets, pp. 33–35	ASSESSMENT ADVANTAGE	**Teacher Works** includes: • Interactive Teacher Edition • Lesson Planner with calendar • Access to all program blacklines • Correlations to standards • Web links
Need materials? Contact Science Kit at 1-800-828-7777 or www.sciencekit.com on the Internet.	**Chapter *FAST FILE* Resources** Transparency Activity, p. 44 Lab Activity, pp. 9–12 Enrichment, p. 30 Reinforcement, p. 27 Directed Reading, p. 20 **Earth Science Critical Thinking/Problem Solving,** p. 10	Portfolio Use Science Words, p. 160 Performance Applying Math, p. 160 Applying Math, p. 161 Content Section Review, p. 161	Section Focus Transparency Guided Reading Audio Program Interactive Chalkboard CD-ROM
MiniLAB: glass, ice, water, 2 coffee cups, clock or watch **MiniLAB:** 250-mL beaker, water, hot plate, 50-mL beaker, penny, metal tongs, dropper, food coloring **Lab:** 5 thermometers, 400-mL beakers (5), stopwatch, refrigerator, stirring rod, hot plate, water, ice	**Chapter *FAST FILE* Resources** Transparency Activity, p. 45 MiniLABS, pp. 3, 4 Lab Activity, pp. 13–16 Enrichment, p. 31 Reinforcement, p. 28 Directed Reading, p. 20 Lab Worksheets, pp. 5–6 **Physical Science Critical Thinking/Problem Solving,** p. 5 **Cultural Diversity,** p. 41	Portfolio Active Reading, p. 164 Performance MiniLAB, p. 164 MiniLAB, p. 165 Applying Skills, p. 167 Content Section Review, p. 167	Section Focus Transparency Virtual Labs CD-ROM Guided Reading Audio Program Interactive Chalkboard CD-ROM Video Lab
Lab: hot plate, large beaker, water, graduated cylinder, thermometers, various beverage containers (each about the same size and shape), covers for the containers, tongs, stopwatch, thermal gloves or mitts	**Chapter *FAST FILE* Resources** Transparency Activity, p. 46 Enrichment, p. 32 Reinforcement, p. 29 Directed Reading, pp. 21, 22 Transparency Activity, pp. 47–48 Lab Worksheets, pp. 7–8 **Home and Community Involvement,** p. 49	Portfolio Differentiated Instruction, p. 170 Performance Applying Skills, p. 173 Content Section Review, p. 173	Section Focus Transparency Teaching Transparency Guided Reading Audio Program Interactive Chalkboard CD-ROM

End of Chapter Assessment

ASSESSMENT ADVANTAGE

Blackline Masters	Technology	Professional Series
Chapter *FAST FILE* Resources Chapter Review, pp. 37–38 Chapter Tests, pp. 39–42 **Standardized Test Practice,** pp. 27–30	MindJogger Videoquiz Virtual Labs CD-ROM ExamView® Pro Testmaker TeacherWorks CD-ROM Interactive Chalkboard CD-ROM	**Performance Assessment in the Science Classroom (PASC)**

Transparencies

Section Focus

This is a representation of key blackline masters available in the Teacher Classroom Resources. See Resource Manager boxes within the chapter for additional information.

Key to Teaching Strategies

The following designations will help you decide which activities are appropriate for your students.

L1 Level 1 activities should be appropriate for students with learning difficulties.

L2 Level 2 activities should be within the ability range of all students.

L3 Level 3 activities are designed for above-average students.

ELL ELL activities should be within the ability range of English Language Learners.

COOP LEARN Cooperative Learning activities are designed for small group work.

LS Multiple Learning Styles logos, as described on page 6T, are used throughout to indicate strategies that address different learning styles.

P These strategies represent student products that can be placed into a best-work portfolio.

PBL Problem-Based Learning activities apply real-world situations to learning.

Assessment

Teaching

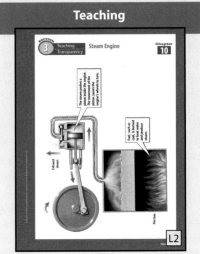

Hands-on Activities

Student Text Lab Worksheet

Laboratory Activities

Meeting Different Ability Levels

Content Outline

Reinforcement

Enrichment

Directed Reading (English/Spanish)

Study Guide

Reading Essentials

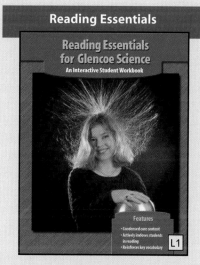

Assessment

Test Practice Workbook

Chapter Review

Chapter Tests

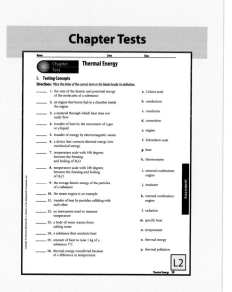

Science Content Background

Temperature and Thermal Energy

What's hot? What's cold?

The atoms and molecules that make up all matter are in random motion, moving in all directions. It is this random motion that gives rise to the physical property of temperature. At room temperature, for example, the oxygen molecules in air are moving in all directions with an average speed of about 440 m/s. All the molecules in air are constantly colliding with each other and with the surfaces of the room. On average, a molecule in air travels about 10^{-5} cm, or about 1,000 times its diameter, before it collides with another molecule. Each molecule undergoes about five billion collisions each second.

Atoms and molecules in motion have kinetic energy. The temperature of an object is proportional to the average kinetic energy associated with the random motion of the atoms or molecules in the object. The faster the molecules are moving, the more kinetic energy they have, and the higher the temperature.

Temperature is related only to the random motion of the atoms or molecules. The organized motion of the molecules that occurs as an object moves does not affect the random molecular motion. Even though the kinetic energy of a falling ball increases as its speed increases, ignoring the effects of air resistance, the temperature of the ball doesn't change as it falls because the random motion of its molecules hasn't changed.

Thermal Energy

The thermal energy of a material or an object is the total energy of the atoms and molecules associated with their random motions. A molecule has kinetic energy as it moves through space. However, the molecule might be rotating like a top, and its atoms might be vibrating back and forth as if they were connected by springs. These rotational and vibrational motions also contribute to the total energy of a molecule.

Molecules in a substance also can exert intermolecular forces on each other. For example, as two molecules in a gas approach each other, the electric charges on each molecule exert forces

chapter content resources

Internet Resources
For additional content background, visit
bookm.msscience.com to:
- access your book online
- find references to related articles in popular science magazines
- access Web links with related content background
- access current events with science journal topics

Print Resources
Introduction to Thermal Sciences: Thermodynamics, Fluid Dynamics, and Heat Transfer, Schmidt, Frank W., Henderson, Robert E., Wolgemuth, Carl H., Wiley, 1997
Encyclopedia of Applied Physics Volume 19: Storage of Energy to Thermal Processes, Trig, G.L. (Editor), Vera, E.S. (Editor), Ammergut, Emund H., John Wiley and Sons, 1997
Thermal Physics: Entropy and Free Energies, Lee, Joon Chang, World Scientific Publishing Co., Inc., 2002

that rearrange the charges on the other molecule. Even though the molecules are electrically neutral, this rearrangement of charge produces attractive electric forces between them.

Just as objects attracted to each other by the gravity have potential energy, molecules that are affected by intermolecular forces also have potential energy. If the electric force between molecules is attractive, a molecule's potential energy decreases as the molecules come closer. This potential energy also contributes to the thermal energy of an object.

As a result, the thermal energy of a substance is the sum of the kinetic energy associated with the random motion of its molecules through space, as well as the energy associated with rotational and vibrational motions, and the potential energy due to the electric forces between molecules.

Heat

section 2

Heat and Thermal Energy

Suppose two materials with different temperatures are brought into contact. At places where the materials are in contact, the molecules in the different materials can interact with each other. As these molecules collide with each other, kinetic energy is transferred from one molecule to another. The result of these collisions is the transfer of kinetic energy from the molecules in the warmer object to the molecules in the cooler object.

Because the kinetic energy of the molecules in the warmer object decreases, its thermal energy and its temperature decreases. At the same time, the thermal energy and the temperature of the cooler object increases as its molecules gain kinetic energy. Thermal energy has been transferred from the warmer object to the cooler object. This transfer of thermal energy is heat.

When a substance changes state, such as when ice melts or water boils, the temperature of the substance remains constant while the change in state is occurring. The average kinetic energy of the molecules doesn't change as the change in state occurs; instead, the potential energy of the molecules changes.

Thermal Expansion

Most substances expand when heated. As the temperature of a substance increases, its molecules move faster on average, and the distance between molecules increases. Water is unusual in that water is most dense at 4°C, so that water expands as it's cooled from 4°C to 0°C. One consequence is that an entire body of water must cool to 4°C before it can cool any further. So the temperature at the bottom of a pond or lake is above freezing as long as the lake isn't frozen solid. This means that aquatic life can survive at the bottom of large bodies of water during winter.

Teacher to Teacher
Steve Federman
Loveland Middle School
Loveland, Ohio

"To help students see that thermal energy is transferred from the Sun by radiation; we paint one plastic 2-liter bottle white and paint another one black. Next, place a small balloon over the mouth of each bottle, making sure they are airtight, and place both bottles in the sunlight. Within a few minutes the balloon on the black bottle will begin to expand and feel warm as the black bottle absorbs thermal energy, and the air inside expands. The balloon on the white bottle remains limp and the bottle remains cool to the touch, as it absorbs less of the Sun's radiant energy."

Steve Federman

chapter
6

chapter
6

Chapter Vocabulary

temperature, p. 158
thermal energy, p. 161
heat, p. 162
conduction, p. 163
radiation, p. 163
convection, p. 164
conductor, p. 165
specific heat, p. 166
thermal pollution, p. 167
heat engine, p. 169
internal combustion engine,
  p. 170

Science Journal Possible responses: fanning yourself, jumping into a pool, removing a jacket, putting on a jacket, jumping up and down, standing by a fire.

INTERACTIVE CHALKBOARD
with Image Bank

PowerPoint® Presentations

This CD-ROM is an editable Microsoft® PowerPoint® presentation that includes:
- a pre-made presentation for every chapter
- interactive graphics
- animations
- audio clips
- image bank
- all new section and chapter questions
- Standardized Test Practice
- transparencies
- pre-lab questions for all labs
- Foldables directions
- links to bookm.msscience.com

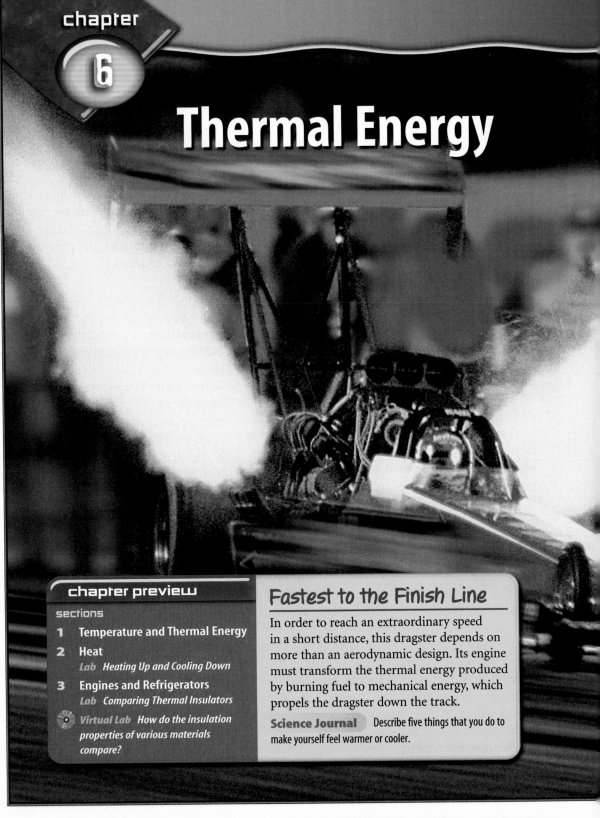

Thermal Energy

chapter preview

sections

1 Temperature and Thermal Energy

2 Heat
  Lab Heating Up and Cooling Down

3 Engines and Refrigerators
  Lab Comparing Thermal Insulators

 Virtual Lab How do the insulation properties of various materials compare?

Fastest to the Finish Line

In order to reach an extraordinary speed in a short distance, this dragster depends on more than an aerodynamic design. Its engine must transform the thermal energy produced by burning fuel to mechanical energy, which propels the dragster down the track.

Science Journal Describe five things that you do to make yourself feel warmer or cooler.

Theme Connection

Energy The thermal energy of a material is the sum of the kinetic and potential energy of its particles. Thermal energy can be converted into work in engines and refrigerators.

About the Photo

Dragsters Top fuel dragsters, like this one, can accelerate from 0 to 100 mph in less than one second. These machines have engines that produce over 6,000 horsepower—more than 40 times that of a typical car—and consume more than a gallon of fuel per second. The velocity of the exhaust gases is so high that even a slight variation in the exhaust angle will cause the dragster to veer sideways.

Start-Up Activities

Measuring Temperature

When you leave a glass of ice water on a kitchen table, the ice gradually melts and the temperature of the water increases. What is temperature, and why does the temperature of the ice water increase? In this lab you will explore one way of determining temperature.

1. Obtain three pans. Fill one pan with luke-warm water. Fill a second pan with cold water and crushed ice. Fill a third pan with very warm tap water. Label each pan.

2. Soak one of your hands in the warm water for one minute. Remove your hand from the warm water and put it in the luke-warm water. Does the lukewarm water feel cool or warm?

3. Now soak your hand in the cold water for one minute. Remove your hand from the cold water and place it in the lukewarm water. Does the lukewarm water feel cool or warm?

4. **Think Critically** Write a paragraph in your Science Journal discussing whether your sense of touch would make a useful thermometer.

 Thermal Energy Make the following Foldable to help you identify how thermal energy, heat, and temperature are related.

STEP 1 **Fold** a vertical piece of paper into thirds.

STEP 2 **Turn** the paper horizontally. **Unfold and label** the three columns as shown.

Read for Main Ideas Before you read the chapter, write down what you know about temperature, thermal energy, and heat on the appropriate tab. As you read, add to and correct what you wrote. Write what you have learned about the relationship between heat and thermal energy on the back of your Foldable.

 Preview this chapter's content and activities at bookm.msscience.com

---

Purpose Use the Launch Lab to introduce the idea that the physical sensation of temperature is not accurate enough to be used as a thermometer. [L2]

Preparation Obtain enough pans so that students can be divided into small groups.

Materials three pans for each group of students, water, ice

Teaching Strategy Groups should be small enough that the water temperature in the pans doesn't change much over the time needed for all students in the group to carry out the activity. Do not use water hotter than 60°C.

Think Critically

To the hand that was initially in the cold water, the lukewarm water felt warm. To the hand that was initially in the hot water, the lukewarm water felt cool. A hand is not a good thermometer because an accurate thermometer would determine the temperature of the lukewarm water to be the same, regardless of which pan the thermometer was placed in earlier.

Assessment

Process Have students predict how the cold water will feel if they first place their hand in the hot water for a few minutes. Then have them test their predictions. Use **Performance Assessment in the Science Classroom**, p. 103. [L2]

FOLDABLES Study Organizer **Dinah Zike Study Fold**

Student preparation materials for this Foldable are available in the **Chapter** *FAST FILE* **Resources**.

Probeware Labs

This chapter's data-collection lab using Probeware technology can be found in the *Probeware Lab Manual* pages 49–52.

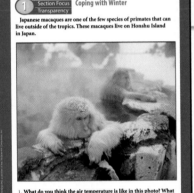
Temperature and Thermal Energy

as you read

What You'll Learn
- **Explain** how temperature is related to kinetic energy.
- **Describe** three scales used for measuring temperature.
- **Define** thermal energy.

Why It's Important
The movement of thermal energy toward or away from your body determines whether you feel too cold, too hot, or just right.

Review Vocabulary
kinetic energy: energy a moving object has that increases as the speed of the object increases

New Vocabulary
- temperature
- thermal energy

What is temperature?

Imagine it's a hot day and you jump into a swimming pool to cool off. When you first hit the water, you might think it feels cold. Perhaps someone else, who has been swimming for a few minutes, thinks the water feels warm. When you swim in water, touch a hot pan, or swallow a cold drink, your sense of touch tells you whether something is hot or cold. However, the words *cold, warm,* and *hot* can mean different things to different people.

Temperature How hot or cold something feels is related to its temperature. To understand temperature, think of a glass of water sitting on a table. The water might seem perfectly still, but water is made of molecules that are in constant, random motion. Because these molecules are always moving, they have energy of motion, or kinetic energy.

However, water molecules in random motion don't all move at the same speed. Some are moving faster and some are moving slower. **Temperature** is a measure of the average value of the kinetic energy of the molecules in random motion. The more kinetic energy the molecules have, the higher the temperature. Molecules have more kinetic energy when they are moving faster. So the higher the temperature, the faster the molecules are moving, as shown in **Figure 1.**

Figure 1 The temperature of a substance depends on how fast its molecules are moving. Water molecules are moving faster in the hot water on the left than in the cold water on the right.

Cold water

Hot water

Section 1 Resource Manager

Chapter *FAST FILE* Resources
Transparency Activity, p. 44
Directed Reading for Content Mastery, pp. 19, 20
Note-taking Worksheets, pp. 33–35

Lab Activity, pp. 9–12
Enrichment, p. 30
Reinforcement, p. 27
Mathematics Skill Activities, p. 11

Thermal Expansion It wasn't an earthquake that caused the sidewalk to buckle in **Figure 2.** Hot weather caused the concrete to expand so much that it cracked, and the pieces squeezed each other upward. When the temperature of an object is increased, its molecules speed up and tend to move farther apart. This causes the object to expand. When the object is cooled, its molecules slow down and move closer together. This causes the object to shrink, or contract.

Almost all substances expand when they are heated and contract when they are cooled. The amount of expansion or contraction depends on the type of material and the change in temperature. For example, liquids usually expand more than solids. Also, the greater the change in temperature, the more an object expands or contracts.

 Why do materials expand when their temperatures increase?

Measuring Temperature

The temperature of an object depends on the average kinetic energy of all the molecules in an object. However, molecules are so small and objects contain so many of them, that it is impossible to measure the kinetic energy of all the individual molecules.

A more practical way to measure temperature is to use a thermometer. Thermometers usually use the expansion and contraction of materials to measure temperature. One common type of thermometer uses a glass tube containing a liquid. When the temperature of the liquid increases, it expands so that the height of the liquid in the tube depends on the temperature.

Temperature Scales To be able to give a number for the temperature, a thermometer has to have a temperature scale. Two common temperature scales are the Fahrenheit and Celsius scales, shown in **Figure 3.**

On the Fahrenheit scale, the freezing point of water is given the temperature 32°F and the boiling point 212°F. The space between the boiling point and the freezing point is divided into 180 equal degrees. The Fahrenheit scale is used mainly in the United States.

On the Celsius temperature scale, the freezing point of water is given the temperature 0°C and the boiling point is given the temperature 100°C. Because there are only 100 Celsius degrees between the boiling and freezing point of water, Celsius degrees are bigger than Fahrenheit degrees.

Figure 2 Most objects expand as their temperatures increase. Pieces of this concrete sidewalk forced each other upward when the concrete expanded on a hot day.

Freezing point of water (32°F)

Freezing point of water (0°C)

Figure 3 The Fahrenheit and Celsius scales are commonly used temperature scales.

---

2 Teach

☑ Reading Check

Answer When the temperature of an object is increased, its molecules speed up and tend to move farther apart.

Discussion

Accepting Celsius Why do you think people in the United States have not accepted the Celsius temperature scale? Answers will vary, but could include that it would be too hard to get used to and that it would take a lot of money to change all of the Fahrenheit-oriented thermometers to Celsius. L2

Visual Learning

Figure 3 Point out the liquid in the thermometer that indicates the temperature. What temperature does this thermometer show in °F? about 78°F In °C? about 26°C L2 Ⓝ **Visual-Spatial**

Activity

Who uses Celsius? The U.S. is the only major industrialized country that still uses the Fahrenheit temperature scale. Have your students discover this for themselves by choosing five countries and investigating what temperature scale each country uses. When the research is finished, list all of the countries researched on the chalkboard and share the results with the entire class.

Differentiated Instruction

Challenge Many liquid thermometers use mercury or alcohol. Have students investigate why these liquids are used instead of water. The volume of both mercury and alcohol changes uniformly over the measured temperatures, and neither alcohol nor mercury sticks to the glass tube. Water cannot be used because its molecular structure causes its volume to increase as its temperature decreases from 4°C to 0°C. Also, water freezes at 0°C, so thermometers using it would not be able to measure temperatures below that point. L3 Ⓝ **Linguistic**

Curriculum Connection

Music Like many other objects, musical instruments undergo thermal expansion. Have students find out what problems this causes for musicians. Thermal expansion and contraction cause the vibrating parts of instruments, including the strings of stringed instruments, to change size. This changes the rate at which they vibrate, causing the instruments to go out of tune. L2 Ⓝ **Linguistic**

Use Science Words

Word Meaning Have students find out why the three temperature scales discussed in this section are called the Fahrenheit, Celsius, and Kelvin scales. Ask them to write their findings in their Science Journals. The Fahrenheit scale was developed by the German physicist Daniel Gabriel Fahrenheit in 1724. The Celsius scale was developed by Anders Celsius in 1742. The Kelvin scale was proposed by Lord Kelvin (William Thomson) in 1848. L2 ELL
IS Linguistic P

Applying Math

National Math Standards
Correlation to Mathematics Objectives
2, 4, 9

Answers to Practice Problems

1. °C = 5(98.6 − 32)/9 = 37.0°C
2. °F = 9(57)/5 + 32 = 134.6°F

Quick Demo

Fahrenheit and Celsius Boil some water on a hotplate and measure the temperature on a Fahrenheit thermometer and on a Celsius thermometer. Let the class see the two thermometers. Do the same with an ice-water bath.

Converting Fahrenheit and Celsius You can convert temperatures back and forth between the two temperature scales by using the following equations.

Temperature Conversion Equations

To convert temperature in °F to °C: $°C = (\frac{5}{9})(°F - 32)$

To convert temperature in °C to °F: $°F = (\frac{9}{5})(°C) + 32$

For example, to convert 68°F to degrees Celsius, first subtract 32, multiply by 5, then divide by 9. The result is 20°C.

The Kelvin Scale Another temperature scale that is sometimes used is the Kelvin scale. On this scale, 0 K is the lowest temperature an object can have. This temperature is known as absolute zero. The size of a degree on the Kelvin scale is the same as on the Celsius scale. You can change from Celsius degrees to Kelvin degrees by adding 273 to the Celsius temperature.

$$K = °C + 273$$

Applying Math   Solving a Simple Equation

CONVERTING TO CELSIUS On a hot summer day, a Fahrenheit thermometer shows the temperature to be 86°F. What is this temperature on the Celsius scale?

Solution

1 *This is what you know:*   Fahrenheit temperature: °F = 86

2 *This is what you need to find:*   Celsius temperature: °C

3 *This is the procedure you need to use:*   Substitute the Fahrenheit temperature into the equation that converts temperature in °F to °C.

$°C = (\frac{5}{9})(°F - 32) = \frac{5}{9}(86 - 32) = \frac{5}{9}(54) = 30°C$

4 *Check the answer:*   Add 32 to your answer and multiply by 9/5. The result should be the given Fahrenheit temperature.

Practice Problems

1. A student's body temperature is 98.6°F. What is this temperature on the Celsius scale?

2. A temperature of 57°C was recorded in 1913 at Death Valley, California. What is this temperature on the Fahrenheit scale?

 For more practice visit bookm.msscience.com/math_practice

Teacher FYI

Absolute Zero Sometimes the claim is made that at absolute zero all molecular motion stops. In fact, at absolute zero molecules still have vibrational energy known as zero point energy.

Differentiated Instruction

Learning Disabled To help learning disabled students understand the Celsius temperature scale, tell them that their clothing requirements will change every ten degrees Celsius from 0°C–30°C. At 0°C, they will need a winter coat. At 10°C, they will only need a jacket. At 20°C, a long sleeve shirt will be warm enough, and at 30°C, shorts and a t-shirt will be most comfortable.

Thermal Energy

The temperature of an object is related to the average kinetic energy of molecules in random motion. But molecules also have potential energy. Potential energy is energy that the molecules have that can be converted into kinetic energy. The sum of the kinetic and potential energy of all the molecules in an object is the **thermal energy** of the object.

The Potential Energy of Molecules When you hold a ball above the ground, it has potential energy. When you drop the ball, its potential energy is converted into kinetic energy as the ball falls toward Earth. It is the attractive force of gravity between Earth and the ball that gives the ball potential energy.

The molecules in a material also exert attractive forces on each other. As a result, the molecules in a material have potential energy. As the molecules get closer together or farther apart, their potential energy changes.

Increasing Thermal Energy Temperature and thermal energy are different. Suppose you have two glasses filled with the same amount of milk, and at the same temperature. If you pour both glasses of milk into a pitcher, as shown in **Figure 4,** the temperature of the milk won't change. However, because there are more molecules of milk in the pitcher than in either glass, the thermal energy of the milk in the pitcher is greater than the thermal energy of the milk in either glass.

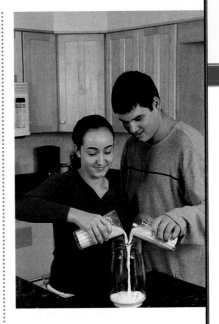

Figure 4 At the same temperature, the larger volume of milk in the pitcher has more thermal energy than the smaller volumes of milk in either glass.

DAILY INTERVENTION

Check for Understanding

Logical-Mathematical If the temperature of a liquid is 8°C, what is its temperature on the Fahrenheit scale? 46.4°F On the Kelvin scale? 281 K L3

Reteach

Daytime Temperature Have students work in pairs using the Internet and other reference sources to determine the typical daytime temperature in your community for each season. Ask them to give the temperatures in Fahrenheit, Celsius, and kelvin. L2 IS **Naturalist**

Design a Temperature Scale Have students work in small groups to design a temperature scale based on something other than the boiling and freezing points of water. L3 IS **Logical-Mathematical**

✓ Assessment

Oral Have small groups of students practice converting between Fahrenheit and Celsius. One student will say a Fahrenheit temperature and see which of the other students can first calculate the temperature in Celsius. Use **Performance Assessment in the Science Classroom,** p. 101. L2

---

section 1 review

Summary

Temperature
- Temperature is related to the average kinetic energy of the molecules an object contains.
- Most materials expand when their temperatures increase.

Measuring Temperature
- On the Celsius scale the freezing point of water is 0°C and the boiling point is 100°C.
- On the Fahrenheit scale the freezing point of water is 32°F and the boiling point is 212°F.

Thermal Energy
- The thermal energy of an object is the sum of the kinetic and potential energy of all the molecules in an object.

Self Check

1. **Explain** the difference between temperature and thermal energy. How are they related?
2. **Determine** which temperature is always larger—an object's Celsius temperature or its Kelvin temperature.
3. **Explain** how kinetic energy and thermal energy are related.
4. **Describe** how a thermometer uses the thermal expansion of a material to measure temperature.

Applying Math

5. **Convert Temperatures** A turkey cooking in an oven will be ready when the internal temperature reaches 180°F. Convert this temperature to °C and K.

---

section 1 review

1. Temperature is the average kinetic energy of the particles in matter. Thermal energy is the total kinetic and potential energy of the particles.
2. The temperature on the Kelvin scale is always a larger number because 273 is added to the Celsius temperature.
3. The thermal energy of a material is the sum of the kinetic energy and the potential energy of all the molecules in the material. The thermal energy increases as the kinetic energy of the molecules increases.
4. As the temperature increases, molecules in a material move faster, causing the material to expand. As a result, the amount of expansion is related to the increase in temperature.
5. 82.2°C; 355.2 K

Bellringer

Section Focus Transparencies also are available on the Interactive Chalkboard CD-ROM.
L2 ELL

Section Focus Transparency — Hot Times

The image below was made with heat sensitive camera on a cool day. The colors show thermal energy escaping from this building. The color green indicates the coolest areas of the building while the color white shows the warmest. Purple, red, and yellow respresent the stages from green to white.

1. From which parts of the house is the most thermal energy escaping?
2. In what ways might the information from the photo be useful?
3. How do you feel if you sit in the shade on a sunny day? How do you feel in the sun?

L2

Tie to Prior Knowledge

Heat Ask students to name some ways things are heated. They might mention heating food in a microwave, a furnace heating a home, or heat from the Sun on a summer day. This section explores heat and the ways thermal energy is transferred. L2

as you read

What **You'll Learn**

- **Explain** the difference between thermal energy and heat.
- **Describe** three ways heat is transferred.
- **Identify** materials that are insulators or conductors.

Why **It's Important**

To keep you comfortable, the flow of heat into and out of your house must be controlled.

 Review Vocabulary
electromagnetic wave: a wave produced by vibrating electric charges that can travel in matter and empty space

New Vocabulary
- heat
- conduction
- radiation
- convection
- conductor
- specific heat
- thermal pollution

Heat and Thermal Energy

It's the heat of the day. Heat the oven to 375°F. A heat wave has hit the Midwest. You've often heard the word *heat*, but what is it? Is it something you can see? Can an object have heat? Is heat anything like thermal energy? **Heat** is thermal energy that is transferred from one object to another when the objects are at different temperatures. The amount of heat that is transferred when two objects are brought into contact depends on the difference in temperature between the objects.

For example, no heat is transferred when two pots of boiling water are touching, because the water in both pots is at the same temperature. However, heat is transferred from the pot of hot water in **Figure 5** that is touching a pot of cold water. The hot water cools down and the cold water gets hotter. Heat continues to be transferred until both objects are the same temperature.

Transfer of Heat When heat is transferred, thermal energy always moves from warmer to cooler objects. Heat never flows from a cooler object to a warmer object. The warmer object loses thermal energy and becomes cooler as the cooler object gains thermal energy and becomes warmer. This process of heat transfer can occur in three ways—by conduction, radiation, or convection.

Figure 5 Heat is transferred only when two objects are at different temperatures. Heat always moves from the warmer object to the cooler object.

Section 2 Resource Manager

Chapter FAST FILE Resources
Transparency Activity, p. 45
Directed Reading for Content Mastery, p. 20
MiniLAB, pp. 3, 4
Lab Activity, pp. 13–16

Enrichment, p. 31
Reinforcement, p. 28
Lab Worksheets, pp. 5–6
Reading and Writing Skill Activities, pp. 13, 33

Conduction

When you eat hot pizza, you experience conduction. As the hot pizza touches your mouth, heat moves from the pizza to your mouth. This transfer of heat by direct contact is called conduction. **Conduction** occurs when the particles in a material collide with neighboring particles.

Imagine holding an ice cube in your hand, as in **Figure 6.** The faster-moving molecules in your warm hand bump against the slower-moving molecules in the cold ice. In these collisions, energy is passed from molecule to molecule. Heat flows from your warmer hand to the colder ice, and the slow-moving molecules in the ice move faster. As a result, the ice becomes warmer and its temperature increases. Molecules in your hand move more slowly as they lose thermal energy, and your hand becomes cooler.

Conduction usually occurs most easily in solids and liquids, where atoms and molecules are close together. Then atoms and molecules need to move only a short distance before they bump into one another and transfer energy. As a result, heat is transferred more rapidly by conduction in solids and liquids than in gases.

Reading Check *Why does conduction occur more easily in solids and liquids than in gases?*

Radiation

On a beautiful, clear day, you walk outside and notice the warmth of the Sun. You know that the Sun heats Earth, but how does this transfer of thermal energy occur? Heat transfer does not occur by conduction because almost no matter exists between the Sun and Earth. Instead, heat is transferred from the Sun to Earth by radiation. Heat transfer by **radiation** occurs when energy is transferred by electromagnetic waves. These waves carry energy through empty space, as well as through matter. The transfer of thermal energy by radiation can occur in empty space, as well as in solids, liquids, and gases.

The Sun is not the only source of radiation. All objects emit electromagnetic radiation, although warm objects emit more radiation than cool objects. The warmth you feel when you sit next to a fireplace is due to heat transferred by radiation from the fire to your skin.

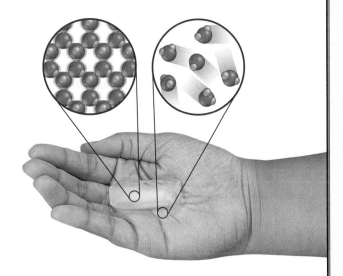

Figure 6 An ice cube in your hand melts because of conduction. The solid ice melts, becoming liquid water. Molecules in the water move faster than molecules in the ice.
Explain *how the thermal energy of the ice cube changes.*

Teacher FYI

Electromagnetic Radiation The wavelength of electromagnetic radiation an object emits is determined in part by its temperature. Objects at higher temperatures emit radiation with shorter wavelengths, and objects at lower temperatures emit radiation with longer wavelengths.

2 Teach

Activity

Passing Cards To demonstrate the difference between thermal energy and heat, cut out several large cardboard circles. On one side of each circle write "thermal energy," and on the other side write "heat." Have two groups of students stand near each other. Have one group hold cards with the "thermal energy" side showing. Then have the group pass the cards to the other group. During the transfer, the "heat" side should be showing. When the other group receives the cards, they should be turned again to show the "thermal energy" side. L2 **Kinesthetic**

Caption Answer

Figure 6 The thermal energy of the ice cube increases.

Reading Check

Answer The atoms and molecules are closer to one another.

Inquiry Lab

Kinetic Energy and Diffusion

Purpose To explore and observe the effects of kinetic energy on the diffusion of molecules in a liquid, have students design experiments using water at various temperatures and food coloring. L2

Materials three containers, hot water, warm water, cold water, food coloring

Estimated Time half class session

Teaching Strategy Students should observe, summarize, and hypothesize about the rates of diffusion of food coloring through water samples of different temperatures.

For additional inquiry activities, see *Science Inquiry Labs.*

Mini LAB

Purpose Students observe the effect of ice water on melting ice. L2 IS **Kinesthetic**

Materials glass, ice, water, two coffee cups, timer

Teaching Strategy If possible, use clear cups so students can watch the ice melt.

Analysis

1. The ice cube in the ice water melted faster. Ice water is a poor insulator.

2. Air is a better insulator. The molecules in air are farther apart than those in water, so they don't collide as often and therefore they don't transfer thermal energy as fast.

Assessment

Process Have students write up their results as lab reports. Suggest they include illustrations. Use **Performance Assessment in the Science Classroom,** p. 119.

Discussion

Rising Air Why is it usually warmer near the ceiling of a room rather than near the floor? Warmer air is less dense than the cooler air around it, and is pushed upward by the denser, cooler air. L3 IS **Logical-Mathematical**

Mini LAB

Comparing Rates of Melting

Procedure

1. Prepare ice water by filling a **glass** with ice and then adding water. Let the glass sit until all the ice melts.
2. Place an ice cube in a **coffee cup**.
3. Place a similar-sized ice cube in another **coffee cup** and add ice water to a depth of about 1 cm.
4. Time how long it takes both ice cubes to melt.

Analysis

1. Which ice cube melted fastest? Why?
2. Is air or water a better insulator? Explain.

Try at Home

Figure 7 Wind movement near a lake or ocean can result from natural convection. Air is heated by the land and becomes less dense. Denser cool air rushes in, pushing the warm air up. The cooler air then is heated by the land and the cycle is repeated.

Convection

When you heat a pot of water on a stove, heat can be transferred through the water by a process other than conduction and radiation. In a gas or liquid, molecules can move much more easily than they can in a solid. As a result, the more energetic molecules can travel from one place to another, and carry their energy along with them. This transfer of thermal energy by the movement of molecules from one part of a material to another is called **convection.**

Transferring Heat by Convection As a pot of water is heated, heat is transferred by convection. First, thermal energy is transferred to the water molecules at the bottom of the pot from the stove. These water molecules move faster as their thermal energy increases. The faster-moving molecules tend to be farther apart than the slower-moving molecules in the cooler water above. Because the molecules are farther apart in the warm water, this water is less dense than the cooler water. As a result, the warm water rises and is replaced at the bottom of the pot by cooler water. The cooler water is heated, rises, and the cycle is repeated until all the water in the pan is at the same temperature.

Natural Convection Natural convection occurs when a warmer, less dense fluid is pushed away by a cooler, denser fluid. For example, imagine the shore of a lake. During the day, the water is cooler than the land. As shown in **Figure 7,** air above the warm land is heated by conduction. When the air gets hotter, its particles move faster and get farther from each other, making the air less dense. The cooler, denser air from over the lake flows in over the land, pushing the less dense air upward. You feel this movement of incoming cool air as wind. The cooler air then is heated by the land and also begins to rise.

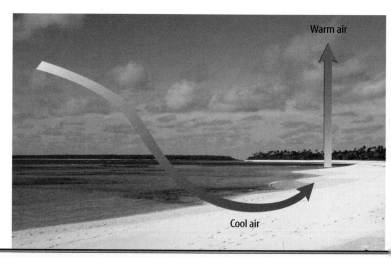

Warm air

Cool air

Heatless Objects Students may think that an object can have heat. Stress that heat is thermal energy that is transferred from one object to another. An object has thermal energy, but it doesn't have heat.

Active Reading

Cause-and-Effect Chart This strategy is used to focus on cause-and-effect reasoning. In the center, students write the topic that they are trying to understand. On the left side, they write the apparent causes of the topic. On the right side, they write the apparent effects of the topic. Have students design a Cause-and-Effect chart for convection. P L2

Fluid is heated.		Warmer fluid is less dense.
Less dense fluid is pushed upward.	Convection	Rising fluid cools.
Fluid becomes more dense as it cools.		Cool fluid sinks.

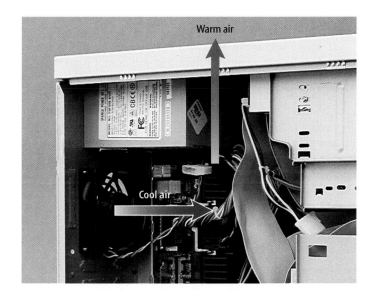

Warm air

Cool air

Figure 8 This computer uses forced convection to keep the electronic components surrounded by cooler air.
Identify *another example of forced convection.*

Forced Convection

Sometimes convection can be forced. Forced convection occurs when an outside force pushes a fluid, such as air or water, to make it move and transfer heat. A fan is one type of device that is used to move air. For example, computers use fans to keep their electronic components from getting too hot, which can damage them. The fan blows cool air onto the hot electronic components, as shown in **Figure 8.** Heat from the electronic components is transferred to the air around them by conduction. The warm air is pushed away as cool air rushes in. The hot components then continue to lose heat as the fan blows cool air over them.

Thermal Conductors

Why are cooking pans usually made of metal? Why does the handle of a metal spoon in a bowl of hot soup become warm? The answer to both questions is that metal is a good conductor. A **conductor** is any material that easily transfers heat. Some materials are good conductors because of the types of atoms or chemical compounds they are made up of.

> ✔ **Reading Check** *What is a conductor?*

Remember that an atom has a nucleus surrounded by one or more electrons. Certain materials, such as metals, have some electrons that are not held tightly by the nucleus and are freer to move around. These loosely held electrons can bump into other atoms and help transfer thermal energy. The best conductors of heat are metals such as gold and copper.

Mini LAB

Observing Convection

Procedure

1. Fill a **250-mL beaker** with room-temperature **water** and let it stand undisturbed for at least 1 min.
2. Using a **hot plate,** heat a small amount of water in a **50-mL beaker** until it is almost boiling.
   WARNING: *Do not touch the heated hot plate.*
3. Carefully drop a **penny** into the hot water and let it stand for about 1 min.
4. Take the penny out of the hot water with **metal tongs** and place it on a table. Immediately place the 250-mL beaker on the penny.
5. Using a **dropper,** gently place one drop of **food coloring** on the bottom of the 250-mL beaker of water.
6. Observe what happens in the beaker for several minutes.

Analysis
What happened when you placed the food coloring in the 250-mL beaker? Why?

Differentiated Instruction

English-Language Learners To help English Language Learners understand the distinction between convection and conduction, explain that conduction is like when you touch something hot, your hand is heated by conduction. Convection is like being heated up in a sauna. L2 **Linguistic**

Visual Learning

Figure 8 In order for forced convection to be possible, the computer must be designed to allow sufficient air flow. Have students describe how this is done in this picture. Ask students to suggest an alternate method for dissipating thermal energy in computers. Some computers are designed to use natural, rather than forced, convection. L2 IS **Visual-Spatial**

Caption Answer
Figure 8 The use of an electric fan to make a person feel cooler.

Mini LAB

Purpose Students observe convection. L2 IS **Kinesthetic**

Materials 250-mL beaker, hot plate, water, 50-mL beaker, penny, metal tongs, dropper, food coloring

Teaching Strategy Students should observe that the column of water directly above the penny (the heat source) is most affected by the convection currents.

Safety Precautions Remind students not to touch the hot plate.

Troubleshooting Be sure that the water is as still as possible when adding the food coloring.

Analysis
A column of colored water rose through the clear water, then fell on the sides. The hot water is less dense than the cool water, so the hot water was pushed upward.

Assessment

Process Ask students to predict what would happen to the water in the beaker if they continued to apply thermal energy only to the center part. The food coloring would be completely mixed in so that all of the water would become colored. Use **Performance Assessment in the Science Classroom,** p. 89.

> ✔ **Reading Check**

Answer any material that easily transfers heat

Animal Insulation A polar bear's long, outer "guard hairs" are hollow in order to trap heat from the Sun. A thick undercoat of fur provides insulation, and the bear's black skin absorbs heat from the guard hairs. Blubber is a layer of fat cells and connective tissue that serves as insulation to help retain body heat.

Make a Model

Energy Efficiency Have students work in small groups to make models of an energy-efficient room. Ceilings of the rooms should be removable so students can demonstrate and explain the design to the rest of the class. Students should be encouraged to use what they have learned about the transfer of thermal energy, insulators, and conductors in their designs. Models can be tested and compared by heating them with a lamp and measuring the change in temperature over a period of time. L3 ELL COOP LEARN LS **Kinesthetic**

Virtual Labs

Insulation *How do the insulation properties of various materials compare?*

INTEGRATE
Life Science

Animal Insulation
To survive in its arctic environment, a polar bear needs good insulation against the cold. Underneath its fur, a polar bear has 10 cm of insulating blubber. Research how animals in polar regions are able to keep themselves warm. Summarize the different ways in your Science Journal.

Figure 9 The insulation in houses and buildings helps reduce the transfer of heat between the air inside and air outside.

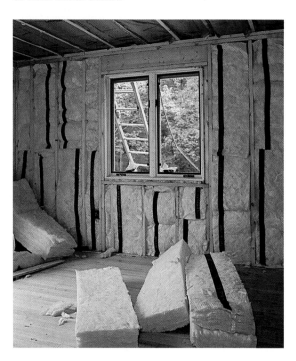

Thermal Insulators

If you're cooking food, you want the pan to conduct heat easily from the stove to your food, but you do not want the heat to move easily to the handle of the pan. An insulator is a material in which heat doesn't flow easily. Most pans have handles that are made from insulators. Liquids and gases are usually better insulators than solids are. Air is a good insulator, and many insulating materials contain air spaces that reduce the transfer of heat by conduction within the material. Materials that are good conductors, such as metals, are poor insulators, and poor conductors are good insulators.

Houses and buildings are made with insulating materials to reduce heat conduction between the inside and outside. Fluffy insulation like that shown in **Figure 9** is put in the walls. Some windows have double layers of glass that sandwich a layer of air or other insulating gas. This reduces the outward flow of heat in the winter and the inward flow of heat in the summer.

Heat Absorption

On a hot day, you can walk barefoot across the lawn, but the asphalt pavement of a street is too hot to walk on. Why is the pavement hotter than the grass? The change in temperature of an object as it absorbs heat depends on the material it is made of.

Specific Heat The amount of heat needed to change the temperature of a substance is related to its specific heat. The **specific heat** of a substance is the amount of heat needed to raise the temperature of 1 kg of that substance by 1°C.

More heat is needed to change the temperature of a material with a high specific heat than one with a low specific heat. For example, the sand on a beach has a lower specific heat than water. When you're at the beach during the day, the sand feels much warmer than the water does. Radiation from the Sun warms the sand and the water. Because of its lower specific heat, the sand heats up faster than the water. At night, however, the sand feels cool and the water feels warmer. The temperature of the water changes more slowly than the temperature of the sand as they both lose thermal energy to the cooler night air.

LAB DEMONSTRATION

Purpose to observe how water conducts thermal energy away from a container so that it doesn't overheat and burn L2

Materials balloon; water; candle flame; sheet of paper cut, folded, and taped into a paper box with top open and all edges sealed with tape

Procedure Fill the balloon with water. Place the candle flame directly in contact with the balloon. You may hold it there for some time. Fill the paper box with water and hold the flame in contact with the box.

Expected Outcome The balloon and the box will get warm, but they will not ignite.

Assessment

The candle flame was very hot. Why didn't it catch the paper or balloon on fire? The water conducted the thermal energy away from the balloon and the paper. Water has a high specific heat, so it could absorb a large amount of thermal energy without a large temperature change.

Thermal Pollution

Some electric power plants and factories that use water for cooling produce hot water as a by-product. If this hot water is released into an ocean, lake, or river, it will raise the temperature of the water nearby. This increase in the temperature of a body of water caused by adding warmer water is called **thermal pollution.** Rainwater that is heated after it falls on warm roads or parking lots also can cause thermal pollution if it runs off into a river or lake.

Effects of Thermal Pollution Increasing the water temperature causes fish and other aquatic organisms to use more oxygen. Because warmer water contains less dissolved oxygen than cooler water, some organisms can die due to a lack of oxygen. Also, in warmer water, many organisms become more sensitive to chemical pollutants, parasites, and diseases.

Reducing Thermal Pollution Thermal pollution can be reduced by cooling the warm water produced by factories, power plants, and runoff before it is released into a body of water. Cooling towers like the ones shown in **Figure 10** are used to cool the water from some power plants and factories.

Figure 10 This power plant uses cooling towers to cool its waste water before releasing it into the lake.

Check for Understanding
Linguistic Have students use what they have learned about conductivity to write a journal entry explaining why stainless-steel pans often have a copper coating on the bottom. Copper has a high conductivity, so it provides even cooking. L3

IS **Logical-Mathematical**

Reteach
Have students identify ways that knowledge about the heat absorption properties of materials can be used in their everyday lives. Possible answers: it can help them choose the best colors of clothing to wear in summer, and whether to sit on a plastic bench or a wooden bench on a hot summer day. L2

IS **Logical-Mathematical**

✔ Assessment

Process Show pictures illustrating the transfer of thermal energy, such as boiling water or people warming themselves near an open fire. Have students explain how thermal energy is transferred in each picture. Use **Performance Assessment in the Science Classroom,** p. 89. L2

---

section ② review

Summary

Heat and Thermal Energy
- Heat is the transfer of thermal energy due to a temperature difference.
- Heat always moves from a higher temperature to a lower temperature.

Conduction, Radiation, and Convection
- Conduction is the transfer of thermal energy when substances are in direct contact.
- Radiation is the transfer of thermal energy by electromagnetic waves.
- Convection is the transfer of thermal energy by the movement of matter.

Thermal Conductors and Specific Heat
- A thermal conductor is a material in which heat moves easily.
- The specific heat of a substance is the amount of heat needed to raise the temperature of 1 kg of the substance by 1°C.

Self Check

1. **Explain** why materials such as plastic foam, feathers, and fur are poor conductors of heat.
2. **Explain** why the sand on a beach cools down at night more quickly than the ocean water.
3. **Infer** If a substance can contain thermal energy, can a substance also contain heat?
4. **Describe** how heat is transferred from one place to another by convection.
5. **Explain** why a blanket keeps you warm.
6. **Think Critically** In order to heat a room evenly, should heating vents be placed near the floor or near the ceiling of the room? Explain.

Applying Skills

7. **Design an Experiment** to determine whether wood or iron is a better thermal conductor. Identify the dependent and independent variables in your experiment.

---

section ② review

1. They contain small pockets of air, which is a poor heat conductor. The trapped air prevents heat from moving easily through the material.
2. The sand on a beach has a lower specific heat than the water. As a result, its temperature changes more than the water temperature as the water and sand transfer heat to their surroundings.
3. No, heat is thermal energy that is transferred from one place to another.
4. As the temperature in one part of a fluid increases, the fluid becomes less dense and is pushed upward by the cooler surrounding fluid. As the warmer fluid moves upward, it transfers heat to the cooler fluid around, until it becomes cool enough to sink.
5. A blanket is an insulator that reduces the rate at which heat is transferred from your body to your surroundings.
6. near the floor, so that warm air rises and transfers thermal energy to the cooler air at all levels in the room
7. Place a piece of wax at one end of an iron rod and a wood rod of equal dimensions, then place the other end of each rod in a beaker of hot water. The wax will melt from the better conductor first. Independent variables: temperature of hot water, dimensions of rods; dependent variable: composition of rod.

Real-World Question

Purpose Students observe how the initial temperature of a liquid affects how quickly it warms or cools. L2

Process Skills observe, compare, measure in SI, make and use tables, record data, make and use graphs, infer

Time Required 45 min

Procedure

Safety Precautions 👓 Caution students to use oven mitts when removing hot beakers from the plate.

Teaching Strategies

• Remind students to fill each beaker to exactly the 100-mL line.

• Students should allow the hot plate to heat up before placing the first beaker of water on the hot plate. Remind students NOT to change the heat setting on the hot plate.

• Suggest students use different colored pencils to plot each of the five lines on the graph.

Conclude and Apply

1. Graphics may vary, but should indicate that the colder the initial temperature of the water, the lower its temperature will be after 10 min. The boiling water and the hot tap water will decrease in temperature over 10 minutes.

2. The rates of heating and cooling should be greater for the water with the greater difference between its initial temperature and the room temperature.

3. The greater the difference between room temperature and initial temperature, the greater the heating or cooling rate.

Heating Up and Cooling Down

Do you remember how long it took for a cup of hot chocolate to cool before you could take a sip? The hotter the chocolate, the longer it seemed to take to cool.

Real-World Question

How does the temperature of a liquid affect how quickly it warms or cools?

Goals

■ **Measure** the temperature change of water at different temperatures.

■ **Infer** how the rate of heating or cooling depends on the initial water temperature.

Materials

thermometers (5)
400-mL beakers (5)
stopwatch
*watch with second hand
hot plate
*Alternate materials

Safety Precautions

👓 🧤

WARNING: *Do not use mercury thermometers. Use caution when heating with a hot plate. Hot and cold glass appears the same.*

Procedure

1. Make a data table to record the temperature of water in five beakers every minute from 0 to 10 min.

2. Fill one beaker with 100 mL of water. Place the beaker on a hot plate and bring the water to a boil. Carefully remove the hot beaker from the hot plate.

3. Record the water temperature at minute 0, and then every minute for 10 min.

4. Repeat step 3 starting with hot tap water, cold tap water, refrigerated water, and ice water with the ice removed.

Conclude and Apply

1. **Graph** your data. **Plot and label** lines for all five beakers on one graph.

2. **Calculate** the rate of heating or cooling for the water in each beaker by subtracting the initial temperature of the water from the final temperature and then dividing this answer by 10 min.

3. **Infer** from your results how the difference between room temperature and the initial temperature of the water affected the rate at which it heated up or cooled down.

Communicating Your Data

Share your data and graphs with other classmates and explain any differences among your data.

Process Ask students to hypothesize what happens to the rate of cooling or warming as the temperature of the water in the beakers becomes closer to room temperature. The rate of warming or cooling will slow as the difference in temperature between the water and room temperature becomes smaller. Use **Performance Assessment in the Science Classroom**, p. 93. L2

Communicating Your Data

Suggest students use a spreadsheet program to graph their results. Students should discuss why their data and graphs did or did not agree.

Engines and Refrigerators

Heat Engines

The engines used in cars, motorcycles, trucks, and other vehicles, like the one shown in **Figure 11,** are heat engines. A **heat engine** is a device that converts thermal energy into mechanical energy. Mechanical energy is the sum of the kinetic and potential energy of an object. The heat engine in a car converts thermal energy into mechanical energy when it makes the car move faster, causing the car's kinetic energy to increase.

Forms of Energy There are other forms of energy besides thermal energy and mechanical energy. For example, chemical energy is energy stored in the chemical bonds between atoms. Radiant energy is the energy carried by electromagnetic waves. Nuclear energy is energy stored in the nuclei of atoms. Electrical energy is the energy carried by electric charges as they move in a circuit. Devices such as heat engines convert one form of energy into other useful forms.

The Law of Conservation of Energy When energy is transformed from one form to another, the total amount of energy doesn't change. According to the law of conservation of energy, energy cannot be created or destroyed. Energy only can be transformed from one form to another. No device, including a heat engine, can produce energy or destroy energy.

as you read

What **You'll Learn**

- **Describe** what a heat engine does.
- **Explain** that energy can exist in different forms, but is never created or destroyed.
- **Describe** how an internal combustion engine works.
- **Explain** how refrigerators move heat.

Why **It's Important**

Heat engines enable you to travel long distances.

🔎 **Review Vocabulary**

work: a way of transferring energy by exerting a force over a distance

New Vocabulary

- heat engine
- internal combustion engine

Figure 11 The engine in this earth mover transforms thermal energy into mechanical energy that can perform useful work.

SECTION 3 Engines and Refrigerators **619**

Section 3 Resource Manager

Chapter FAST FILE Resources

Transparency Activity, pp. 46, 47–48

Directed Reading for Content Mastery, pp. 21, 22

Reinforcement, p. 29

Enrichment, p. 32

Lab Worksheets, pp. 7–8

Reading Check

Answer When the fuel mixture is ignited, it burns explosively and pushes the piston down.

Fun Fact

Aluminum foil has one side that is shinier than the other. The shiny side reflects radiant heat better. So if you want something to stay cool, wrap it with the shiny side out. If you want something to stay warm, wrap it with the shiny side in.

Quick Demo

Fuel Injector

Materials spray bottle

Estimated Time 2 min

Procedure Have a water squirt bottle with the nozzle set on spray so that a fine mist sprays out. Explain that a fuel injector in the internal combustion engine of a car sprays fuel into the cylinders in a fine mist like this spray bottle. The fine spray allows the fuel to burn more evenly resulting in a higher efficiency burn in the cylinder resulting in better engine performance and fuel efficiency.

Figure 12 Internal combustion engines are found in many tools and machines.

Science Online

Topic: Automobile Engines
Visit bookm.msscience.com for Web links to information on how internal combustion engines were developed for use in cars.

Activity Make a time line showing the five important events in the development of the automobile engine.

Internal Combustion Engines The heat engine you are probably most familiar with is the internal combustion engine. In **internal combustion engines,** the fuel burns in a combustion chamber inside the engine. Many machines, including cars, airplanes, buses, boats, trucks, and lawn mowers, use internal combustion engines, as shown in **Figure 12.**

Most cars have an engine with four or more combustion chambers, or cylinders. Usually the more cylinders an engine has, the more power it can produce. Each cylinder contains a piston that can move up and down. A mixture of fuel and air is injected into a combustion chamber and ignited by a spark. When the fuel mixture is ignited, it burns explosively and pushes the piston down. The up-and-down motion of the pistons turns a rod called a crankshaft, which turns the wheels of the car. **Figure 13** shows how an internal combustion engine converts thermal energy to mechanical energy in a process called the four-stroke cycle.

Several kinds of internal combustion engines have been designed. In diesel engines, the air in the cylinder is compressed to such a high pressure that the highly flammable fuel ignites without the need for a spark plug. Many lawn mowers use a two-stroke gasoline engine. The first stroke is a combination of intake and compression. The second stroke is a combination of power and exhaust.

 Reading Check *How does the burning of fuel mixture cause a piston to move?*

Science Journal

Steam Engines The earliest documented steam engine was produced by Heron of Alexandria in ancient Greece. Have students find out more about this engine and draw illustrations of it in their Science Journals. Ask them to include descriptions of how the engine worked. The recoil of steam from inside a ball made the ball rotate. L2 IS
Visual-Spatial

Differentiated Instruction

Challenge Have students research how a jet engine works and prepare a computer presentation about it. A jet engine is a gas turbine engine. As air rushes into the engine, a compressor increases its pressure and temperature. A fine spray of fuel is injected into the high-pressure air and burned. This causes the air to expand, so that it turns a turbine. Part of the energy from the turbine is used to power the compressor. The remainder leaves the system as exhaust to propel the plane forward. L3 IS **Logical-Mathematical** P

Figure 13

Most modern cars are powered by fuel-injected internal combustion engines that have a four-stroke combustion cycle. Inside the engine, thermal energy is converted into mechanical energy as gasoline is burned under pressure inside chambers known as cylinders. The steps in the four-stroke cycle are shown here.

COMPRESSION STROKE

Fuel-air mixture

EXHAUST STROKE

Exhaust valve

Exhaust gases

POWER STROKE

Spark plug

INTAKE STROKE

Intake valve

Fuel injector

Cylinder

Piston

Ⓐ During the intake stroke, the piston inside the cylinder moves downward. As it does, air fills the cylinder through the intake valve, and a mist of fuel is injected into the cylinder.

Ⓑ The piston moves up, compressing the fuel-air mixture.

Crankshaft

Ⓒ At the top of the compression stroke, a spark ignites the fuel-air mixture. The hot gases that are produced expand, pushing the piston down and turning the crankshaft.

Ⓓ The exhaust valve opens as the piston moves up, pushing the exhaust gases out of the cylinder.

SECTION 3 Engines and Refrigerators **M ◆ 171**

Visualizing the Four-Stroke Cycle

Have students examine the pictures and read the captions. Then ask the following questions:

During the intake stroke, the volume of the cylinder is increased. How does this affect the pressure in the cylinder? The pressure decreases.

How does the density and pressure of the air/gas mixture change during the compression stroke? They all increase.

Does the thermal energy of the air/gas mixture increase or decrease during the power stroke? It decreases. What happens to this energy? The gas exerts a force on the piston, so the thermal energy is used to do work on the piston.

Activity

Diesel Engine Poster Ask students to work in pairs to make posters similar to this figure, but showing the operation of a typical diesel engine. When presenting their posters to the class, students should explain how the process differs from that of a four-stroke engine. L3 LS **Visual-Spatial**

Differentiated Instruction

Challenge Have students find out how a spark plug works and write a paragraph explaining what they find. Suggest students include illustrations with their paragraphs. L3 LS **Logical-Mathematical**

Figure 14 A refrigerator uses a coolant to move heat from inside to outside the refrigerator. The compressor supplies the energy that enables the coolant to transfer heat to the room.
Diagram how the temperature of the coolant changes as it moves in a refrigerator.

Refrigerators

If thermal energy will only flow from something that is warm to something that is cool, how can a refrigerator be cooler inside than the air in the kitchen? A refrigerator is a heat mover. It absorbs heat from the food and other materials inside the refrigerator. Then it carries the heat to outside the refrigerator, where it is transferred to the surrounding air.

A refrigerator contains a material called a coolant that is pumped through pipes inside and outside the refrigerator. The coolant is the substance that carries heat from the inside to the outside of the refrigerator.

Absorbing Heat Figure 14 shows how a refrigerator operates. Liquid coolant is forced up a pipe toward the freezer unit. The liquid passes through an expansion valve where it changes into a gas. When it changes into a gas, it becomes cold. The cold gas passes through pipes around the inside of the refrigerator. Because the coolant gas is so cold, it absorbs heat from inside the refrigerator, and becomes warmer.

Releasing Heat However, the gas is still colder than the outside air. So, the heat absorbed by the coolant cannot be transferred to the air. The warm coolant gas then passes through a compressor that compresses the gas. When the gas is compressed, it becomes warmer than room temperature. The gas then flows through the condenser coils, where it transfers heat to the cooler air in the room. As the coolant gas cools, it changes into a liquid. The liquid is pumped through the expansion valve, changes into a gas, and the cycle is repeated.

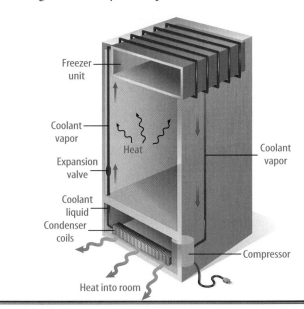

Freezer unit

Coolant vapor

Expansion valve

Coolant liquid

Condenser coils

Heat

Coolant vapor

Compressor

Heat into room

Air Conditioners Most air conditioners cool in the same way that a refrigerator does. You've probably seen air-conditioning units outside of many houses. As in a refrigerator, heat from inside the house is absorbed by the coolant within pipes inside the air conditioner. The coolant then is compressed by a compressor, and becomes warmer. The warmed coolant travels through pipes that are exposed to the outside air. Here the heat is transferred to the outside air.

Cool air

Expansion valve

Outside coils

Inside coils   Compressor

Warm air

Heat Pumps Some buildings use a heat pump for heating as well as cooling. Like an air conditioner or refrigerator, a heat pump moves heat from one place to another. In heating mode, shown in **Figure 15,** the coolant absorbs heat through the outside coils. The coolant is warmed when it is compressed and transfers heat to the house through the inside coils. When a heat pump is used for cooling, it removes thermal energy from the indoor air and transfers it outdoors.

Figure 15 A heat pump heats a building by absorbing thermal energy from the outside air and transferring this heat inside.

section 3 review

Summary

Heat Engines and Energy

- A heat engine is a device that converts thermal energy into mechanical energy.
- Energy cannot be created or destroyed. It only can be transformed from one form to another.
- An internal combustion engine is a heat engine that burns fuel in a combustion chamber inside the engine.

Refrigerators and Heat Pumps

- A refrigerator uses a coolant to transfer heat from inside to outside the refrigerator.
- When the coolant is a gas, it absorbs heat from inside the refrigerator.
- When the coolant is compressed, it changes to a liquid and transfers heat to the air outside.
- A heat pump heats by absorbing heat from the air outside, and transferring it inside a building.

Self Check

1. **Diagram** the movement of coolant and the flow of heat when a heat pump is used to cool a building.
2. **Explain** why diesel engines don't use spark plugs.
3. **Identify** the source of thermal energy in an internal combustion engine.
4. **Determine** whether you could cool a kitchen by keeping the refrigerator door open.
5. **Describe** how a refrigerator uses a coolant to keep the food compartment cool.
6. **Think Critically** Explain how an air conditioner could also be used to heat a room.

Applying Skills

7. **Make a Concept Map** Make an events-chain concept map showing the sequence of steps in a four-stroke cycle.

3 Assess

DAILY INTERVENTION

Check for Understanding

Logical-Mathematical The efficiency of an ideal engine is given by the equation

Efficiency =
$$(T_2 - T_1)/T_2 \times 100\%$$

Here T_2 is the kelvin temperature of the heat source inside the engine. T_1 is the kelvin temperature of the surrounding air the exhaust gases are expelled into. Use this equation to determine what the temperature of the surrounding air must be for the engine to have 100% efficiency. An ideal engine would have an efficiency of 100% only if T_1 were 0 K, or absolute zero. L3 **IS** **Logical-Mathematical**

Reteach

Have students draw diagrams to help them see that a refrigerator is like an engine working in reverse. L2 **IS** **Visual-Spatial**

✓ Assessment

Performance Have students design an engine that uses a heat source other than combustion to perform work. Use **Performance Assessment in the Science Classroom,** p. 117.

section 3 review

1. The coolant absorbs heat from the building interior, is warmed as it passes through the compressor, and releases the heat through the outside coils. It passes through the expansion valve and is cooled, and then passes through the inside coils.

2. The fuel-air mixture becomes so hot during the compression stroke that the mixture ignites.

3. the ignition of the fuel-air mixture

4. No. The heat extracted from the air in the room by having the door open is released back into the room by the condenser coils.

5. The coolant expands, changing to a gas and becoming cooler. It then absorbs heat from inside the refrigerator. The coolant is compressed and becomes warm, so that heat is transferred from the coolant to the outside air. The cycle repeats.

6. The air conditioner could be placed in the window so that the condenser coils were inside the room. Then the air conditioner would absorb heat from the outside air and release the heat into the room.

7. Answers should include fuel-air mixture being drawn into the cylinder, fuel-air mixture being ignited, hot gases expanding and pushing piston down, hot gases being forced out of the cylinder.

Real-World Question

Purpose Students design an experiment to determine which type of beverage containers best insulate hot drinks. L2 LS **Logical-Mathematical**

Process Skills design an experiment, form a hypothesis, observe, identify and control variables, make and use tables, measure in SI, make and use graphs, analyze results, draw conclusions

Time Required two 45-min periods

Materials a variety of disposable drink containers

Safety Precautions 👓

Form a Hypothesis

Possible Hypothesis Beverage containers made of polystyrene, plastic, and paper will block heat transfer from hot liquids better than containers made of glass, ceramic, or metal.

Data Table Data will vary, but the best insulators will show a slower decrease in temperature of liquid over time.

Test Your Hypothesis

Possible Procedures Heat 500 mL of water to boiling. Measure and pour 100 mL of hot water into each of the five different beverage containers. Cover each container with aluminum foil. Insert a thermometer through the foil into each container. Measure and record the temperature of the liquid in each container at the beginning and each minute for ten min.

Design Your Own

Comparing Thermal Insulators

Goals

- **Predict** the temperature change of a hot drink in various types of containers over time.
- **Design** an experiment to test the hypothesis and collect data that can be graphed.
- **Interpret** the data.

Possible Materials

hot plate
large beaker
water
100-mL graduated cylinder
alcohol thermometers
various beverage
   containers
material to cover the
   containers
stopwatch
tongs
thermal gloves or mitts

Safety Precautions

👓 🔥

WARNING: *Use caution when heating liquids. Use tongs or thermal gloves when handling hot materials. Hot and cold glass appear the same. Treat thermometers with care and keep them away from the edges of tables.*

Real-World Question

Insulated beverage containers are used to reduce heat transfer. What kinds of containers do you most often drink from? Aluminum soda cans? Paper, plastic, or foam cups? Glass containers? In this investigation, compare how well several different containers block heat transfer. Which types of beverage containers are most effective at blocking heat transfer from a hot drink?

Form a Hypothesis

Predict the temperature change of a hot liquid in several containers made of different materials over a time interval.

Test Your Hypothesis

Make a Plan

1. **Decide** what types of containers you will test. Design an experiment to test your hypothesis. This is a group activity, so make certain that everyone gets to contribute to the discussion.

Temp. (°C)	foam	paper	plastic	glass	metal
Start					
1 min					
2 min					
3 min					
4 min					
5 min					
6 min					
7 min					
8 min					
9 min					
10 min					

2. **List** the materials you will use in your experiment. Describe exactly how you will use these materials. Which liquid will you test? What temperature will the liquid begin at? How will you cover the hot liquids in the container? What material will you use as a cover?

3. **Identify** the variables and controls in your experiment.

4. **Design** a data table in your Science Journal to record the observations you make.

Follow Your Plan

1. Ask your teacher to examine the steps of your experiment and your data table before you start.

2. To see the pattern of how well various containers retain heat, you will need to graph your data. What kind of graph will you use? Make certain you take enough measurements during the experiment to make your graph.

3. The time intervals between measurements should be the same. Be sure to keep track of time as the experiment goes along. For how long will you measure the temperature?

4. Carry out your investigation and record your observations.

▶ *Analyze Your Data*

1. **Graph** your data. Use one graph to show the data collected from all your containers. Label each line on your graph.

2. **Interpret Data** How can you tell by looking at your graphs which containers retain heat best?

3. **Evaluate** Did the water temperature change as you had predicted? Use your data and graph to explain your answers.

▶ *Conclude and Apply*

1. **Explain** why the rate of temperature change varies among the containers. Did the size of the containers affect the rate of cooling?

2. **Conclude** which containers were the best insulators.

Communicating Your Data

Compare your data and graphs with other classmates and explain any differences in your results or conclusions.

LAB M ◆ 175

Teaching Strategies Suggest that students use different colored pencils to graph temperatures of beverages in different containers.

Troubleshooting Check students' procedures to be sure they have identified and controlled variables.

Expected Outcome Most results will show that a container made from plastic foam or plastic is best at blocking heat transfer.

▶ *Analyze Your Data*

1. Graphs should be consistent with data in the data table. The containers that are least effective at blocking heat transfer will show the steepest curves.

2. The containers that retain heat best show the least steep curves (the temperature will drop less over the same period of time).

3. Answers will vary depending on students' hypotheses.

Error Analysis Have students compare their results and their hypotheses and explain why differences occurred.

▶ *Conclude and Apply*

1. The rate of temperature change varied because some containers conducted heat more slowly than others. The size of the containers would not have much effect on the rate of cooling.

2. Answers will vary depending on containers chosen for testing. In general, cups made from plastic foam or other types of plastic are the best insulators.

☑ Assessment

Process Show students a picnic cooler. Remind them that people place food in picnic coolers to keep the food cold on a warm day. Ask them if a cooler really cools the food. If not, how does it work? The cooler slows heat transfer between the food and the outside (warm) environment. Use **Performance Assessment in the Science Classroom,** p. 89.

Communicating Your Data

Students can use an electronic database to plot their data and graphs. Printouts of each group's data can be given to the other groups for easier comparison and discussion.

Content Background

NASA scientists have used airplanes equipped with heat-sensitive cameras to generate thermal images of several cities. These images showed that darker colors and certain building materials, such as asphalt, absorb and retain far more heat than do lighter colors and materials like concrete. The images also identify areas that are cooler because of an abundance of foliage.

It is estimated that the additional air-conditioning used due to this urban heat-island effect accounts for as much as ten percent of electricity used during peak periods. In Los Angeles, this adds up to more than 100 million dollars per year.

Discussion

Planning Expansion What factors should be considered when planning expansion of cities? Possible answers include: use lighter colors and materials that reflect rather than absorb heat. Tracts of trees and other vegetation should be incorporated into urban and suburban design. Strategic planting of shade trees will reduce heat absorption by buildings. ☐L2 ☐IS **Logical-Mathematical**

Activity

Making Models Divide the class into two groups. Have them use simple materials such as shoeboxes or other cardboard materials to make models of buildings. Have the two groups decorate their models with colors that would make them hotter or cooler. Make other components of cities, such as streets, some dark, some light, to represent asphalt and concrete. Collect pictures of trees, of people who look comfortable, and of people who appear distressed in heat. Save these for construction of two model cities in the activity on the right.

The Heat's On

You may live far from water, but still live on an island—a heat island

Think about all the things that are made of asphalt and concrete in a city. As far as the eye can see, there are buildings and parking lots, sidewalks and streets. The combined effect of these paved surfaces and towering structures can make a city sizzle in the summer. There's even a name for this effect. It's called the heat island effect.

Hot Times

You can think of a city as an island surrounded by an ocean of green trees and other vegetation. In the midst of those green trees, the air can be up to 8°C cooler than it is downtown. During the day in rural areas, the Sun's energy is absorbed by plants and soil. Some of this energy causes water to evaporate, so less energy is available to heat the surroundings. This keeps the temperature lower.

Higher temperatures aren't the only problems caused by heat islands. People crank up their air conditioners for relief, so the use of energy skyrockets. Also, the added heat speeds up the rates of chemical reactions in the atmosphere. Smog is due to chemical reactions caused by the interaction of sunlight and vehicle emissions. So hotter air means more smog. And more smog means more health problems.

Cool Cures

Several U.S. cities are working with NASA scientists to come up with a cure for the summertime blues. For instance, dark materials absorb heat more efficiently than light materials. So painting buildings, especially roofs, white can reduce heat and save on cooling bills.

Dark materials, such as asphalt, absorb more heat than light materials. In extreme heat, it's even possible to fry an egg on dark pavement!

Design and Research Visit the Web Site to the right to research NASA's Urban Heat Island Project. What actions are cities taking to reduce the heat-island effect? Design a city area that would help reduce this effect.

Science Online

For more information, visit bookm.msscience.com/time

Design and Research Have students use the building models and collected pictures from the activity to construct two model cities. One should illustrate a city that absorbs a great deal of heat. The other should illustrate the benefits of a plan that includes the use of color, materials, trees, and parks to reduce the heat absorbed in the city.

Resources for Teachers and Students

Heat Islands—And How To Cool Them, Center For Building Science Newsletter, Spring 1994

"Cities trap heat, make their own weather, study indicates," *Seattle Times*, July 10, 2000

Reviewing Main Ideas

Section 1 — Temperature and Thermal Energy

1. Molecules of matter are moving constantly. Temperature is related to the average value of the kinetic energy of the molecules.

2. Thermometers measure temperature. Three common temperature scales are the Celsius, Fahrenheit, and Kelvin scales.

3. Thermal energy is the total kinetic and potential energy of the particles in matter.

Section 2 — Heat

1. Heat is thermal energy that is transferred from a warmer object to a colder object.

2. Heat can be transferred by conduction, convection, and radiation.

3. A material that easily transfers heat is called a conductor. A material that resists the flow of heat is an insulator.

4. The specific heat of a substance is the amount of heat needed to change the temperature of 1 kg of the substance 1°C.

5. Thermal pollution occurs when warm water is added to a body of water.

Section 3 — Engines and Refrigerators

1. A device that converts thermal energy into mechanical energy is an engine.

2. In an internal combustion engine, fuel is burned in combustion chambers inside the engine using a four-stroke cycle.

3. Refrigerators and air conditioners use a coolant to move heat.

Visualizing Main Ideas

Copy and complete the following cycle map about the four-stroke cycle.

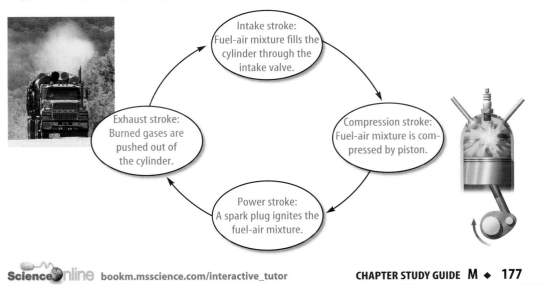

Intake stroke: Fuel-air mixture fills the cylinder through the intake valve.

Compression stroke: Fuel-air mixture is compressed by piston.

Power stroke: A spark plug ignites the fuel-air mixture.

Exhaust stroke: Burned gases are pushed out of the cylinder.

 bookm.msscience.com/interactive_tutor

Reviewing Main Ideas

Summary statements can be used by students to review the major concepts of the chapter.

Visualizing Main Ideas

See student page.

Science **online**

Visit **bookm.msscience.com**
/self_check_quiz
/interactive_tutor
/vocabulary_puzzlemaker
/chapter_review
/standardized_test

Assessment Transparency

For additional assessment questions, use the *Assessment Transparency* located in the transparency book.

Assessment

Assessment Transparency — **Thermal Energy**

Directions: *Carefully review the table and answer the following questions.*

Types of Heat Transfer

Type	Example	Transfer method
Conduction	stove heating a pan	particle collision
Forced convection	furnace fan	particle movement from area to area
Natural convection	boiling water	particle movement from area to area
Radiation	Sun	electromagnetic waves

1. According to the table all of these types of heat transfer involve molecules in motion EXCEPT ___.
   A conduction   C natural convection
   B forced convection   D radiation

2. Rowena is studying outside on a sunny day. She notices she feels warmer. The Sun is most likely transferring heat to Rowena by ___.
   F forced convection   H natural convection
   G radiation   I conduction

3. According to the table, heating a pot of water on a stove until it boils would demonstrate ___.
   A conduction and forced convection
   B radiation and conduction
   C natural convection and conduction
   D natural convection and forced convection

L2

Thermal Energy

Using Vocabulary

1. An engine converts thermal energy to mechanical energy. In an internal combustion engine, fuel is burned in chambers inside the engine.

2. Temperature is the average value of the kinetic energy of the molecules in a material. Thermal energy is the sum of all the kinetic and potential energy of the molecules in the material.

3. Thermal energy is the sum of the kinetic and potential energy of the molecules in a material. Thermal pollution is an increase in the temperature of a natural body of water caused by adding warmer water.

4. Both are methods of transferring thermal energy. Conduction transfers thermal energy by direct contact. Convection transfers thermal energy by movement of fluids from one place to another.

5. Conduction is the transfer of thermal energy by direct contact. Heat is thermal energy transferred from warmer to cooler objects.

6. Heat is thermal energy transferred from one object to another. Specific heat is the amount of heat needed to change the temperature of 1 kg of a substance 1°C.

7. Both are methods of transferring thermal energy. Conduction transfers thermal energy by direct contact. Radiation transfers thermal energy by electromagnetic waves.

8. Both are methods of transferring thermal energy. Convection transfers thermal energy by movement of fluids from one place to another. Radiation transfers thermal energy by electromagnetic waves.

9. A conductor is any material that easily transfers thermal energy. Heat is thermal energy that is transferred from warmer to cooler objects.

Using Vocabulary

conduction p. 163
conductor p. 165
convection p. 164
heat p. 162
heat engine p. 169
internal combustion
  engine p. 170
radiation p. 163
specific heat p. 166
temperature p. 158
thermal energy p. 161
thermal pollution p. 167

Explain the differences in the vocabulary words given below. Then explain how the words are related. Use complete sentences in your answers.

1. internal combustion engine—heat engine
2. temperature—thermal energy
3. thermal energy—thermal pollution
4. conduction—convection
5. conduction—heat
6. heat—specific heat
7. conduction—radiation
8. convection—radiation
9. conductor—heat

Checking Concepts

Choose the word or phrase that best answers the question.

10. What source of thermal energy does an internal combustion engine use?
    A) steam
    B) hot water
    C) burning fuel
    D) refrigerant

11. What happens to most materials when they become warmer?
    A) They contract.
    B) They float.
    C) They vaporize.
    D) They expand.

12. Which occurs if two objects at different temperatures are in contact?
    A) convection
    B) radiation
    C) condensation
    D) conduction

Science Online bookm.msscience.com/vocabulary_puzzlemaker

13. Which of the following describes the thermal energy of particles in a substance?
    A) average value of all kinetic energy
    B) total value of all kinetic energy
    C) total value of all kinetic and potential energy
    D) average value of all kinetic and potential energy

14. Heat being transferred from the Sun to Earth is an example of which process?
    A) convection
    B) expansion
    C) radiation
    D) conduction

15. Many insulating materials contain spaces filled with air because air is what type of material?
    A) conductor
    B) coolant
    C) radiator
    D) insulator

16. A recipe calls for a cake to be baked at a temperature of 350°F. What is this temperature on the Celsius scale?
    A) 162°C
    B) 177°C
    C) 194°C
    D) 212°C

17. Which of the following is true?
    A) Warm air is less dense than cool air.
    B) Warm air is as dense as cool air.
    C) Warm air has no density.
    D) Warm air is denser than cool air.

18. Which of these is the name for thermal energy that moves from a warmer object to a cooler one?
    A) kinetic energy
    B) specific heat
    C) heat
    D) temperature

19. Which of the following is an example of heat transfer by conduction?
    A) water moving in a pot of boiling water
    B) warm air rising from hot pavement
    C) the warmth you feel sitting near a fire
    D) the warmth you feel holding a cup of hot cocoa

Checking Concepts

10. C   15. D
11. D   16. B
12. D   17. A
13. C   18. C
14. C   19. D

Use the Exam*View*® Pro Testmaker CD-ROM to:
- customize tests
- create multiple versions of tests
- generate tests in Spanish
- build tests aligned with state standards

Thinking Critically

20. Infer Water is a poor conductor of heat. Yet when you heat water in a pan, the surface gets hot quickly, even though you are applying heat to the bottom of the water. Explain.

21. Explain why several layers of clothing often keep you warmer than a single layer.

22. Identify The phrase "heat rises" is sometimes used to describe the movement of heat. For what type of materials is this phrase correct? Explain.

23. Describe In a refrigerator, the coolant absorbs heat from inside the refrigerator and then transfers this heat to the air outside. Describe how the temperature of the coolant is changed as it flows through the refrigerator.

24. Design an Experiment Some colors of clothing absorb heat better than other colors. Design an experiment that will test various colors by placing them in the hot Sun for a period of time. Explain your results.

25. Draw Conclusions Would it be possible to cool a kitchen by leaving the refrigerator door open? Explain.

26. Concept Map Copy and complete the following concept map on convection in a liquid.

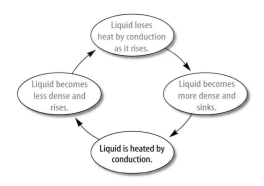

27. Explain A winter jacket is lined with insulating material that contains air spaces. How would the insulating properties of the jacket change if the insulating material in the jacket becomes wet? Explain.

28. Compare Two glasses of water are poured into a pitcher. If the temperature of the water in both glasses was the same before they were mixed, describe how the temperature and thermal energy of the water in the pitcher compares to the water in the glasses.

Performance Activities

29. Poll In the United States, the Fahrenheit temperature scale is used most often. Some people feel that Americans should switch to the Celsius scale. Take a poll of at least 20 people. Find out if they feel the switch to the Celsius scale should be made. Make a list of reasons people give for or against changing.

Applying Math

30. Temperature Order List the following temperatures from coldest to warmest: 80° C, 200 K, 50° F.

31. Temperature Change The high temperature on a summer day is 88°F and the low temperature is 61°F. What is the difference between these two temperatures in degrees Celsius?

32. Global Temperature The average global temperature is 286 K. Convert this temperature to degrees Celsius.

33. Body Temperature A doctor measures a patient's temperature at 38.4°C. Convert this temperature to degrees Fahrenheit.

 bookm.msscience.com/chapter_review

✔ Assessment Resources

Reproducible Masters
Chapter Fast File Resources
Chapter Review, pp. 37–38
Chapter Tests, pp. 39–42
Assessment Transparency Activity, p. 49
Glencoe Science Web site
Chapter Review Test
Standardized Test Practice

Glencoe Technology
Assessment Transparency
ExamView® Pro Testmaker
MindJogger Videoquiz
Interactive Chalkboard

Thinking Critically

20. Convection transfers heat from the bottom of the pan to the water at the surface.

21. Several layers of clothing enable more air to be trapped within and between layers, making the layers a better insulator than a single layer.

22. Fluid. Warm fluid is less dense and is forced upward when convection occurs.

23. Thermal energy is transferred to the glass bulb by convection in the gas and radiation. Thermal energy is then transferred to the air outside by conduction and radiation through the glass.

24. The darker colors will become warmer more quickly.

25. The space prevents the concrete from buckling when it expands in the summer.

26. See student answers.

27. Water fills the air spaces, and because water is a much better conductor of heat than air, the jacket is a better conductor.

28. The thermal energy of the water in the pitcher is the sum of the thermal energy of the water in the glasses. The temperature is the same as the water in the glasses.

Performance Activities

29. Some people might say that switching to Celsius would be too difficult and unnecessary. Others might say that Celsius is easier to use.

Applying Math

National Math Standards
1, 2, 4, 9
30. 200 K, 50°F, 80°C
31. 15°C
32. 13°C
33. 101.1°F

FAST FILE

Answer Sheet A practice answer sheet can be found at bookm.msscience.com/answer_sheet.

SAMPLE

Part 1 | Multiple Choice

1. D   5. C
2. A   6. B
3. C   7. A
4. C

Part 2 | Short Response

8. The water warms the ice. Heat always flows from warm materials to cool materials.

9. You would expect the warmer air mass to rise.

10. Because a diesel engine contains no spark plug, the fuel mixture must be flammable enough to ignite when it is compressed in the cylinder.

11. Air fills the cylinder through the intake valve, and a mist of fuel is injected into the cylinder.

12. Metal is a good heat conductor. The handle is made of a material that is not a good conductor.

13. thermal energy

Part 1 | Multiple Choice

Record your answers on the answer sheet provided by your teacher or on a sheet of paper.

Use the photo below to answer questions 1 and 2.

1. The temperatures of the two glasses of water shown in the photograph above are 30°C and 0°C. Which of the following is a correct statement about the two glasses of water?
   A. The cold water has a higher average kinetic energy.
   B. The warmer water has lower thermal energy.
   C. The molecules of the cold water move faster.
   D. The molecules of the warmer water have more kinetic energy.

2. The difference in temperature of the two glasses of water is 30°C. What is their difference in temperature on the Kelvin scale?
   A. 30 K   **C.** 243 K
   B. 86 K   **D.** 303 K

3. Which of the following describes a refrigerator?
   A. heat engine   **C.** heat mover
   B. heat pump   **D.** conductor

Test-Taking Tip

Avoid rushing on test day. Prepare your clothes and test supplies the night before. Wake up early and arrive at school on time on test day.

4. Which of the following is not a step in the four-stroke cycle of internal combustion engines?
   A. compression   **C.** idling
   B. exhaust   **D.** power

Use the table below to answer question 5.

Material	Specific Heat (J/kg °C)
aluminum	897
copper	385
lead	129
nickel	444
zinc	388

5. A sample of each of the metals in the table above is formed into a 50-g cube. If 100 J of heat are applied to each of the samples, which metal would change temperature by the greatest amount?
   A. aluminum   **C.** lead
   B. copper   **D.** nickel

6. An internal combustion engine converts thermal energy to which of the following forms of energy?
   A. chemical   **C.** radiant
   B. mechanical   **D.** electrical

7. Which of the following is a statement of the law of conservation of energy?
   A. Energy never can be created or destroyed.
   B. Energy can be created, but never destroyed.
   C. Energy can be destroyed, but never created.
   D. Energy can be created and destroyed when it changes form.

Part 3 | Open Ended

14. Coolant constantly flows through the coils that surround the freezer unit. This coolant has been cooled by passing it through the expansion valve. Although heat from the food compartment enters the freezer unit, the coolant in the pipes absorbs this heat, keeping the freezer unit very cold.

15. The expansion valve changes the coolant from a liquid to a vapor. This causes the coolant to expand. The compressor compresses the vapor, making it warmer. The condenser transfers heat from the warmed coolant to the cooler air in the room.

16. Convection is a method of thermal energy transfer by the movement of molecules from one part of a material to another. Natural convection occurs when a warmer, less dense fluid is pushed away by a cooler, denser fluid. An example is the way cooler denser air over a lake flows in over the land, pushing the warmer, less dense air

Part 2 | Short Response/Grid In

Record your answers on the answer sheet provided by your teacher or on a sheet of paper.

8. If you add ice to a glass of room-temperature ice, does the water warm the ice or does the ice cool the water? Explain.

9. Strong winds that occur during a thunderstorm are the result of temperature differences between neighboring air masses. Would you expect the warmer or the cooler air mass to rise above the other?

10. A diesel engine uses a different type of fuel than the fuel used in a gasoline engine. Explain why.

11. What are the two main events that occur while the cylinder moves downward during the intake stroke of an internal combustion engine's four-stroke cycle?

Use the photo below to answer questions 12 and 13.

12. Why are cooking pots like the one in the photograph above often made of metal? Why isn't the handle made of metal?

13. When heating water in the pot, electrical energy from the cooking unit is changed to what other type of energy?

Part 3 | Open Ended

Record your answers on a sheet of paper.

Use the illustration below to answer questions 14 and 15.

14. The illustration above shows how a refrigerator moves heat. Why doesn't the freezer unit shown in the illustration become warm, despite the fact that heat from the food compartment rises? What happens to this heat?

15. What are the functions of the expansion valve, the condenser coils, and the compressor in the illustration?

16. Define convection. Explain the difference between natural and forced convection, and give an example of each.

17. Draw a sketch with arrows showing how conduction, convection, and radiation affect the movement and temperature of air near an ocean.

18. Define temperature and explain how it is related to the movement of molecules in a substance.

19. Explain what makes some materials good thermal conductors.

20. You place a cookie sheet in a hot oven. A few minutes later you hear a sound as the cookie sheet bends slightly. Explain what causes this.

ecules in a substance. The more kinetic energy the molecules have, the higher the temperature. Molecules have more kinetic energy when they are moving faster. Thus the higher the temperature, the faster the molecules are moving.

19. Some materials, such as metals, have some electrons that are not held tightly by the nucleus and are freer to move around. These loosely held electrons can bump into each other. This bumping transfers thermal energy from one part of the material to another.

20. The cookie sheet makes a banging sound because of thermal expansion. Thermal expansion is the increase in length or volume of an object due to changes in temperature. When the temperature of the object increases, its molecules speed up and tend to move farther apart. This increases the size of the object slightly. The cookie sheet may bend when one side experiences more thermal expansion than the other size. Also, some cookie sheets are made of two different metals which experience different amounts of thermal expansion.

Rubrics

For more help evaluating open-ended assessment questions, see the rubric on p. 4T.

Part 3 | Open Ended

upward. Forced convection is when something other than a difference in temperature or density causes the movement of the molecules and transfer of heat. An example is when a fan inside a computer blows cool air onto hot electronic components, causing the warmer

air to move away from the components.

17. Sketches should show heat traveling from the Sun to Earth by radiation. The Sun's energy heats the land and water. The air above the land and water are heated by conduction. Warmer air near the sur-

face of the land rises during the day by convection. This causes cooler air over the ocean to flow toward land. This air becomes heated and rises also as the cycle is repeated.

18. Temperature is a measure of the average kinetic energy of the mol-

Student Resources

CONTENTS

Scientific Methods

Scientists use an orderly approach called scientific methods to solve problems. These include organizing and recording data so others can understand them. Scientists use many variations in these methods when they solve problems.

Identify a Question

The first step in a scientific investigation or experiment is to identify a question to be answered or a problem to be solved. For example, you might ask which gasoline is the most efficient.

Gather and Organize Information

After you have identified your question, begin gathering and organizing information. There are many ways to gather information, such as researching in a library, interviewing those knowledgeable about the subject, testing and working in the laboratory and field. Fieldwork is investigations and observations done outside of a laboratory.

Researching Information Before moving in a new direction, it is important to gather the information that already is known about the subject. Start by asking yourself questions to determine exactly what you need to know. Then you will look for the information in various reference sources, like the student is doing in **Figure 1.** Some sources may include textbooks, encyclopedias, government documents, professional journals, science magazines, and the Internet. Always list the sources of your information.

Figure 1 The Internet can be a valuable research tool.

Evaluate Sources of Information Not all sources of information are reliable. You should evaluate all of your sources of information, and use only those you know to be dependable. For example, if you are researching ways to make homes more energy efficient, a site written by the U.S. Department of Energy would be more reliable than a site written by a company that is trying to sell a new type of weatherproofing material. Also, remember that research always is changing. Consult the most current resources available to you. For example, a 1985 resource about saving energy would not reflect the most recent findings.

Sometimes scientists use data that they did not collect themselves, or conclusions drawn by other researchers. This data must be evaluated carefully. Ask questions about how the data were obtained, if the investigation was carried out properly, and if it has been duplicated exactly with the same results. Would you reach the same conclusion from the data? Only when you have confidence in the data can you believe it is true and feel comfortable using it.

Interpret Scientific Illustrations As you research a topic in science, you will see drawings, diagrams, and photographs to help you understand what you read. Some illustrations are included to help you understand an idea that you can't see easily by yourself, like the tiny particles in an atom in **Figure 2.** A drawing helps many people to remember details more easily and provides examples that clarify difficult concepts or give additional information about the topic you are studying. Most illustrations have labels or a caption to identify or to provide more information.

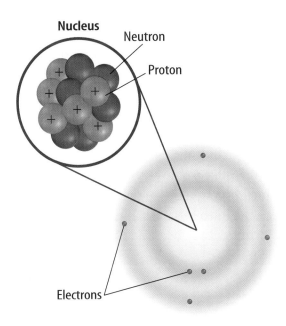

Figure 2 This drawing shows an atom of carbon with its six protons, six neutrons, and six electrons.

Concept Maps One way to organize data is to draw a diagram that shows relationships among ideas (or concepts). A concept map can help make the meanings of ideas and terms more clear, and help you understand and remember what you are studying. Concept maps are useful for breaking large concepts down into smaller parts, making learning easier.

Network Tree A type of concept map that not only shows a relationship, but how the concepts are related is a network tree, shown in **Figure 3.** In a network tree, the words are written in the ovals, while the description of the type of relationship is written across the connecting lines.

When constructing a network tree, write down the topic and all major topics on separate pieces of paper or notecards. Then arrange them in order from general to specific. Branch the related concepts from the major concept and describe the relationship on the connecting line. Continue to more specific concepts until finished.

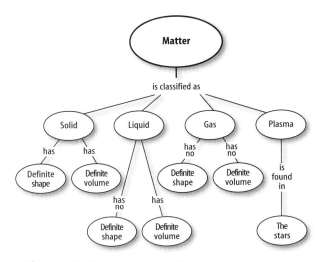

Figure 3 A network tree shows how concepts or objects are related.

Events Chain Another type of concept map is an events chain. Sometimes called a flow chart, it models the order or sequence of items. An events chain can be used to describe a sequence of events, the steps in a procedure, or the stages of a process.

When making an events chain, first find the one event that starts the chain. This event is called the initiating event. Then, find the next event and continue until the outcome is reached, as shown in **Figure 4.**

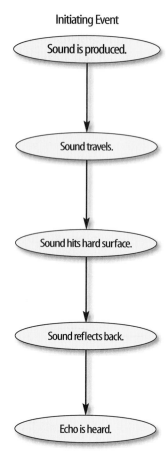

Initiating Event

Sound is produced.

Sound travels.

Sound hits hard surface.

Sound reflects back.

Echo is heard.

Figure 4 Events-chain concept maps show the order of steps in a process or event. This concept map shows how a sound makes an echo.

Cycle Map A specific type of events chain is a cycle map. It is used when the series of events do not produce a final outcome, but instead relate back to the beginning event, such as in **Figure 5.** Therefore, the cycle repeats itself.

To make a cycle map, first decide what event is the beginning event. This is also called the initiating event. Then list the next events in the order that they occur, with the last event relating back to the initiating event. Words can be written between the events that describe what happens from one event to the next. The number of events in a cycle map can vary, but usually contain three or more events.

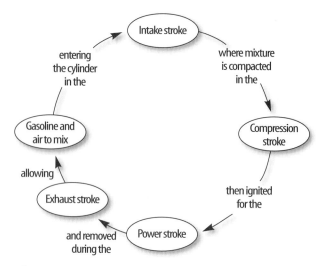

Figure 5 A cycle map shows events that occur in a cycle.

Spider Map A type of concept map that you can use for brainstorming is the spider map. When you have a central idea, you might find that you have a jumble of ideas that relate to it but are not necessarily clearly related to each other. The spider map on sound in **Figure 6** shows that if you write these ideas outside the main concept, then you can begin to separate and group unrelated terms so they become more useful.

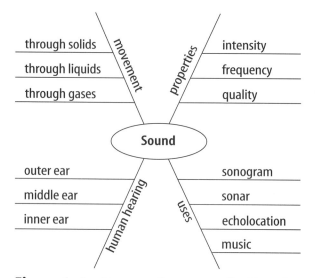

Figure 6 A spider map allows you to list ideas that relate to a central topic but not necessarily to one another.

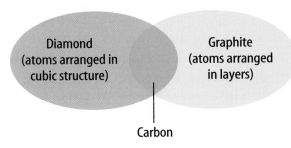

Figure 7 This Venn diagram compares and contrasts two substances made from carbon.

Venn Diagram To illustrate how two subjects compare and contrast you can use a Venn diagram. You can see the characteristics that the subjects have in common and those that they do not, shown in **Figure 7.**

To create a Venn diagram, draw two overlapping ovals that that are big enough to write in. List the characteristics unique to one subject in one oval, and the characteristics of the other subject in the other oval. The characteristics in common are listed in the overlapping section.

Make and Use Tables One way to organize information so it is easier to understand is to use a table. Tables can contain numbers, words, or both.

To make a table, list the items to be compared in the first column and the characteristics to be compared in the first row. The title should clearly indicate the content of the table, and the column or row heads should be clear. Notice that in **Table 1** the units are included.

Table 1 Recyclables Collected During Week			
Day of Week	Paper (kg)	Aluminum (kg)	Glass (kg)
Monday	5.0	4.0	12.0
Wednesday	4.0	1.0	10.0
Friday	2.5	2.0	10.0

Make a Model One way to help you better understand the parts of a structure, the way a process works, or to show things too large or small for viewing is to make a model. For example, an atomic model made of a plastic-ball nucleus and pipe-cleaner electron shells can help you visualize how the parts of an atom relate to each other. Other types of models can by devised on a computer or represented by equations.

Form a Hypothesis

A possible explanation based on previous knowledge and observations is called a hypothesis. After researching gasoline types and recalling previous experiences in your family's car you form a hypothesis—our car runs more efficiently because we use premium gasoline. To be valid, a hypothesis has to be something you can test by using an investigation.

Predict When you apply a hypothesis to a specific situation, you predict something about that situation. A prediction makes a statement in advance, based on prior observation, experience, or scientific reasoning. People use predictions to make everyday decisions. Scientists test predictions by performing investigations. Based on previous observations and experiences, you might form a prediction that cars are more efficient with premium gasoline. The prediction can be tested in an investigation.

Design an Experiment A scientist needs to make many decisions before beginning an investigation. Some of these include: how to carry out the investigation, what steps to follow, how to record the data, and how the investigation will answer the question. It also is important to address any safety concerns.

Test the Hypothesis

Now that you have formed your hypothesis, you need to test it. Using an investigation, you will make observations and collect data, or information. This data might either support or not support your hypothesis. Scientists collect and organize data as numbers and descriptions.

Follow a Procedure In order to know what materials to use, as well as how and in what order to use them, you must follow a procedure. **Figure 8** shows a procedure you might follow to test your hypothesis.

Procedure
1. Use regular gasoline for two weeks.
2. Record the number of kilometers between fill-ups and the amount of gasoline used.
3. Switch to premium gasoline for two weeks.
4. Record the number of kilometers between fill-ups and the amount of gasoline used.

Figure 8 A procedure tells you what to do step by step.

Identify and Manipulate Variables and Controls In any experiment, it is important to keep everything the same except for the item you are testing. The one factor you change is called the independent variable. The change that results is the dependent variable. Make sure you have only one independent variable, to assure yourself of the cause of the changes you observe in the dependent variable. For example, in your gasoline experiment the type of fuel is the independent variable. The dependent variable is the efficiency.

Many experiments also have a control—an individual instance or experimental subject for which the independent variable is not changed. You can then compare the test results to the control results. To design a control you can have two cars of the same type. The control car uses regular gasoline for four weeks. After you are done with the test, you can compare the experimental results to the control results.

Collect Data

Whether you are carrying out an investigation or a short observational experiment, you will collect data, as shown in **Figure 9.** Scientists collect data as numbers and descriptions and organize it in specific ways.

Observe Scientists observe items and events, then record what they see. When they use only words to describe an observation, it is called qualitative data. Scientists' observations also can describe how much there is of something. These observations use numbers, as well as words, in the description and are called quantitative data. For example, if a sample of the element gold is described as being "shiny and very dense" the data are qualitative. Quantitative data on this sample of gold might include "a mass of 30 g and a density of 19.3 g/cm^3."

Figure 9 Collecting data is one way to gather information directly.

Figure 10 Record data neatly and clearly so it is easy to understand.

When you make observations you should examine the entire object or situation first, and then look carefully for details. It is important to record observations accurately and completely. Always record your notes immediately as you make them, so you do not miss details or make a mistake when recording results from memory. Never put unidentified observations on scraps of paper. Instead they should be recorded in a notebook, like the one in **Figure 10.** Write your data neatly so you can easily read it later. At each point in the experiment, record your observations and label them. That way, you will not have to determine what the figures mean when you look at your notes later. Set up any tables that you will need to use ahead of time, so you can record any observations right away. Remember to avoid bias when collecting data by not including personal thoughts when you record observations. Record only what you observe.

Estimate Scientific work also involves estimating. To estimate is to make a judgment about the size or the number of something without measuring or counting. This is important when the number or size of an object or population is too large or too difficult to accurately count or measure.

Sample Scientists may use a sample or a portion of the total number as a type of estimation. To sample is to take a small, representative portion of the objects or organisms of a population for research. By making careful observations or manipulating variables within that portion of the group, information is discovered and conclusions are drawn that might apply to the whole population. A poorly chosen sample can be unrepresentative of the whole. If you were trying to determine the rainfall in an area, it would not be best to take a rainfall sample from under a tree.

Measure You use measurements everyday. Scientists also take measurements when collecting data. When taking measurements, it is important to know how to use measuring tools properly. Accuracy also is important.

Length To measure length, the distance between two points, scientists use meters. Smaller measurements might be measured in centimeters or millimeters.

Length is measured using a metric ruler or meter stick. When using a metric ruler, line up the 0-cm mark with the end of the object being measured and read the number of the unit where the object ends. Look at the metric ruler shown in **Figure 11.** The centimeter lines are the long, numbered lines, and the shorter lines are millimeter lines. In this instance, the length would be 4.50 cm.

Figure 11 This metric ruler has centimeter and millimeter divisions.

Mass The SI unit for mass is the kilogram (kg). Scientists can measure mass using units formed by adding metric prefixes to the unit gram (g), such as milligram (mg). To measure mass, you might use a triple-beam balance similar to the one shown in **Figure 12.** The balance has a pan on one side and a set of beams on the other side. Each beam has a rider that slides on the beam.

When using a triple-beam balance, place an object on the pan. Slide the largest rider along its beam until the pointer drops below zero. Then move it back one notch. Repeat the process for each rider proceeding from the larger to smaller until the pointer swings an equal distance above and below the zero point. Sum the masses on each beam to find the mass of the object. Move all riders back to zero when finished.

Instead of putting materials directly on the balance, scientists often take a tare of a container. A tare is the mass of a container into which objects or substances are placed for measuring their masses. To mass objects or substances, find the mass of a clean container. Remove the container from the pan, and place the object or substances in the container. Find the mass of the container with the materials in it. Subtract the mass of the empty container from the mass of the filled container to find the mass of the materials you are using.

Figure 13 Graduated cylinders measure liquid volume.

Liquid Volume To measure liquids, the unit used is the liter. When a smaller unit is needed, scientists might use a milliliter. Because a milliliter takes up the volume of a cube measuring 1 cm on each side it also can be called a cubic centimeter ($cm^3 = cm \times cm \times cm$).

You can use beakers and graduated cylinders to measure liquid volume. A graduated cylinder, shown in **Figure 13,** is marked from bottom to top in milliliters. In lab, you might use a 10-mL graduated cylinder or a 100-mL graduated cylinder. When measuring liquids, notice that the liquid has a curved surface. Look at the surface at eye level, and measure the bottom of the curve. This is called the meniscus. The graduated cylinder in **Figure 13** contains 79.0 mL, or 79.0 cm^3, of a liquid.

Temperature Scientists often measure temperature using the Celsius scale. Pure water has a freezing point of 0°C and boiling point of 100°C. The unit of measurement is degrees Celsius. Two other scales often used are the Fahrenheit and Kelvin scales.

Figure 12 A triple-beam balance is used to determine the mass of an object.

Figure 14 A thermometer measures the temperature of an object.

Scientists use a thermometer to measure temperature. Most thermometers in a laboratory are glass tubes with a bulb at the bottom end containing a liquid such as colored alcohol. The liquid rises or falls with a change in temperature. To read a glass thermometer like the thermometer in **Figure 14,** rotate it slowly until a red line appears. Read the temperature where the red line ends.

Form Operational Definitions An operational definition defines an object by how it functions, works, or behaves. For example, when you are playing hide and seek and a tree is home base, you have created an operational definition for a tree.

Objects can have more than one operational definition. For example, a ruler can be defined as a tool that measures the length of an object (how it is used). It can also be a tool with a series of marks used as a standard when measuring (how it works).

Analyze the Data

To determine the meaning of your observations and investigation results, you will need to look for patterns in the data. Then you must think critically to determine what the data mean. Scientists use several approaches when they analyze the data they have collected and recorded. Each approach is useful for identifying specific patterns.

Interpret Data The word *interpret* means "to explain the meaning of something." When analyzing data from an experiment, try to find out what the data show. Identify the control group and the test group to see whether or not changes in the independent variable have had an effect. Look for differences in the dependent variable between the control and test groups.

Classify Sorting objects or events into groups based on common features is called classifying. When classifying, first observe the objects or events to be classified. Then select one feature that is shared by some members in the group, but not by all. Place those members that share that feature in a subgroup. You can classify members into smaller and smaller subgroups based on characteristics. Remember that when you classify, you are grouping objects or events for a purpose. Keep your purpose in mind as you select the features to form groups and subgroups.

Compare and Contrast Observations can be analyzed by noting the similarities and differences between two more objects or events that you observe. When you look at objects or events to see how they are similar, you are comparing them. Contrasting is looking for differences in objects or events.

Recognize Cause and Effect A cause is a reason for an action or condition. The effect is that action or condition. When two events happen together, it is not necessarily true that one event caused the other. Scientists must design a controlled investigation to recognize the exact cause and effect.

Draw Conclusions

When scientists have analyzed the data they collected, they proceed to draw conclusions about the data. These conclusions are sometimes stated in words similar to the hypothesis that you formed earlier. They may confirm a hypothesis, or lead you to a new hypothesis.

Infer Scientists often make inferences based on their observations. An inference is an attempt to explain observations or to indicate a cause. An inference is not a fact, but a logical conclusion that needs further investigation. For example, you may infer that a fire has caused smoke. Until you investigate, however, you do not know for sure.

Apply When you draw a conclusion, you must apply those conclusions to determine whether the data supports the hypothesis. If your data do not support your hypothesis, it does not mean that the hypothesis is wrong. It means only that the result of the investigation did not support the hypothesis. Maybe the experiment needs to be redesigned, or some of the initial observations on which the hypothesis was based were incomplete or biased. Perhaps more observation or research is needed to refine your hypothesis. A successful investigation does not always come out the way you originally predicted.

Avoid Bias Sometimes a scientific investigation involves making judgments. When you make a judgment, you form an opinion. It is important to be honest and not to allow any expectations of results to bias your judgments. This is important throughout the entire investigation, from researching to collecting data to drawing conclusions.

Communicate

The communication of ideas is an important part of the work of scientists. A discovery that is not reported will not advance the scientific community's understanding or knowledge. Communication among scientists also is important as a way of improving their investigations.

Scientists communicate in many ways, from writing articles in journals and magazines that explain their investigations and experiments, to announcing important discoveries on television and radio. Scientists also share ideas with colleagues on the Internet or present them as lectures, like the student is doing in **Figure 15.**

Figure 15 A student communicates to his peers about his investigation.

SAFETY SYMBOLS

SAFETY SYMBOLS	HAZARD	EXAMPLES	PRECAUTION	REMEDY
DISPOSAL	Special disposal procedures need to be followed.	certain chemicals, living organisms	Do not dispose of these materials in the sink or trash can.	Dispose of wastes as directed by your teacher.
BIOLOGICAL	Organisms or other biological materials that might be harmful to humans	bacteria, fungi, blood, unpreserved tissues, plant materials	Avoid skin contact with these materials. Wear mask or gloves.	Notify your teacher if you suspect contact with material. Wash hands thoroughly.
EXTREME TEMPERATURE	Objects that can burn skin by being too cold or too hot	boiling liquids, hot plates, dry ice, liquid nitrogen	Use proper protection when handling.	Go to your teacher for first aid.
SHARP OBJECT	Use of tools or glassware that can easily puncture or slice skin	razor blades, pins, scalpels, pointed tools, dissecting probes, broken glass	Practice common-sense behavior and follow guidelines for use of the tool.	Go to your teacher for first aid.
FUME	Possible danger to respiratory tract from fumes	ammonia, acetone, nail polish remover, heated sulfur, moth balls	Make sure there is good ventilation. Never smell fumes directly. Wear a mask.	Leave foul area and notify your teacher immediately.
ELECTRICAL	Possible danger from electrical shock or burn	improper grounding, liquid spills, short circuits, exposed wires	Double-check setup with teacher. Check condition of wires and apparatus.	Do not attempt to fix electrical problems. Notify your teacher immediately.
IRRITANT	Substances that can irritate the skin or mucous membranes of the respiratory tract	pollen, moth balls, steel wool, fiberglass, potassium permanganate	Wear dust mask and gloves. Practice extra care when handling these materials.	Go to your teacher for first aid.
CHEMICAL	Chemicals can react with and destroy tissue and other materials	bleaches such as hydrogen peroxide; acids such as sulfuric acid, hydrochloric acid; bases such as ammonia, sodium hydroxide	Wear goggles, gloves, and an apron.	Immediately flush the affected area with water and notify your teacher.
TOXIC	Substance may be poisonous if touched, inhaled, or swallowed.	mercury, many metal compounds, iodine, poinsettia plant parts	Follow your teacher's instructions.	Always wash hands thoroughly after use. Go to your teacher for first aid.
FLAMMABLE	Flammable chemicals may be ignited by open flame, spark, or exposed heat.	alcohol, kerosene, potassium permanganate	Avoid open flames and heat when using flammable chemicals.	Notify your teacher immediately. Use fire safety equipment if applicable.
OPEN FLAME	Open flame in use, may cause fire.	hair, clothing, paper, synthetic materials	Tie back hair and loose clothing. Follow teacher's instruction on lighting and extinguishing flames.	Notify your teacher immediately. Use fire safety equipment if applicable.

 Eye Safety Proper eye protection should be worn at all times by anyone performing or observing science activities.

 Clothing Protection This symbol appears when substances could stain or burn clothing.

 Animal Safety This symbol appears when safety of animals and students must be ensured.

 Handwashing After the lab, wash hands with soap and water before removing goggles.

Safety in the Science Laboratory

The science laboratory is a safe place to work if you follow standard safety procedures. Being responsible for your own safety helps to make the entire laboratory a safer place for everyone. When performing any lab, read and apply the caution statements and safety symbol listed at the beginning of the lab.

General Safety Rules

1. Obtain your teacher's permission to begin all investigations and use laboratory equipment.

2. Study the procedure. Ask your teacher any questions. Be sure you understand safety symbols shown on the page.

3. Notify your teacher about allergies or other health conditions which can affect your participation in a lab.

4. Learn and follow use and safety procedures for your equipment. If unsure, ask your teacher.

5. Never eat, drink, chew gum, apply cosmetics, or do any personal grooming in the lab. Never use lab glassware as food or drink containers. Keep your hands away from your face and mouth.

6. Know the location and proper use of the safety shower, eye wash, fire blanket, and fire alarm.

Prevent Accidents

1. Use the safety equipment provided to you. Goggles and a safety apron should be worn during investigations.

2. Do NOT use hair spray, mousse, or other flammable hair products. Tie back long hair and tie down loose clothing.

3. Do NOT wear sandals or other open-toed shoes in the lab.

4. Remove jewelry on hands and wrists. Loose jewelry, such as chains and long necklaces, should be removed to prevent them from getting caught in equipment.

5. Do not taste any substances or draw any material into a tube with your mouth.

6. Proper behavior is expected in the lab. Practical jokes and fooling around can lead to accidents and injury.

7. Keep your work area uncluttered.

Laboratory Work

1. Collect and carry all equipment and materials to your work area before beginning a lab.

2. Remain in your own work area unless given permission by your teacher to leave it.

3. Always slant test tubes away from yourself and others when heating them, adding substances to them, or rinsing them.

4. If instructed to smell a substance in a container, hold the container a short distance away and fan vapors towards your nose.

5. Do NOT substitute other chemicals/substances for those in the materials list unless instructed to do so by your teacher.

6. Do NOT take any materials or chemicals outside of the laboratory.

7. Stay out of storage areas unless instructed to be there and supervised by your teacher.

Laboratory Cleanup

1. Turn off all burners, water, and gas, and disconnect all electrical devices.

2. Clean all pieces of equipment and return all materials to their proper places.

3. Dispose of chemicals and other materials as directed by your teacher. Place broken glass and solid substances in the proper containers. Never discard materials in the sink.

4. Clean your work area.

5. Wash your hands with soap and water thoroughly BEFORE removing your goggles.

Emergencies

1. Report any fire, electrical shock, glassware breakage, spill, or injury, no matter how small, to your teacher immediately. Follow his or her instructions.

2. If your clothing should catch fire, STOP, DROP, and ROLL. If possible, smother it with the fire blanket or get under a safety shower. NEVER RUN.

3. If a fire should occur, turn off all gas and leave the room according to established procedures.

4. In most instances, your teacher will clean up spills. Do NOT attempt to clean up spills unless you are given permission and instructions to do so.

5. If chemicals come into contact with your eyes or skin, notify your teacher immediately. Use the eyewash or flush your skin or eyes with large quantities of water.

6. The fire extinguisher and first-aid kit should only be used by your teacher unless it is an extreme emergency and you have been given permission.

7. If someone is injured or becomes ill, only a professional medical provider or someone certified in first aid should perform first-aid procedures.

① Measuring Momentum

Time Required 40 minutes

Materials
- Students can transport the bowling balls in heavy-duty 5-gallon construction buckets.
- You might have to help students find the weights of the bowling balls.

Safety Precautions
- Caution students not to throw or drop the bowling balls.
- Students should use the metersticks with care.

Teaching Strategies
- Students should roll each ball so that it does not bounce.
- Instruct students to use the formula: momentum = mass × velocity to calculate each ball's momentum.

Conclude and Apply
1. Answers will vary, but all answers should have the units kg m/s.
2. The masses of balls varied greatly.

Extra Try at Home Labs

EXTRA Labs
From Your Kitchen, Junk Drawer, or Yard

① Measuring Momentum

▶ **Real-World Question**
How much momentum do rolling balls have?

Possible Materials
- meterstick
- orange cones or tape
- scale
- stopwatch
- bucket
- bowling ball
- plastic baseball
- golf ball
- tennis ball
- calculator

▶ **Procedure**
1. Use a balance to measure the masses of the tennis ball, golf ball, and plastic baseball. Convert their masses from grams to kilograms.
2. Find the weight of the bowling ball in pounds. The weight should be written on the ball. Divide the ball's weight by 2.2 to calculate its mass in kilograms.
3. Go outside and measure a 10-m distance on a blacktop or concrete surface. Mark the distance with orange cones or tape.
4. Have a partner roll each ball the 10-m distance. Measure the time it takes each ball to roll 10 m.
5. Use the formula: velocity = $\frac{distance}{time}$ to calculate each ball's velocity.

▶ **Conclude and Apply**
1. Calculate the momentum of each ball.
2. Infer why the momentums of the balls differed so greatly.

② Friction in Traffic

▶ **Real-World Question**
How do the various kinds of friction affect the operation of vehicles?

Possible Materials
- erasers taken from the ends of pencils (4)
- needles (2)
- small match box
- toy car

▶ **Procedure**
1. Build a match box car with the materials listed, or use a toy car.
2. Invent ways to demonstrate the effects of static friction, sliding friction, and rolling friction on the car. Think of hills, ice or rain conditions, graveled roads and paved roads, etc.

3. Make drawings of how friction is acting on the car, or how the car uses friction to work.

▶ **Conclude and Apply**
1. In what ways are static, sliding, and rolling friction helpful to drivers?
2. In what ways are static, sliding, and rolling friction unfavorable to car safety and operation?
3. Explain what your experiment taught you about driving in icy conditions.

Adult supervision required for all labs.

These labs are available at bookm.msscience.com.

---

② Friction in Traffic

Time Required one to one-and-a-half hours, including building the car

Materials
- Make the ice the night before.
- For an icy hill, you could use a cookie sheet full of ice, soap, or a sprinkling of cornstarch. Use books to elevate it.

Teaching Strategy Combining this lab with force drawings can help students understand the types of friction.

Conclude and Apply
1. Static friction helps a car park on a hill. Sliding friction helps it stop by braking. Rolling friction is necessary for the wheels to move.

2. The engine needs to work hard to overcome static friction. If there's not enough sliding friction, cars crash (like on wet and/or icy roads). Too much of all three kinds of friction decrease fuel economy.
3. Answers will vary.

3 Submersible Egg

▶ Real-World Question

How can you make an egg float and sink again?

Possible Materials

- egg
- 10 mL (2 teaspoons) of salt
- measuring spoons
- water
- glass (250–300 mL)
- spoon
- marking pen

▶ Procedure

1. Put 150 mL of water in the glass.
2. Gently use a marking pen to write an X on one side of the egg.
3. Put the egg in the glass. Record your observations.

4. Use the spoon to remove the egg. Add 1 mL (1/4 teaspoon) of salt and swirl or stir to dissolve. Put the egg back in. Record your observations.
5. Repeat step 4 until you have used all the salt. Remember to make observations at each step.

▶ Conclude and Apply

1. How could you resink the egg? Try your idea. Did it work?
2. The egg always floats with the same point or side down. Why do you think this is?
3. How does your answer to question 2 relate to real-world applications?

---

4 Simple Machines

▶ Real-World Question

What types of simple machines are found in a toolbox?

Possible Materials

- box of tools

▶ Procedure

1. Obtain a box of tools and lay all the tools and other hardware from the box on a table.
2. Carefully examine all the tools and hardware, and separate all the items that are a type of inclined plane.
3. Carefully examine all the tools and hardware, and separate all the items that are a type of lever.

4. Identify and separate all the items that are a wheel and axle.
5. Identify any pulleys in the toolbox.
6. Identify any tools that are a combination of two or more simple machines.

▶ Conclude and Apply

1. List all the tools you found that were a type of inclined plane, lever, wheel and axle, or pulley.
2. List all the tools that were a combination of two or more simple machines.
3. Infer how a hammer could be used as both a first class lever and a third class lever.

---

3 Submersible Egg

Time Required one class period

Safety Precaution Make sure students wash their hands after handling the egg.

Teaching Strategies

- You may tell students to begin with 4 mL of salt to speed up the process.
- The egg begins to rise between 6 and 7 mL of salt. If students are careful around this point, they may see the egg hover halfway.

Conclude and Apply

1. Add more water. If students add the water slowly, they will be able to see the egg slowly sink down and hover halfway on the way to the bottom.
2. There is an air sac in the egg. It is lighter than the rest of the egg, so that side of the egg (usually the wide end) always rises to the top.
3. Answers will vary. One answer is that a submarine has compressed gas that is used to fill air chambers to get the sub to the surface.

Time Required 40 minutes

Safety Precaution Caution students to handle sharp tools with care.

Teaching Strategy To help students match each tool with a type of simple machine, instruct them to think about how each is used.

Conclude and Apply

1. Answers will vary. Wedge (inclined plane): utility knife, putty knife, doorstop, nail. Screw (inclined plane): screw, flashlight top, clamp, nut and bolt. Lever: hammer, pliers, wrench. Wheel and axle: clamp, faucet, doorknob, screwdriver. Pulley:

4 Simple Machines

window blind pulley.
2. Answers will vary. A clamp is a combination of a screw and wheel and axle. A wrench is screw, wheel and axle, and a lever.
3. A hammer is a first class lever when its claw is used to remove a nail and a third class lever when using it to hammer a nail.

5 The Heat is On

Time Required ten minutes

Materials
- Use an incandescent, not fluorescent, lightbulb.
- The lightbulbs should not be turned on before the lab.
- Black cloth can be used instead of the paper.

Safety Precaution
Warn students never to touch a lightbulb even if it is not lit.

Teaching Strategies
- Have students lay the sheet of paper in direct sunlight first, complete the other parts of the lab, and then return to the paper after ten minutes.
- Extend the lab by using thermometers.

Conclude and Apply
1. solar energy to heat energy
2. kinetic energy (energy of motion) to heat energy
3. electrical energy to heat energy

---

5 The Heat is On

▶ **Real-World Question**
How can different types of energy be transformed into thermal energy?

Possible Materials
- lamp
- incandescent light bulb
- black construction paper or cloth

▶ **Procedure**
1. Feel the temperature of a black sheet of paper. Lay the paper in direct sunlight, wait 10 min, and observe how it feels.

2. Rub the palms of your hands together quickly for 10 s and observe how they feel.
3. Switch on a lamp that has a bare light bulb. *Without touching the lightbulb,* cup your hand 2 cm above the bulb for 30 s and observe what you feel.

▶ **Conclude and Apply**
1. Infer the type of energy transformation that happened on the paper.
2. Infer the type of energy transformation that happened between the palms of your hands.
3. Infer the type of energy transformation that happened to the lightbulb.

6 Estimate Temperature

▶ **Real-World Question**
How can we learn to estimate temperatures?

Possible Materials
- thermometer • water
- bowl • ice

▶ **Procedure**
1. If you have a dual-scale weather thermometer, you can learn twice as much by trying to do your estimation in degrees Fahrenheit and Celsius each time.
2. Fill a bowl with ice water. Submerge your fingers in the water and estimate the water temperature.
3. Place the thermometer in the bowl and observe the temperature.
4. Place a bowl of warm water in direct sunlight for 20 min. Submerge your fingers in the water and estimate the water temperature.

5. Place the thermometer in the bowl and observe the temperature.
6. Place the thermometer outside in a location where you can see it each day.
7. Each day for a month, step outside and estimate the temperature. Check the accuracy of your estimates with the thermometer. Record the weather conditions as well.

▶ **Conclude and Apply**
1. Describe how well you can estimate air temperatures after estimating the temperature each day for a month. Did the cloudiness of the day affect your estimation skills?
2. Infer why understanding the Celsius scale might be helpful to you in the future.

Adult supervision required for all labs.

These labs are available at bookm.msscience.com.

---

6 Estimate Temperature

Time Required 20 minutes set up time, plus three minutes to observe and record each day for a month

Materials If students do not have dual scale thermometers at home, set one up outside school and have students check it each day.

Safety Precautions
- Caution students not to touch the glass of a broken thermometer.
- Use nonmercury thermometers.

Teaching Strategy Encourage students to estimate air temperature before they observe temperatures on display.

Conclude and Apply
1. Answers will vary.
2. Students will use the Celsius scale during future science classes, science careers, and foreign travel.

Computer Skills

People who study science rely on computers, like the one in **Figure 16,** to record and store data and to analyze results from investigations. Whether you work in a laboratory or just need to write a lab report with tables, good computer skills are a necessity.

Using the computer comes with responsibility. Issues of ownership, security, and privacy can arise. Remember, if you did not author the information you are using, you must provide a source for your information. Also, anything on a computer can be accessed by others. Do not put anything on the computer that you would not want everyone to know. To add more security to your work, use a password.

Use a Word Processing Program

A computer program that allows you to type your information, change it as many times as you need to, and then print it out is called a word processing program. Word processing programs also can be used to make tables.

Figure 16 A computer will make reports neater and more professional looking.

Learn the Skill To start your word processing program, a blank document, sometimes called "Document 1," appears on the screen. To begin, start typing. To create a new document, click the *New* button on the standard tool bar. These tips will help you format the document.

- The program will automatically move to the next line; press *Enter* if you wish to start a new paragraph.
- Symbols, called non-printing characters, can be hidden by clicking the *Show/Hide* button on your toolbar.
- To insert text, move the cursor to the point where you want the insertion to go, click on the mouse once, and type the text.
- To move several lines of text, select the text and click the *Cut* button on your toolbar. Then position your cursor in the location that you want to move the cut text and click *Paste.* If you move to the wrong place, click *Undo.*
- The spell check feature does not catch words that are misspelled to look like other words, like "cold" instead of "gold." Always reread your document to catch all spelling mistakes.
- To learn about other word processing methods, read the user's manual or click on the *Help* button.
- You can integrate databases, graphics, and spreadsheets into documents by copying from another program and pasting it into your document, or by using desktop publishing (DTP). DTP software allows you to put text and graphics together to finish your document with a professional look. This software varies in how it is used and its capabilities.

Technology Skill Handbook

Use a Database

A collection of facts stored in a computer and sorted into different fields is called a database. A database can be reorganized in any way that suits your needs.

Learn the Skill A computer program that allows you to create your own database is a database management system (DBMS). It allows you to add, delete, or change information. Take time to get to know the features of your database software.

- Determine what facts you would like to include and research to collect your information.
- Determine how you want to organize the information.
- Follow the instructions for your particular DBMS to set up fields. Then enter each item of data in the appropriate field.
- Follow the instructions to sort the information in order of importance.
- Evaluate the information in your database, and add, delete, or change as necessary.

Use the Internet

The Internet is a global network of computers where information is stored and shared. To use the Internet, like the students in **Figure 17,** you need a modem to connect your computer to a phone line and an Internet Service Provider account.

Learn the Skill To access internet sites and information, use a "Web browser," which lets you view and explore pages on the World Wide Web. Each page is its own site, and each site has its own address, called a URL. Once you have found a Web browser, follow these steps for a search (this also is how you search a database).

Figure 17 The Internet allows you to search a global network for a variety of information.

- Be as specific as possible. If you know you want to research "gold," don't type in "elements." Keep narrowing your search until you find what you want.
- Web sites that end in *.com* are commercial Web sites; *.org, .edu,* and *.gov* are non-profit, educational, or government Web sites.
- Electronic encyclopedias, almanacs, indexes, and catalogs will help locate and select relevant information.
- Develop a "home page" with relative ease. When developing a Web site, NEVER post pictures or disclose personal information such as location, names, or phone numbers. Your school or community usually can host your Web site. A basic understanding of HTML (hypertext mark-up language), the language of Web sites, is necessary. Software that creates HTML code is called authoring software, and can be downloaded free from many Web sites. This software allows text and pictures to be arranged as the software is writing the HTML code.

Use a Spreadsheet

A spreadsheet, shown in **Figure 18,** can perform mathematical functions with any data arranged in columns and rows. By entering a simple equation into a cell, the program can perform operations in specific cells, rows, or columns.

Learn the Skill Each column (vertical) is assigned a letter, and each row (horizontal) is assigned a number. Each point where a row and column intersect is called a cell, and is labeled according to where it is located— Column A, Row 1 (A1).

- Decide how to organize the data, and enter it in the correct row or column.
- Spreadsheets can use standard formulas or formulas can be customized to calculate cells.
- To make a change, click on a cell to make it activate, and enter the edited data or formula.
- Spreadsheets also can display your results in graphs. Choose the style of graph that best represents the data.

Figure 18 A spreadsheet allows you to perform mathematical operations on your data.

Use Graphics Software

Adding pictures, called graphics, to your documents is one way to make your documents more meaningful and exciting. This software adds, edits, and even constructs graphics. There is a variety of graphics software programs. The tools used for drawing can be a mouse, keyboard, or other specialized devices. Some graphics programs are simple. Others are complicated, called computer-aided design (CAD) software.

Learn the Skill It is important to have an understanding of the graphics software being used before starting. The better the software is understood, the better the results. The graphics can be placed in word-processing document.

- Clip art can be found on a variety of internet sites, and on CDs. These images can be copied and pasted into your document.
- When beginning, try editing existing drawings, then work up to creating drawings.
- The images are made of tiny rectangles of color called pixels. Each pixel can be altered.
- Digital photography is another way to add images. The photographs in the memory of a digital camera can be downloaded into a computer, then edited and added to the document.
- Graphics software also can allow animation. The software allows drawings to have the appearance of movement by connecting basic drawings automatically. This is called in-betweening, or tweening.
- Remember to save often.

Presentation Skills

Develop Multimedia Presentations

Most presentations are more dynamic if they include diagrams, photographs, videos, or sound recordings, like the one shown in **Figure 19.** A multimedia presentation involves using stereos, overhead projectors, televisions, computers, and more.

Learn the Skill Decide the main points of your presentation, and what types of media would best illustrate those points.

- Make sure you know how to use the equipment you are working with.
- Practice the presentation using the equipment several times.
- Enlist the help of a classmate to push play or turn lights out for you. Be sure to practice your presentation with him or her.
- If possible, set up all of the equipment ahead of time, and make sure everything is working properly.

Figure 19 These students are engaging the audience using a variety of tools.

Computer Presentations

There are many different interactive computer programs that you can use to enhance your presentation. Most computers have a compact disc (CD) drive that can play both CDs and digital video discs (DVDs). Also, there is hardware to connect a regular CD, DVD, or VCR. These tools will enhance your presentation.

Another method of using the computer to aid in your presentation is to develop a slide show using a computer program. This can allow movement of visuals at the presenter's pace, and can allow for visuals to build on one another.

Learn the Skill In order to create multimedia presentations on a computer, you need to have certain tools. These may include traditional graphic tools and drawing programs, animation programs, and authoring systems that tie everything together. Your computer will tell you which tools it supports. The most important step is to learn about the tools that you will be using.

- Often, color and strong images will convey a point better than words alone. Use the best methods available to convey your point.
- As with other presentations, practice many times.
- Practice your presentation with the tools you and any assistants will be using.
- Maintain eye contact with the audience. The purpose of using the computer is not to prompt the presenter, but to help the audience understand the points of the presentation.

Math Review

Use Fractions

A fraction compares a part to a whole. In the fraction $\frac{2}{3}$, the 2 represents the part and is the numerator. The 3 represents the whole and is the denominator.

Reduce Fractions To reduce a fraction, you must find the largest factor that is common to both the numerator and the denominator, the greatest common factor (GCF). Divide both numbers by the GCF. The fraction has then been reduced, or it is in its simplest form.

Example Twelve of the 20 chemicals in the science lab are in powder form. What fraction of the chemicals used in the lab are in powder form?

Step 1 Write the fraction.

$$\frac{part}{whole} = \frac{12}{20}$$

Step 2 To find the GCF of the numerator and denominator, list all of the factors of each number.

Factors of 12: 1, 2, 3, 4, 6, 12 (the numbers that divide evenly into 12)

Factors of 20: 1, 2, 4, 5, 10, 20 (the numbers that divide evenly into 20)

Step 3 List the common factors.

1, 2, 4.

Step 4 Choose the greatest factor in the list.

The GCF of 12 and 20 is 4.

Step 5 Divide the numerator and denominator by the GCF.

$$\frac{12 \div 4}{20 \div 4} = \frac{3}{5}$$

In the lab, $\frac{3}{5}$ of the chemicals are in powder form.

Practice Problem At an amusement park, 66 of 90 rides have a height restriction. What fraction of the rides, in its simplest form, has a height restriction?

Add and Subtract Fractions To add or subtract fractions with the same denominator, add or subtract the numerators and write the sum or difference over the denominator. After finding the sum or difference, find the simplest form for your fraction.

Example 1 In the forest outside your house, $\frac{1}{8}$ of the animals are rabbits, $\frac{3}{8}$ are squirrels, and the remainder are birds and insects. How many are mammals?

Step 1 Add the numerators.

$$\frac{1}{8} + \frac{3}{8} = \frac{(1 + 3)}{8} = \frac{4}{8}$$

Step 2 Find the GCF.

$$\frac{4}{8} \quad (\text{GCF, 4})$$

Step 3 Divide the numerator and denominator by the GCF.

$$\frac{4}{4} = 1, \ \frac{8}{4} = 2$$

$\frac{1}{2}$ of the animals are mammals.

Example 2 If $\frac{7}{16}$ of the Earth is covered by freshwater, and $\frac{1}{16}$ of that is in glaciers, how much freshwater is not frozen?

Step 1 Subtract the numerators.

$$\frac{7}{16} - \frac{1}{16} = \frac{(7 - 1)}{16} = \frac{6}{16}$$

Step 2 Find the GCF.

$$\frac{6}{16} \quad (\text{GCF, 2})$$

Step 3 Divide the numerator and denominator by the GCF.

$$\frac{6}{2} = 3, \ \frac{16}{2} = 8$$

$\frac{3}{8}$ of the freshwater is not frozen.

Practice Problem A bicycle rider is going 15 km/h for $\frac{4}{9}$ of his ride, 10 km/h for $\frac{2}{9}$ of his ride, and 8 km/h for the remainder of the ride. How much of his ride is he going over 8 km/h?

Reduce Fractions

$$\frac{66 \div 6}{90 \div 6} = \frac{11}{15}$$

Add and Subtract Fractions

$$\frac{4}{9} + \frac{2}{9} = \frac{6}{9}$$

$$\frac{6 \div 3}{9 \div 3} = \frac{2}{3}$$

Unlike Denominators

Problem 1

$1 \times 5 = 5, 8 \times 5 = 40$

$1 \times 4 = 4, 10 \times 4 = 40$

$\frac{5}{40} + \frac{4}{40} = \frac{9}{40}$

Problem 2

If $\frac{7}{10}$ are involuntary, the remainder are voluntary.

$\frac{10}{10} - \frac{7}{10} = \frac{3}{10}$

Math Skill Handbook

Unlike Denominators To add or subtract fractions with unlike denominators, first find the least common denominator (LCD). This is the smallest number that is a common multiple of both denominators. Rename each fraction with the LCD, and then add or subtract. Find the simplest form if necessary.

Example 1 A chemist makes a paste that is $\frac{1}{2}$ table salt (NaCl), $\frac{1}{3}$ sugar ($C_6H_{12}O_6$), and the rest water (H_2O). How much of the paste is a solid?

Step 1 Find the LCD of the fractions.

$\frac{1}{2} + \frac{1}{3}$ (LCD, 6)

Step 2 Rename each numerator and each denominator with the LCD.

$1 \times 3 = 3, \quad 2 \times 3 = 6$

$1 \times 2 = 2, \quad 3 \times 2 = 6$

Step 3 Add the numerators.

$\frac{3}{6} + \frac{2}{6} = \frac{(3 + 2)}{6} = \frac{5}{6}$

$\frac{5}{6}$ of the paste is a solid.

Example 2 The average precipitation in Grand Junction, CO, is $\frac{7}{10}$ inch in November, and $\frac{3}{5}$ inch in December. What is the total average precipitation?

Step 1 Find the LCD of the fractions.

$\frac{7}{10} + \frac{3}{5}$ (LCD, 10)

Step 2 Rename each numerator and each denominator with the LCD.

$7 \times 1 = 7, \quad 10 \times 1 = 10$

$3 \times 2 = 6, \quad 5 \times 2 = 10$

Step 3 Add the numerators.

$\frac{7}{10} + \frac{6}{10} = \frac{(7 + 6)}{10} = \frac{13}{10}$

$\frac{13}{10}$ inches total precipitation, or $1\frac{3}{10}$ inches.

Practice Problem On an electric bill, about $\frac{1}{8}$ of the energy is from solar energy and about $\frac{1}{10}$ is from wind power. How much of the total bill is from solar energy and wind power combined?

Example 3 In your body, $\frac{7}{10}$ of your muscle contractions are involuntary (cardiac and smooth muscle tissue). Smooth muscle makes $\frac{3}{15}$ of your muscle contractions. How many of your muscle contractions are made by cardiac muscle?

Step 1 Find the LCD of the fractions.

$\frac{7}{10} - \frac{3}{15}$ (LCD, 30)

Step 2 Rename each numerator and each denominator with the LCD.

$7 \times 3 = 21, \quad 10 \times 3 = 30$

$3 \times 2 = 6, \quad 15 \times 2 = 30$

Step 3 Subtract the numerators.

$\frac{21}{30} - \frac{6}{30} = \frac{(21 - 6)}{30} = \frac{15}{30}$

Step 4 Find the GCF.

$\frac{15}{30}$ (GCF, 15)

$\frac{1}{2}$

$\frac{1}{2}$ of all muscle contractions are cardiac muscle.

Example 4 Tony wants to make cookies that call for $\frac{3}{4}$ of a cup of flour, but he only has $\frac{1}{3}$ of a cup. How much more flour does he need?

Step 1 Find the LCD of the fractions.

$\frac{3}{4} - \frac{1}{3}$ (LCD, 12)

Step 2 Rename each numerator and each denominator with the LCD.

$3 \times 3 = 9, \quad 4 \times 3 = 12$

$1 \times 4 = 4, \quad 3 \times 4 = 12$

Step 3 Subtract the numerators.

$\frac{9}{12} - \frac{4}{12} = \frac{(9 - 4)}{12} = \frac{5}{12}$

$\frac{5}{12}$ of a cup of flour.

Practice Problem Using the information provided to you in Example 3 above, determine how many muscle contractions are voluntary (skeletal muscle).

Math Skill Handbook

Math Skill Handbook

Multiply Fractions To multiply with fractions, multiply the numerators and multiply the denominators. Find the simplest form if necessary.

Example Multiply $\frac{3}{5}$ by $\frac{1}{3}$.

Step 1 Multiply the numerators and denominators.

$$\frac{3}{5} \times \frac{1}{3} = \frac{(3 \times 1)}{(5 \times 3)} = \frac{3}{15}$$

Step 2 Find the GCF.

$$\frac{3}{15} \ \ (\text{GCF}, 3)$$

Step 3 Divide the numerator and denominator by the GCF.

$$\frac{3}{3} = 1, \ \ \frac{15}{3} = 5$$

$$\frac{1}{5}$$

$\frac{3}{5}$ multiplied by $\frac{1}{3}$ is $\frac{1}{5}$.

Practice Problem Multiply $\frac{3}{14}$ by $\frac{5}{16}$.

Find a Reciprocal Two numbers whose product is 1 are called multiplicative inverses, or reciprocals.

Example Find the reciprocal of $\frac{3}{8}$.

Step 1 Inverse the fraction by putting the denominator on top and the numerator on the bottom.

$$\frac{8}{3}$$

The reciprocal of $\frac{3}{8}$ is $\frac{8}{3}$.

Practice Problem Find the reciprocal of $\frac{4}{9}$.

Divide Fractions To divide one fraction by another fraction, multiply the dividend by the reciprocal of the divisor. Find the simplest form if necessary.

Example 1 Divide $\frac{1}{9}$ by $\frac{1}{3}$.

Step 1 Find the reciprocal of the divisor.

The reciprocal of $\frac{1}{3}$ is $\frac{3}{1}$.

Step 2 Multiply the dividend by the reciprocal of the divisor.

$$\frac{\frac{1}{9}}{\frac{1}{3}} = \frac{1}{9} \times \frac{3}{1} = \frac{(1 \times 3)}{(9 \times 1)} = \frac{3}{9}$$

Step 3 Find the GCF.

$$\frac{3}{9} \ \ (\text{GCF}, 3)$$

Step 4 Divide the numerator and denominator by the GCF.

$$\frac{3}{3} = 1, \ \ \frac{9}{3} = 3$$

$$\frac{1}{3}$$

$\frac{1}{9}$ divided by $\frac{1}{3}$ is $\frac{1}{3}$.

Example 2 Divide $\frac{3}{5}$ by $\frac{1}{4}$.

Step 1 Find the reciprocal of the divisor.

The reciprocal of $\frac{1}{4}$ is $\frac{4}{1}$.

Step 2 Multiply the dividend by the reciprocal of the divisor.

$$\frac{\frac{3}{5}}{\frac{1}{4}} = \frac{3}{5} \times \frac{4}{1} = \frac{(3 \times 4)}{(5 \times 1)} = \frac{12}{5}$$

$\frac{3}{5}$ divided by $\frac{1}{4}$ is $\frac{12}{5}$ or $2\frac{2}{5}$.

Practice Problem Divide $\frac{3}{11}$ by $\frac{7}{10}$.

Multiply Fractions

$$\frac{3}{14} \times \frac{5}{16} = \frac{(3 \times 5)}{(14 \times 16)} = \frac{15}{224}$$

Find a Reciprocal

$$\frac{9}{4}$$

Divide Fractions

The reciprocal of $\frac{7}{10}$ is $\frac{10}{7}$.

$$\frac{3}{11} \times \frac{10}{7} = \frac{(3 \times 10)}{(11 \times 7)} = \frac{30}{77}$$

Math Skill Handbook

Math Skill Handbook

Use Ratios

$$\frac{100 \text{ cm}}{144 \text{ cm}} = \frac{100 \div 4}{144 \div 4} = \frac{25}{36}$$

25:36

Add or Subtract Decimals

$$\begin{array}{r} {}^{1} \\ 1.245 \\ + 3.842 \\ \hline 5.087 \end{array}$$

Use Ratios

When you compare two numbers by division, you are using a ratio. Ratios can be written 3 to 5, 3:5, or $\frac{3}{5}$. Ratios, like fractions, also can be written in simplest form.

Ratios can represent probabilities, also called odds. This is a ratio that compares the number of ways a certain outcome occurs to the number of outcomes. For example, if you flip a coin 100 times, what are the odds that it will come up heads? There are two possible outcomes, heads or tails, so the odds of coming up heads are 50:100. Another way to say this is that 50 out of 100 times the coin will come up heads. In its simplest form, the ratio is 1:2.

Example 1 A chemical solution contains 40 g of salt and 64 g of baking soda. What is the ratio of salt to baking soda as a fraction in simplest form?

Step 1 Write the ratio as a fraction.

$$\frac{\text{salt}}{\text{baking soda}} = \frac{40}{64}$$

Step 2 Express the fraction in simplest form.
The GCF of 40 and 64 is 8.

$$\frac{40}{64} = \frac{40 \div 8}{64 \div 8} = \frac{5}{8}$$

The ratio of salt to baking soda in the sample is 5:8.

Example 2 Sean rolls a 6-sided die 6 times. What are the odds that the side with a 3 will show?

Step 1 Write the ratio as a fraction.

$$\frac{\text{number of sides with a 3}}{\text{number of sides}} = \frac{1}{6}$$

Step 2 Multiply by the number of attempts.

$$\frac{1}{6} \times 6 \text{ attempts} = \frac{6}{6} \text{ attempts} = 1 \text{ attempt}$$

1 attempt out of 6 will show a 3.

Practice Problem Two metal rods measure 100 cm and 144 cm in length. What is the ratio of their lengths in simplest form?

Use Decimals

A fraction with a denominator that is a power of ten can be written as a decimal. For example, 0.27 means $\frac{27}{100}$. The decimal point separates the ones place from the tenths place.

Any fraction can be written as a decimal using division. For example, the fraction $\frac{5}{8}$ can be written as a decimal by dividing 5 by 8. Written as a decimal, it is 0.625.

Add or Subtract Decimals When adding and subtracting decimals, line up the decimal points before carrying out the operation.

Example 1 Find the sum of 47.68 and 7.80.

Step 1 Line up the decimal places when you write the numbers.

$$\begin{array}{r} 47.68 \\ + \ 7.80 \\ \hline \end{array}$$

Step 2 Add the decimals.

$$\begin{array}{r} 47.68 \\ + \ 7.80 \\ \hline 55.48 \end{array}$$

The sum of 47.68 and 7.80 is 55.48.

Example 2 Find the difference of 42.17 and 15.85.

Step 1 Line up the decimal places when you write the number.

$$\begin{array}{r} 42.17 \\ - 15.85 \\ \hline \end{array}$$

Step 2 Subtract the decimals.

$$\begin{array}{r} 42.17 \\ - 15.85 \\ \hline 26.32 \end{array}$$

The difference of 42.17 and 15.85 is 26.32.

Practice Problem Find the sum of 1.245 and 3.842.

Math Skill Handbook

Math Skill Handbook

Multiply Decimals To multiply decimals, multiply the numbers like any other number, ignoring the decimal point. Count the decimal places in each factor. The product will have the same number of decimal places as the sum of the decimal places in the factors.

Example Multiply 2.4 by 5.9.

Step 1 Multiply the factors like two whole numbers.
$24 \times 59 = 1416$

Step 2 Find the sum of the number of decimal places in the factors. Each factor has one decimal place, for a sum of two decimal places.

Step 3 The product will have two decimal places.
14.16

The product of 2.4 and 5.9 is 14.16.

Practice Problem Multiply 4.6 by 2.2.

Divide Decimals When dividing decimals, change the divisor to a whole number. To do this, multiply both the divisor and the dividend by the same power of ten. Then place the decimal point in the quotient directly above the decimal point in the dividend. Then divide as you do with whole numbers.

Example Divide 8.84 by 3.4.

Step 1 Multiply both factors by 10.
$3.4 \times 10 = 34$, $8.84 \times 10 = 88.4$

Step 2 Divide 88.4 by 34.

$$
\begin{array}{r}
2.6 \\
34\overline{)88.4} \\
-68 \\
\hline
204 \\
-204 \\
\hline
0
\end{array}
$$

8.84 divided by 3.4 is 2.6.

Practice Problem Divide 75.6 by 3.6.

Use Proportions

An equation that shows that two ratios are equivalent is a proportion. The ratios $\frac{2}{4}$ and $\frac{5}{10}$ are equivalent, so they can be written as $\frac{2}{4} = \frac{5}{10}$. This equation is a proportion.

When two ratios form a proportion, the cross products are equal. To find the cross products in the proportion $\frac{2}{4} = \frac{5}{10}$, multiply the 2 and the 10, and the 4 and the 5. Therefore $2 \times 10 = 4 \times 5$, or $20 = 20$.

Because you know that both proportions are equal, you can use cross products to find a missing term in a proportion. This is known as solving the proportion.

Example The heights of a tree and a pole are proportional to the lengths of their shadows. The tree casts a shadow of 24 m when a 6-m pole casts a shadow of 4 m. What is the height of the tree?

Step 1 Write a proportion.
$$\frac{\text{height of tree}}{\text{height of pole}} = \frac{\text{length of tree's shadow}}{\text{length of pole's shadow}}$$

Step 2 Substitute the known values into the proportion. Let h represent the unknown value, the height of the tree.
$$\frac{h}{6} = \frac{24}{4}$$

Step 3 Find the cross products.
$$h \times 4 = 6 \times 24$$

Step 4 Simplify the equation.
$$4h = 144$$

Step 5 Divide each side by 4.
$$\frac{4h}{4} = \frac{144}{4}$$
$$h = 36$$

The height of the tree is 36 m.

Practice Problem The ratios of the weights of two objects on the Moon and on Earth are in proportion. A rock weighing 3 N on the Moon weighs 18 N on Earth. How much would a rock that weighs 5 N on the Moon weigh on Earth?

Multiply Decimals

Multiply 4.6 and 2.2 by 10.
$46 \times 22 = 1012$
Each factor had one decimal place.
10.12

Divide Decimals

Multiply both factors by 10.
Divide 756 by 36.

$$
\begin{array}{r}
21 \\
36\overline{)756} \\
72 \\
\hline
36 \\
36 \\
\hline
0
\end{array}
$$

Use Proportions

$$\frac{3}{18} = \frac{5}{w}$$
$$w \times 3 = 5 \times 18$$
$$\frac{3w}{3} = \frac{90}{3}$$
$$w = 30$$

Math Skill Handbook

Math Skill Handbook

Use Percentages

$$\frac{73}{365} = \frac{x}{100}$$

$$\frac{7300}{365} = \frac{365x}{365}$$

$$20\% = x$$

Solve One-Step Equations

$$h = gd$$

$$\frac{17.4}{12.3} = \frac{12.3d}{12.3}$$

$$1.41 = d$$

Use Percentages

The word *percent* means "out of one hundred." It is a ratio that compares a number to 100. Suppose you read that 77 percent of the Earth's surface is covered by water. That is the same as reading that the fraction of the Earth's surface covered by water is $\frac{77}{100}$. To express a fraction as a percent, first find the equivalent decimal for the fraction. Then, multiply the decimal by 100 and add the percent symbol.

Example Express $\frac{13}{20}$ as a percent.

Step 1 Find the equivalent decimal for the fraction.

$$
\begin{array}{r}
0.65 \\
20\overline{)13.00} \\
\underline{12\,0} \\
1\,00 \\
\underline{1\,00} \\
0
\end{array}
$$

Step 2 Rewrite the fraction $\frac{13}{20}$ as 0.65.

Step 3 Multiply 0.65 by 100 and add the % sign.
$$0.65 \times 100 = 65 = 65\%$$

So, $\frac{13}{20} = 65\%$.

This also can be solved as a proportion.

Example Express $\frac{13}{20}$ as a percent.

Step 1 Write a proportion.
$$\frac{13}{20} = \frac{x}{100}$$

Step 2 Find the cross products.
$$1300 = 20x$$

Step 3 Divide each side by 20.
$$\frac{1300}{20} = \frac{20x}{20}$$
$$65\% = x$$

Practice Problem In one year, 73 of 365 days were rainy in one city. What percent of the days in that city were rainy?

Solve One-Step Equations

A statement that two things are equal is an equation. For example, $A = B$ is an equation that states that A is equal to B.

An equation is solved when a variable is replaced with a value that makes both sides of the equation equal. To make both sides equal the inverse operation is used. Addition and subtraction are inverses, and multiplication and division are inverses.

Example 1 Solve the equation $x - 10 = 35$.

Step 1 Find the solution by adding 10 to each side of the equation.
$$x - 10 = 35$$
$$x - 10 + 10 = 35 + 10$$
$$x = 45$$

Step 2 Check the solution.
$$x - 10 = 35$$
$$45 - 10 = 35$$
$$35 = 35$$

Both sides of the equation are equal, so $x = 45$.

Example 2 In the formula $a = bc$, find the value of c if $a = 20$ and $b = 2$.

Step 1 Rearrange the formula so the unknown value is by itself on one side of the equation by dividing both sides by b.
$$a = bc$$
$$\frac{a}{b} = \frac{bc}{b}$$
$$\frac{a}{b} = c$$

Step 2 Replace the variables a and b with the values that are given.
$$\frac{a}{b} = c$$
$$\frac{20}{2} = c$$
$$10 = c$$

Step 3 Check the solution.
$$a = bc$$
$$20 = 2 \times 10$$
$$20 = 20$$

Both sides of the equation are equal, so $c = 10$ is the solution when $a = 20$ and $b = 2$.

Practice Problem In the formula $h = gd$, find the value of d if $g = 12.3$ and $h = 17.4$.

Math Skill Handbook

Math Skill Handbook

Use Statistics

The branch of mathematics that deals with collecting, analyzing, and presenting data is statistics. In statistics, there are three common ways to summarize data with a single number—the mean, the median, and the mode.

The **mean** of a set of data is the arithmetic average. It is found by adding the numbers in the data set and dividing by the number of items in the set.

The **median** is the middle number in a set of data when the data are arranged in numerical order. If there were an even number of data points, the median would be the mean of the two middle numbers.

The **mode** of a set of data is the number or item that appears most often.

Another number that often is used to describe a set of data is the range. The **range** is the difference between the largest number and the smallest number in a set of data.

A **frequency table** shows how many times each piece of data occurs, usually in a survey. **Table 2** below shows the results of a student survey on favorite color.

Table 2 Student Color Choice		
Color	Tally	Frequency
red	||||	4
blue	++++	5
black	||	2
green	|||	3
purple	++++ ||	7
yellow	++++		6

Based on the frequency table data, which color is the favorite?

Example The speeds (in m/s) for a race car during five different time trials are 39, 37, 44, 36, and 44.

To find the mean:

Step 1 Find the sum of the numbers.

$$39 + 37 + 44 + 36 + 44 = 200$$

Step 2 Divide the sum by the number of items, which is 5.

$$200 \div 5 = 40$$

The mean is 40 m/s.

To find the median:

Step 1 Arrange the measures from least to greatest.

36, 37, 39, 44, 44

Step 2 Determine the middle measure.

36, 37, 39, 44, 44

The median is 39 m/s.

To find the mode:

Step 1 Group the numbers that are the same together.

44, 44, 36, 37, 39

Step 2 Determine the number that occurs most in the set.

44, 44, 36, 37, 39

The mode is 44 m/s.

To find the range:

Step 1 Arrange the measures from largest to smallest.

44, 44, 39, 37, 36

Step 2 Determine the largest and smallest measures in the set.

44, 44, 39, 37, 36

Step 3 Find the difference between the largest and smallest measures.

$$44 - 36 = 8$$

The range is 8 m/s.

Practice Problem Find the mean, median, mode, and range for the data set 8, 4, 12, 8, 11, 14, 16.

Use Statistics

mean

$$8 + 4 + 12 + 8 + 11 + 14 + 16 = 73$$
$$73 \div 7 = 10.4$$

median

4, 8, 8, 11, 12, 14, 16

mode

4, 8, 8, 11, 12, 14, 16

range

4, 8, 8, 11, 12, 14, 16

$$16 - 4 = 12$$

Perimeter

Problem 1

$P = 2(18\,m + 7\,m)$

$P = 2(25\,m)$

$P = 50\,m$

Problem 2

$P = 1.6\,cm + 2.4\,cm + 2.4\,cm$

$P = 6.4\,cm$

Area of a Rectangle

$A = (4\,m \times 4\,m)$

$A = 16\,m^2$

Area of a Triangle

$A = \frac{1}{2}(27\,cm \times 17\,cm)$

$A = \frac{1}{2}(459\,cm^2)$

$A = 229.5\,cm^2$

Use Geometry

The branch of mathematics that deals with the measurement, properties, and relationships of points, lines, angles, surfaces, and solids is called geometry.

Perimeter The **perimeter** (P) is the distance around a geometric figure. To find the perimeter of a rectangle, add the length and width and multiply that sum by two, or $2(l + w)$. To find perimeters of irregular figures, add the length of the sides.

Example 1 Find the perimeter of a rectangle that is 3 m long and 5 m wide.

Step 1 You know that the perimeter is 2 times the sum of the width and length.

$P = 2(3\,m + 5\,m)$

Step 2 Find the sum of the width and length.

$P = 2(8\,m)$

Step 3 Multiply by 2.

$P = 16\,m$

The perimeter is 16 m.

Example 2 Find the perimeter of a shape with sides measuring 2 cm, 5 cm, 6 cm, 3 cm.

Step 1 You know that the perimeter is the sum of all the sides.

$P = 2 + 5 + 6 + 3$

Step 2 Find the sum of the sides.

$P = 2 + 5 + 6 + 3$

$P = 16$

The perimeter is 16 cm.

Practice Problem Find the perimeter of a rectangle with a length of 18 m and a width of 7 m.

Practice Problem Find the perimeter of a triangle measuring 1.6 cm by 2.4 cm by 2.4 cm.

Area of a Rectangle The **area** (A) is the number of square units needed to cover a surface. To find the area of a rectangle, multiply the length times the width, or $l \times w$. When finding area, the units also are multiplied. Area is given in square units.

Example Find the area of a rectangle with a length of 1 cm and a width of 10 cm.

Step 1 You know that the area is the length multiplied by the width.

$A = (1\,cm \times 10\,cm)$

Step 2 Multiply the length by the width. Also multiply the units.

$A = 10\,cm^2$

The area is 10 cm².

Practice Problem Find the area of a square whose sides measure 4 m.

Area of a Triangle To find the area of a triangle, use the formula:

$$A = \frac{1}{2}(\text{base} \times \text{height})$$

The base of a triangle can be any of its sides. The height is the perpendicular distance from a base to the opposite endpoint, or vertex.

Example Find the area of a triangle with a base of 18 m and a height of 7 m.

Step 1 You know that the area is $\frac{1}{2}$ the base times the height.

$A = \frac{1}{2}(18\,m \times 7\,m)$

Step 2 Multiply $\frac{1}{2}$ by the product of 18×7. Multiply the units.

$A = \frac{1}{2}(126\,m^2)$

$A = 63\,m^2$

The area is 63 m².

Practice Problem Find the area of a triangle with a base of 27 cm and a height of 17 cm.

Math Skill Handbook

Circumference of a Circle The **diameter** (*d*) of a circle is the distance across the circle through its center, and the **radius** (*r*) is the distance from the center to any point on the circle. The radius is half of the diameter. The distance around the circle is called the **circumference** (C). The formula for finding the circumference is:

$$C = 2\pi r \ or \ C = \pi d$$

The circumference divided by the diameter is always equal to 3.1415926... This nonterminating and nonrepeating number is represented by the Greek letter π (pi). An approximation often used for π is 3.14.

Example 1 Find the circumference of a circle with a radius of 3 m.

Step 1 You know the formula for the circumference is 2 times the radius times π.
$C = 2\pi(3)$

Step 2 Multiply 2 times the radius.
$C = 6\pi$

Step 3 Multiply by π.
$C = 19$ m

The circumference is 19 m.

Example 2 Find the circumference of a circle with a diameter of 24.0 cm.

Step 1 You know the formula for the circumference is the diameter times π.
$C = \pi(24.0)$

Step 2 Multiply the diameter by π.
$C = 75.4$ cm

The circumference is 75.4 cm.

Practice Problem Find the circumference of a circle with a radius of 19 cm.

Area of a Circle The formula for the area of a circle is:
$A = \pi r^2$

Example 1 Find the area of a circle with a radius of 4.0 cm.

Step 1 $A = \pi(4.0)^2$

Step 2 Find the square of the radius.
$A = 16\pi$

Step 3 Multiply the square of the radius by π.
$A = 50$ cm^2

The area of the circle is 50 cm^2.

Example 2 Find the area of a circle with a radius of 225 m.

Step 1 $A = \pi(225)^2$

Step 2 Find the square of the radius.
$A = 50625\pi$

Step 3 Multiply the square of the radius by π.
$A = 158962.5$

The area of the circle is 158,962 m^2.

Example 3 Find the area of a circle whose diameter is 20.0 mm.

Step 1 You know the formula for the area of a circle is the square of the radius times π, and that the radius is half of the diameter.
$A = \pi\left(\dfrac{20.0}{2}\right)^2$

Step 2 Find the radius.
$A = \pi(10.0)^2$

Step 3 Find the square of the radius.
$A = 100\pi$

Step 4 Multiply the square of the radius by π.
$A = 314$ mm^2

The area is 314 mm^2.

Practice Problem Find the area of a circle with a radius of 16 m.

Circumference of a Circle

$C = 2\pi r$
$C = 2\pi(19)$
$C = 38\pi$
$C = 119.3$

Area of a Circle

$A = \pi r^2$
$A = \pi(16\text{ m})^2$
$A = \pi\ 256\text{ m}^2$
$A = 803.8\text{ m}^2$

Volume

Problem 1

$V = 8\,m \times 4\,m \times 4\,m$

$V = 128\,m^3$

Problem 2

$V = \pi r^2 \times \text{height}$

$V = \left[\pi\left(\frac{1}{2} \times 7\right)^2\right] \times 16$

$V = [\pi(3.5)^2] \times 16$

$V = [\pi(12.25)] \times 16$

$V = 38.46 \times 16$

$V = 615.36$

Volume The measure of space occupied by a solid is the **volume** (V). To find the volume of a rectangular solid multiply the length times width times height, or $V = l \times w \times h$. It is measured in cubic units, such as cubic centimeters (cm^3).

Example Find the volume of a rectangular solid with a length of 2.0 m, a width of 4.0 m, and a height of 3.0 m.

Step 1 You know the formula for volume is the length times the width times the height.

$V = 2.0\,m \times 4.0\,m \times 3.0\,m$

Step 2 Multiply the length times the width times the height.

$V = 24\,m^3$

The volume is 24 m³.

Practice Problem Find the volume of a rectangular solid that 8 m long, 4 m wide, and 4 m high.

To find the volume of other solids, multiply the area of the base times the height.

Example 1 Find the volume of a solid that has a triangular base with a length of 8.0 m and a height of 7.0 m. The height of the entire solid is 15.0 m.

Step 1 You know that the base is a triangle, and the area of a triangle is $\frac{1}{2}$ the base times the height, and the volume is the area of the base times the height.

$V = \left[\frac{1}{2}(b \times h)\right] \times 15$

Step 2 Find the area of the base.

$V = \left[\frac{1}{2}(8 \times 7)\right] \times 15$

$V = \left(\frac{1}{2} \times 56\right) \times 15$

Step 3 Multiply the area of the base by the height of the solid.

$V = 28 \times 15$

$V = 420\,m^3$

The volume is 420 m³.

Example 2 Find the volume of a cylinder that has a base with a radius of 12.0 cm, and a height of 21.0 cm.

Step 1 You know that the base is a circle, and the area of a circle is the square of the radius times π, and the volume is the area of the base times the height.

$V = (\pi r^2) \times 21$

$V = (\pi 12^2) \times 21$

Step 2 Find the area of the base.

$V = 144\pi \times 21$

$V = 452 \times 21$

Step 3 Multiply the area of the base by the height of the solid.

$V = 9490\,cm^3$

The volume is 9490 cm³.

Example 3 Find the volume of a cylinder that has a diameter of 15 mm and a height of 4.8 mm.

Step 1 You know that the base is a circle with an area equal to the square of the radius times π. The radius is one-half the diameter. The volume is the area of the base times the height.

$V = (\pi r^2) \times 4.8$

$V = \left[\pi\left(\frac{1}{2} \times 15\right)^2\right] \times 4.8$

$V = (\pi 7.5^2) \times 4.8$

Step 2 Find the area of the base.

$V = 56.25\pi \times 4.8$

$V = 176.63 \times 4.8$

Step 3 Multiply the area of the base by the height of the solid.

$V = 847.8$

The volume is 847.8 mm³.

Practice Problem Find the volume of a cylinder with a diameter of 7 cm in the base and a height of 16 cm.

Math Skill Handbook

Math Skill Handbook

Science Applications

Measure in SI

The metric system of measurement was developed in 1795. A modern form of the metric system, called the International System (SI), was adopted in 1960 and provides the standard measurements that all scientists around the world can understand.

The SI system is convenient because unit sizes vary by powers of 10. Prefixes are used to name units. Look at **Table 3** for some common SI prefixes and their meanings.

Table 3 Common SI Prefixes			
Prefix	**Symbol**	**Meaning**	
kilo-	k	1,000	thousand
hecto-	h	100	hundred
deka-	da	10	ten
deci-	d	0.1	tenth
centi-	c	0.01	hundredth
milli-	m	0.001	thousandth

Example How many grams equal one kilogram?

Step 1 Find the prefix *kilo* in **Table 3.**

Step 2 Using **Table 3,** determine the meaning of *kilo*. According to the table, it means 1,000. When the prefix *kilo* is added to a unit, it means that there are 1,000 of the units in a "*kilo*unit."

Step 3 Apply the prefix to the units in the question. The units in the question are grams. There are 1,000 grams in a kilogram.

Practice Problem Is a milligram larger or smaller than a gram? How many of the smaller units equal one larger unit? What fraction of the larger unit does one smaller unit represent?

Dimensional Analysis

Convert SI Units In science, quantities such as length, mass, and time sometimes are measured using different units. A process called dimensional analysis can be used to change one unit of measure to another. This process involves multiplying your starting quantity and units by one or more conversion factors. A conversion factor is a ratio equal to one and can be made from any two equal quantities with different units. If 1,000 mL equal 1 L then two ratios can be made.

$$\frac{1,000 \text{ mL}}{1 \text{ L}} = \frac{1 \text{ L}}{1,000 \text{ mL}} = 1$$

One can covert between units in the SI system by using the equivalents in **Table 3** to make conversion factors.

Example 1 How many cm are in 4 m?

Step 1 Write conversion factors for the units given. From **Table 3,** you know that 100 cm = 1 m. The conversion factors are

$$\frac{100 \text{ cm}}{1 \text{ m}} \quad and \quad \frac{1 \text{ m}}{100 \text{ cm}}$$

Step 2 Decide which conversion factor to use. Select the factor that has the units you are converting from (m) in the denominator and the units you are converting to (cm) in the numerator.

$$\frac{100 \text{ cm}}{1 \text{ m}}$$

Step 3 Multiply the starting quantity and units by the conversion factor. Cancel the starting units with the units in the denominator. There are 400 cm in 4 m.

$$4 \text{ m} \times \frac{100 \text{ cm}}{1 \text{ m}} = 400 \text{ cm}$$

Practice Problem How many milligrams are in one kilogram? (Hint: You will need to use two conversion factors from **Table 3.**)

Measure in SI

smaller; 1000; one thousandth

Dimensional Analysis

$$x \text{ mg} = 1 \text{ kg} \times \frac{1000 \text{ g}}{1 \text{ kg}} \times \frac{1000 \text{ mg}}{1 \text{ g}} =$$

1,000,000 mg

1,000,000 mg = 1 kg

Convert Between Unit Systems

$$\frac{(1 \text{ in})^3}{(2.54 \text{ cm})^3}$$

$$= \frac{1 \text{ in} \times 1 \text{ in} \times 1 \text{ in}}{2.54 \text{ cm} \times 2.54 \text{ cm} \times 2.54 \text{ cm}}$$

$$= \frac{1 \text{ in}^3}{16.39 \text{ cm}^3}$$

Table 4 Unit System Equivalents

Type of Measurement	Equivalent
Length	1 in = 2.54 cm
	1 yd = 0.91 m
	1 mi = 1.61 km
Mass and Weight*	1 oz = 28.35 g
	1 lb = 0.45 kg
	1 ton (short) = 0.91 tonnes (metric tons)
	1 lb = 4.45 N
Volume	1 in^3 = 16.39 cm^3
	1 qt = 0.95 L
	1 gal = 3.78 L
Area	1 in^2 = 6.45 cm^2
	1 yd^2 = 0.83 m^2
	1 mi^2 = 2.59 km^2
	1 acre = 0.40 hectares
Temperature	$°C = \dfrac{(°F - 32)}{1.8}$
	K = °C + 273

*Weight is measured in standard Earth gravity.

Convert Between Unit Systems Table 4 gives a list of equivalents that can be used to convert between English and SI units.

Example If a meterstick has a length of 100 cm, how long is the meterstick in inches?

Step 1 Write the conversion factors for the units given. From **Table 4,** 1 in = 2.54 cm.

$$\frac{1 \text{ in}}{2.54 \text{ cm}} \quad and \quad \frac{2.54 \text{ cm}}{1 \text{ in}}$$

Step 2 Determine which conversion factor to use. You are converting from cm to in. Use the conversion factor with cm on the bottom.

$$\frac{1 \text{ in}}{2.54 \text{ cm}}$$

Step 3 Multiply the starting quantity and units by the conversion factor. Cancel the starting units with the units in the denominator. Round your answer based on the number of significant figures in the conversion factor.

$$100 \text{ cm} \times \frac{1 \text{ in}}{2.54 \text{ cm}} = 39.37 \text{ in}$$

The meterstick is 39.4 in long.

Practice Problem A book has a mass of 5 lbs. What is the mass of the book in kg?

Practice Problem Use the equivalent for in and cm (1 in = 2.54 cm) to show how 1 in^3 = 16.39 cm^3.

Precision and Significant Digits

When you make a measurement, the value you record depends on the precision of the measuring instrument. This precision is represented by the number of significant digits recorded in the measurement. When counting the number of significant digits, all digits are counted except zeros at the end of a number with no decimal point such as 2,050, and zeros at the beginning of a decimal such as 0.03020. When adding or subtracting numbers with different precision, round the answer to the smallest number of decimal places of any number in the sum or difference. When multiplying or dividing, the answer is rounded to the smallest number of significant digits of any number being multiplied or divided.

Example The lengths 5.28 and 5.2 are measured in meters. Find the sum of these lengths and record your answer using the correct number of significant digits.

Step 1 Find the sum.

5.28 m	2 digits after the decimal
+ 5.2 m	1 digit after the decimal
10.48 m	

Step 2 Round to one digit after the decimal because the least number of digits after the decimal of the numbers being added is 1.

The sum is 10.5 m.

Practice Problem How many significant digits are in the measurement 7,071,301 m? How many significant digits are in the measurement 0.003010 g?

Practice Problem Multiply 5.28 and 5.2 using the rule for multiplying and dividing. Record the answer using the correct number of significant digits.

Scientific Notation

Many times numbers used in science are very small or very large. Because these numbers are difficult to work with scientists use scientific notation. To write numbers in scientific notation, move the decimal point until only one non-zero digit remains on the left. Then count the number of places you moved the decimal point and use that number as a power of ten. For example, the average distance from the Sun to Mars is 227,800,000,000 m. In scientific notation, this distance is 2.278×10^{11} m. Because you moved the decimal point to the left, the number is a positive power of ten.

The mass of an electron is about 0.000 000 000 000 000 000 000 000 000 000 911 kg. Expressed in scientific notation, this mass is 9.11×10^{-31} kg. Because the decimal point was moved to the right, the number is a negative power of ten.

Example Earth is 149,600,000 km from the Sun. Express this in scientific notation.

Step 1 Move the decimal point until one non-zero digit remains on the left.
1.496 000 00

Step 2 Count the number of decimal places you have moved. In this case, eight.

Step 3 Show that number as a power of ten, 10^8.

The Earth is 1.496×10^8 km from the Sun.

Practice Problem How many significant digits are in 149,600,000 km? How many significant digits are in 1.496×10^8 km?

Practice Problem Parts used in a high performance car must be measured to 7×10^{-6} m. Express this number as a decimal.

Practice Problem A CD is spinning at 539 revolutions per minute. Express this number in scientific notation.

Precision and Significant Digits

Problem 1
7; 4

Problem 2
$5.28 \times 5.2 = 27.456$

5.28 has 3 significant digits.

5.2 has 2 significant digits.

When multiplying and dividing, the answer is rounded to the smallest number of significant digits of the numbers being multiplied or divided—in this case, 2.

27.456 is rounded to 27.

Scientific Notation

Problem 1
4; 4

Problem 2
0.000007

Problem 3
5.39×10^2

Line Graph

x	y
3	52
6	72
9	83
12	86

Puppy Growth

Make and Use Graphs

Data in tables can be displayed in a graph—a visual representation of data. Common graph types include line graphs, bar graphs, and circle graphs.

Line Graph A line graph shows a relationship between two variables that change continuously. The independent variable is changed and is plotted on the *x*-axis. The dependent variable is observed, and is plotted on the *y*-axis.

Example Draw a line graph of the data below from a cyclist in a long-distance race.

Table 5 Bicycle Race Data	
Time (h)	**Distance (km)**
0	0
1	8
2	16
3	24
4	32
5	40

Step 1 Determine the *x*-axis and *y*-axis variables. Time varies independently of distance and is plotted on the *x*-axis. Distance is dependent on time and is plotted on the *y*-axis.

Step 2 Determine the scale of each axis. The *x*-axis data ranges from 0 to 5. The *y*-axis data ranges from 0 to 40.

Step 3 Using graph paper, draw and label the axes. Include units in the labels.

Step 4 Draw a point at the intersection of the time value on the *x*-axis and corresponding distance value on the *y*-axis. Connect the points and label the graph with a title, as shown in **Figure 20.**

Distance v. Time

Figure 20 This line graph shows the relationship between distance and time during a bicycle ride.

Practice Problem A puppy's shoulder height is measured during the first year of her life. The following measurements were collected: (3 mo, 52 cm), (6 mo, 72 cm), (9 mo, 83 cm), (12 mo, 86). Graph this data.

Find a Slope The slope of a straight line is the ratio of the vertical change, rise, to the horizontal change, run.

$$\text{Slope} = \frac{\text{vertical change (rise)}}{\text{horizontal change (run)}} = \frac{\text{change in } y}{\text{change in } x}$$

Example Find the slope of the graph in **Figure 20.**

Step 1 You know that the slope is the change in *y* divided by the change in *x*.
$$\text{Slope} = \frac{\text{change in } y}{\text{change in } x}$$

Step 2 Determine the data points you will be using. For a straight line, choose the two sets of points that are the farthest apart.
$$\text{Slope} = \frac{(40-0) \text{ km}}{(5-0) \text{ hr}}$$

Step 3 Find the change in *y* and *x*.
$$\text{Slope} = \frac{40 \text{ km}}{5 \text{ h}}$$

Step 4 Divide the change in *y* by the change in *x*.
$$\text{Slope} = \frac{8 \text{ km}}{\text{h}}$$

The slope of the graph is 8 km/h.

Math Skill Handbook

Math Skill Handbook

Bar Graph To compare data that does not change continuously you might choose a bar graph. A bar graph uses bars to show the relationships between variables. The *x*-axis variable is divided into parts. The parts can be numbers such as years, or a category such as a type of animal. The *y*-axis is a number and increases continuously along the axis.

Example A recycling center collects 4.0 kg of aluminum on Monday, 1.0 kg on Wednesday, and 2.0 kg on Friday. Create a bar graph of this data.

Step 1 Select the *x*-axis and *y*-axis variables. The measured numbers (the masses of aluminum) should be placed on the *y*-axis. The variable divided into parts (collection days) is placed on the *x*-axis.

Step 2 Create a graph grid like you would for a line graph. Include labels and units.

Step 3 For each measured number, draw a vertical bar above the *x*-axis value up to the *y*-axis value. For the first data point, draw a vertical bar above Monday up to 4.0 kg.

Aluminum Collected During Week

Practice Problem Draw a bar graph of the gases in air: 78% nitrogen, 21% oxygen, 1% other gases.

Circle Graph To display data as parts of a whole, you might use a circle graph. A circle graph is a circle divided into sections that represent the relative size of each piece of data. The entire circle represents 100%, half represents 50%, and so on.

Example Air is made up of 78% nitrogen, 21% oxygen, and 1% other gases. Display the composition of air in a circle graph.

Step 1 Multiply each percent by 360° and divide by 100 to find the angle of each section in the circle.

$$78\% \times \frac{360°}{100} = 280.8°$$

$$21\% \times \frac{360°}{100} = 75.6°$$

$$1\% \times \frac{360°}{100} = 3.6°$$

Step 2 Use a compass to draw a circle and to mark the center of the circle. Draw a straight line from the center to the edge of the circle.

Step 3 Use a protractor and the angles you calculated to divide the circle into parts. Place the center of the protractor over the center of the circle and line the base of the protractor over the straight line.

Practice Problem Draw a circle graph to represent the amount of aluminum collected during the week shown in the bar graph to the left.

Bar Graph

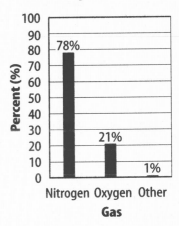

Composition of Air

Circle Graph

The total amount of aluminum collected is:

$$4.0 \text{ kg} + 1.0 \text{ kg} + 2.0 \text{ kg} = 7.0 \text{ kg}$$

$$\frac{4.0 \text{ kg}}{7.0 \text{ kg}} = \frac{x}{360°};\ x = 206°$$

$$\frac{1.0 \text{ kg}}{7.0 \text{ kg}} = \frac{x}{360°};\ x = 51°$$

$$\frac{2.0 \text{ kg}}{7.0 \text{ kg}} = \frac{x}{360°};\ x = 103°$$

Physical Science Reference Tables

Standard Units

Symbol	Name	Quantity
m	meter	length
kg	kilogram	mass
Pa	pascal	pressure
K	kelvin	temperature
mol	mole	amount of a substance
J	joule	energy, work, quantity of heat
s	second	time
C	coulomb	electric charge
V	volt	electric potential
A	ampere	electric current
Ω	ohm	resistance

Physical Constants and Conversion Factors

Acceleration due to gravity	g	9.8 m/s/s or m/s^2
Avogadro's Number	N_A	6.02×10^{23} particles per mole
Electron charge	e	1.6×10^{-19} C
Electron rest mass	m_e	9.11×10^{-31} kg
Gravitation constant	G	6.67×10^{-11} N $\times$ m^2/kg^2
Mass-energy relationship		1 u (amu) $= 9.3 \times 10^2$ MeV
Speed of light in a vacuum	c	3.00×10^8 m/s
Speed of sound at STP		331 m/s
Standard Pressure		1 atmosphere
		101.3 kPa
		760 Torr or mmHg
		14.7 lb/in.^{2}

Wavelengths of Light in a Vacuum

Violet	$4.0 - 4.2 \times 10^{-7}$ m
Blue	$4.2 - 4.9 \times 10^{-7}$ m
Green	$4.9 - 5.7 \times 10^{-7}$ m
Yellow	$5.7 - 5.9 \times 10^{-7}$ m
Orange	$5.9 - 6.5 \times 10^{-7}$ m
Red	$6.5 - 7.0 \times 10^{-7}$ m

The Index of Refraction for Common Substances
($\lambda = 5.9 \times 10^{-7}$ m)

Air	1.00
Alcohol	1.36
Canada Balsam	1.53
Corn Oil	1.47
Diamond	2.42
Glass, Crown	1.52
Glass, Flint	1.61
Glycerol	1.47
Lucite	1.50
Quartz, Fused	1.46
Water	1.33

Heat Constants

	Specific Heat (average) (kJ/kg $\times$ °C) (J/g $\times$ °C)	Melting Point (°C)	Boiling Point (°C)	Heat of Fusion (kJ/kg) (J/g)	Heat of Vaporization (kJ/kg) (J/g)
Alcohol (ethyl)	2.43 (liq.)	−117	79	109	855
Aluminum	0.90 (sol.)	660	2467	396	10500
Ammonia	4.71 (liq.)	−78	−33	332	1370
Copper	0.39 (sol.)	1083	2567	205	4790
Iron	0.45 (sol.)	1535	2750	267	6290
Lead	0.13 (sol.)	328	1740	25	866
Mercury	0.14 (liq.)	−39	357	11	295
Platinum	0.13 (sol.)	1772	3827	101	229
Silver	0.24 (sol.)	962	2212	105	2370
Tungsten	0.13 (sol.)	3410	5660	192	4350
Water (solid)	2.05 (sol.)	0	–	334	–
Water (liquid)	4.18 (liq.)	–	100	–	–
Water (vapor)	2.01 (gas)	–	–	–	2260
Zinc	0.39 (sol.)	420	907	113	1770

Standard Units

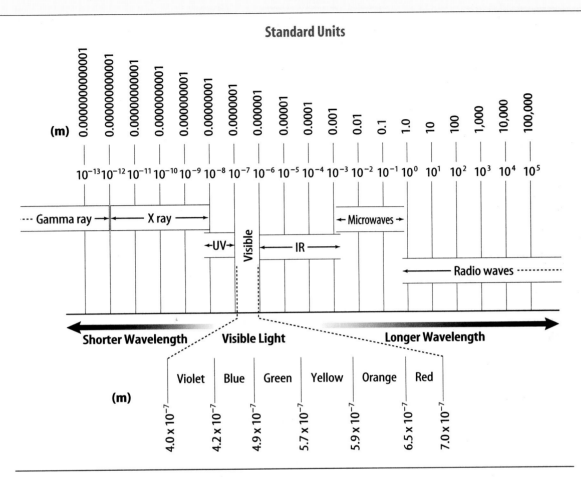

| (m) | 0.0000000000001 | 0.000000000001 | 0.00000000001 | 0.0000000001 | 0.000000001 | 0.00000001 | 0.0000001 | 0.000001 | 0.00001 | 0.0001 | 0.001 | 0.01 | 0.1 | 1.0 | 10 | 100 | 1,000 | 10,000 | 100,000 |

10^{-13} 10^{-12} 10^{-11} 10^{-10} 10^{-9} 10^{-8} 10^{-7} 10^{-6} 10^{-5} 10^{-4} 10^{-3} 10^{-2} 10^{-1} 10^{0} 10^{1} 10^{2} 10^{3} 10^{4} 10^{5}

← Gamma ray → ← X ray → ←UV→ Visible ← IR → ← Microwaves → ← Radio waves

Shorter Wavelength   **Visible Light**   **Longer Wavelength**

| Violet | Blue | Green | Yellow | Orange | Red |

(m)

4.0×10^{-7} 4.2×10^{-7} 4.9×10^{-7} 5.7×10^{-7} 5.9×10^{-7} 6.5×10^{-7} 7.0×10^{-7}

Heat Constants

Atomic number and chemical symbol

	82	84	86	88	90	92
	Pb	Bi	Po	At	Rn	Fr	Ra	Ac	Th	Pa	U

Mass number: 238, 234, 230, 226, 222, 218, 214, 210, 206

$^{4}_{2}$He (α particle) Helium nucleus emission

$^{0}_{-1}$e (β particle) electron emission

PERIODIC TABLE OF THE ELEMENTS

Columns of elements are called groups. Elements in the same group have similar chemical properties.

Gas

Liquid

Solid

Synthetic

Element — Hydrogen
Atomic number — 1
Symbol — H
Atomic mass — 1.008

State of matter

The first three symbols tell you the state of matter of the element at room temperature. The fourth symbol identifies elements that are not present in significant amounts on Earth. Useful amounts are made synthetically.

Group 1

1	2	3	4	5	6	7	8	9
1 Hydrogen 1 H 1.008								
2 Lithium 3 Li 6.941	Beryllium 4 Be 9.012							
3 Sodium 11 Na 22.990	Magnesium 12 Mg 24.305							
4 Potassium 19 K 39.098	Calcium 20 Ca 40.078	Scandium 21 Sc 44.956	Titanium 22 Ti 47.867	Vanadium 23 V 50.942	Chromium 24 Cr 51.996	Manganese 25 Mn 54.938	Iron 26 Fe 55.845	Cobalt 27 Co 58.933
5 Rubidium 37 Rb 85.468	Strontium 38 Sr 87.62	Yttrium 39 Y 88.906	Zirconium 40 Zr 91.224	Niobium 41 Nb 92.906	Molybdenum 42 Mo 95.94	Technetium 43 Tc (98)	Ruthenium 44 Ru 101.07	Rhodium 45 Rh 102.906
6 Cesium 55 Cs 132.905	Barium 56 Ba 137.327	Lanthanum 57 La 138.906	Hafnium 72 Hf 178.49	Tantalum 73 Ta 180.948	Tungsten 74 W 183.84	Rhenium 75 Re 186.207	Osmium 76 Os 190.23	Iridium 77 Ir 192.217
7 Francium 87 Fr (223)	Radium 88 Ra (226)	Actinium 89 Ac (227)	Rutherfordium 104 Rf (261)	Dubnium 105 Db (262)	Seaborgium 106 Sg (266)	Bohrium 107 Bh (264)	Hassium 108 Hs (277)	Meitnerium 109 Mt (268)

The number in parentheses is the mass number of the longest-lived isotope for that element.

Rows of elements are called periods. Atomic number increases across a period.

The arrow shows where these elements would fit into the periodic table. They are moved to the bottom of the table to save space.

Lanthanide series

Cerium 58 Ce 140.116	Praseodymium 59 Pr 140.908	Neodymium 60 Nd 144.24	Promethium 61 Pm (145)	Samarium 62 Sm 150.36

Actinide series

Thorium 90 Th 232.038	Protactinium 91 Pa 231.036	Uranium 92 U 238.029	Neptunium 93 Np (237)	Plutonium 94 Pu (244)

Metal
Metalloid
Nonmetal

The color of an element's block tells you if the element is a metal, nonmetal, or metalloid.

Science Online
Visit bookm.msscience.com for updates to the periodic table.

						18
						Helium 2 He 4.003
13	14	15	16	17		
Boron 5 B 10.811	Carbon 6 C 12.011	Nitrogen 7 N 14.007	Oxygen 8 O 15.999	Fluorine 9 F 18.998	Neon 10 Ne 20.180	

10	11	12						
			Aluminum 13 Al 26.982	Silicon 14 Si 28.086	Phosphorus 15 P 30.974	Sulfur 16 S 32.065	Chlorine 17 Cl 35.453	Argon 18 Ar 39.948
Nickel 28 Ni 58.693	Copper 29 Cu 63.546	Zinc 30 Zn 65.409	Gallium 31 Ga 69.723	Germanium 32 Ge 72.64	Arsenic 33 As 74.922	Selenium 34 Se 78.96	Bromine 35 Br 79.904	Krypton 36 Kr 83.798
Palladium 46 Pd 106.42	Silver 47 Ag 107.868	Cadmium 48 Cd 112.411	Indium 49 In 114.818	Tin 50 Sn 118.710	Antimony 51 Sb 121.760	Tellurium 52 Te 127.60	Iodine 53 I 126.904	Xenon 54 Xe 131.293
Platinum 78 Pt 195.078	Gold 79 Au 196.967	Mercury 80 Hg 200.59	Thallium 81 Tl 204.383	Lead 82 Pb 207.2	Bismuth 83 Bi 208.980	Polonium 84 Po (209)	Astatine 85 At (210)	Radon 86 Rn (222)
Darmstadtium 110 Ds (281)	* Unununium 111 Uuu (272)	* Ununbium 112 Uub (285)		* Ununquadium 114 Uuq (289)		** 116		** 118

* The names and symbols for elements 111–114 are temporary. Final names will be selected when the elements' discoveries are verified.

** Elements 116 and 118 were thought to have been created. The claim was retracted because the experimental results could not be repeated.

Europium 63 Eu 151.964	Gadolinium 64 Gd 157.25	Terbium 65 Tb 158.925	Dysprosium 66 Dy 162.500	Holmium 67 Ho 164.930	Erbium 68 Er 167.259	Thulium 69 Tm 168.934	Ytterbium 70 Yb 173.04	Lutetium 71 Lu 174.967
Americium 95 Am (243)	Curium 96 Cm (247)	Berkelium 97 Bk (247)	Californium 98 Cf (251)	Einsteinium 99 Es (252)	Fermium 100 Fm (257)	Mendelevium 101 Md (258)	Nobelium 102 No (259)	Lawrencium 103 Lr (262)

Glossary/Glosario

Cómo usar el glosario en español:
1. Busca el término en inglés que desees encontrar.
2. El término en español, junto con la definición, se encuentran en la columna de la derecha.

Pronunciation Key

Use the following key to help you sound out words in the glossary.

a	back (BAK)	ew	food (FEWD)
ay	day (DAY)	yoo	pure (PYOOR)
ah	father (FAH thur)	yew	few (FYEW)
ow	flower (FLOW ur)	uh	comma (CAH muh)
ar	car (CAR)	u (+ con)	rub (RUB)
e	less (LES)	sh	shelf (SHELF)
ee	leaf (LEEF)	ch	nature (NAY chur)
ih	trip (TRIHP)	g	gift (GIHFT)
i (i + con + e)	idea (i DEE uh)	j	gem (JEM)
oh	go (GOH)	ing	sing (SING)
aw	soft (SAWFT)	zh	vision (VIH zhun)
or	orbit (OR buht)	k	cake (KAYK)
oy	coin (COYN)	s	seed, cent (SEED, SENT)
oo	foot (FOOT)	z	zone, raise (ZOHN, RAYZ)

English | A | Español

acceleration: equals the change in velocity divided by the time for the change to take place; occurs when an object speeds up, slows down, or turns. (p. 14)

alternative resource: new renewable or inexhaustible energy source; includes solar energy, wind, and geothermal energy. (p. 143)

Archimedes' principle: states that the buoyant force on an object equals the weight of the fluid displaced by the object. (p. 77)

average speed: equals the total distance traveled divided by the total time taken to travel the distance. (p. 11)

aceleración: es igual al cambio de velocidad dividido por el tiempo que toma en realizarse dicho cambio; sucede cuando un objeto aumenta su velocidad, la disminuye o gira. (p. 14)

recurso alternativo: nueva fuente de energía renovable o inagotable; incluye energía solar, eólica y geotérmica. (p. 143)

principio de Arquímedes: establece que la fuerza de flotación de un objeto es igual al peso del fluido desplazado por dicho objeto. (p. 77)

velocidad promedio: es igual al total de la distancia recorrida dividida por el tiempo total necesario para recorrer dicha distancia. (p. 11)

B

balanced forces: two or more forces whose effects cancel each other out and do not change the motion of an object. (p. 37)

Bernoulli's principle: states that when the speed of a fluid increases, the pressure exerted by the fluid decreases. (p. 85)

buoyant force: upward force exerted by a fluid on any object placed in the fluid. (p. 74)

fuerzas balanceadas: dos o más fuerzas cuyos efectos se cancelan mutuamente sin cambiar el movimiento de un objeto. (p. 37)

principio de Bernoulli: establece que cuando se incrementa la velocidad de un fluido, disminuye la presión ejercida por el mismo. (p. 85)

fuerza de flotación: fuerza ascendente ejercida por un fluido sobre cualquier objeto colocado en dicho fluido. (p. 74) center of mass: point in a object that moves as if all of the object's mass were concentrated at that point. (p. 48)

chemical energy: energy stored in chemical bonds. (p. 129)

compound machine: machine made up of a combination of two or more simple machines. (p. 109)

conduction: transfer of thermal energy by direct contact; occurs when energy is transferred by collisions between particles. (p. 163)

conductor: material that transfers heat easily. (p. 165)

convection: transfer of thermal energy by the movement of particles from one place to another in a gas or liquid. (p. 164)

centro de masa: punto en un objeto que se mueve como si toda la masa del objeto estuviera concentrada en ese punto. (p. 48)

energía química: energía almacenada en enlaces químicos. (p. 129)

máquina compuesta: máquina compuesta por la combinación de dos o más máquinas. (p. 109)

conducción: transferencia de energía térmica por contacto directo; se produce cuando la energía se transfiere mediante colisiones entre las partículas. (p. 163)

conductor: material que transfiere calor fácilmente. (p. 165)

convección: transferencia de energía térmica por el movimiento de partículas de un sitio a otro en un líquido o un gas. (p. 164)

density: mass of an object divided by its volume. (p. 78)

densidad: masa de un objeto dividida por su volumen. (p. 78)

efficiency: equals the output work divided by the input work; expressed as a percentage. (p. 107)

electrical energy: energy carried by electric current. (p. 130)

energy: the ability to cause change. (p. 126)

eficiencia: equivale al trabajo aplicado dividido el trabajo generado y se expresa en porcentaje. (p. 107)

energía eléctrica: energía transportada por corriente eléctrica. (p. 130)

energía: capacidad de producir cambios. (p. 126)

fluid: a substance that has no definite shape and can flow. (p. 69)

force: a push or a pull. (p. 36)

friction: force that acts to oppose sliding between two surfaces that are touching. (p. 38)

fluido: sustancia que no tiene forma definida y que puede fluir. (p. 69)

fuerza: presión o tracción. (p. 36)

fricción: fuerza que actúa para oponerse al deslizamiento entre dos superficies que se tocan. (p. 38)

generator: device that transforms kinetic energy into electrical energy. (p. 136)

generador: dispositivo que transforma la energía cinética en energía eléctrica. (p. 136)

Glossary/Glosario

Glossary/Glosario

H

heat: thermal energy transferred from a warmer object to a cooler object. (p. 162)

heat engine: device that converts thermal energy into mechanical energy. (p. 169)

hydraulic system: uses a fluid to increase an applied force. (p. 83)

calor: energía térmica transferida de un objeto con más calor a uno con menos calor. (p. 162)

motor de calor: motor que transforma la energía térmica en energía mecánica. (p. 169)

sistema hidráulico: usa un fluido para incrementar una fuerza aplicada. (p. 83)

I

inclined plane: simple machine that is a flat surface, sloped surface, or ramp. (p. 109)

inertia: tendency of an object to resist a change in its motion. (p. 19)

inexhaustible resource: energy source that can't be used up by humans. (p. 143)

input force: force exerted on a machine. (p. 104)

instantaneous speed: the speed of an object at one instant of time. (p. 11)

internal combustion engine: heat engine in which fuel is burned in a combustion chamber inside the engine. (p. 170)

plano inclinado: máquina simple que consiste en una superficie plana, inclinada, o una rampa. (p. 109)

inercia: tendencia de un objeto a resistirse a un cam bio de movimiento. (p. 19)

recurso inagotable: fuente de energía que no puede ser agotada por los seres humanos. (p. 143)

fuerza aplicada: fuerza que se ejerce sobre una máquina. (p. 104)

velocidad instantánea: la velocidad de un objeto en un instante de tiempo. (p. 11)

motor de combustión interna: motor de calor en el cual el combustible es quemado en una cámara de combustión dentro del motor. (p. 170)

K

kinetic energy: energy an object has due to its motion. (p. 127)

energía cinética: energía que posee un objeto debido a su movimiento. (p. 127)

L

law of conservation of energy: states that energy can change its form but is never created or destroyed. (p. 132)

law of conservation of momentum: states that the total momentum of objects that collide with each other is the same before and after the collision. (p. 21)

lever: simple machine consisting of a rigid rod or plank that pivots or rotates about a fixed point called the fulcrum. (p. 112)

ley de la conservación de la energía: establece que la energía puede cambiar de forma pero nunca puede ser creada ni destruida. (p. 132)

ley de conservación de momento: establece que el momento total de los objetos que chocan entre sí es el mismo antes y después de la colisión. (p. 21)

palanca: máquina simple que consiste en una barra rígida que puede girar sobre un punto fijo llamado punto de apoyo. (p. 112)

M

mass: amount of matter in an object. (p. 19)

masa: cantidad de materia en un objeto. (p. 19)

mechanical advantage: number of times the input force is multiplied by a machine; equal to the output force divided by the input force. (p. 105)

momentum: a measure of how difficult it is to stop a moving object; equals the product of mass and velocity. (p. 20)

ventaja mecánica: número de veces que la fuerza aplicada es multiplicada por una máquina; equivale a la fuerza producida dividida por la fuerza aplicada. (p. 105)

momento: medida de la dificultad para detener un objeto en movimiento; es igual al producto de la masa por la velocidad. (p. 20)

net force: combination of all forces acting on an object. (p. 37)

Newton's first law of motion: states that if the net force acting on an object is zero, the object will remain at rest or move in a straight line with a constant speed. (p. 38)

Newton's second law of motion: states that an object acted upon by a net force will accelerate in the direction of the force, and that the acceleration equals the net force divided by the object's mass. (p. 42)

Newton's third law of motion: states that forces always act in equal but opposite pairs. (p. 49)

nonrenewable resource: energy resource that is used up much faster than it can be replaced. (p. 140)

nuclear energy: energy contained in atomic nuclei. (p. 130)

fuerza neta: la combinación de todas las fuerzas que actúan sobre un objeto. (p. 37)

primera ley de movimiento de Newton: establece que si la fuerza neta que actúa sobre un objeto es igual a cero, el objeto se mantendrá en reposo o se moverá en línea recta a una velocidad constante. (p. 38)

segunda ley de movimiento de Newton: establece que si una fuerza neta se ejerce sobre un objeto, éste se acelerará en la dirección de la fuerza y la aceleración es igual a la fuerza neta dividida por la masa del objeto. (p. 42)

tercera ley de movimiento de Newton: establece que las fuerzas siempre actúan en pares iguales pero opuestos. (p. 49)

recurso no renovable: recurso energético que se agota mucho más rápidamente de lo que puede ser reemplazado. (p. 140)

energía nuclear: energía contenida en los núcleos de los atómos. (p. 130)

output force: force exerted by a machine. (p. 104)

fuerza generada: fuerza producida por una máquina. (p. 104)

P

Pascal's principle: states that the pressure applied to a confined fluid is transmitted equally throughout the fluid. (p. 83)

photovoltaic: device that transforms radiant energy directly into electrical energy. (p. 144)

potential energy: energy stored in an object due to its position. (p. 128)

power: rate at which work is done; equal to the work done divided by the time it takes to do the work; measured in watts (W). (p. 101)

principio de Pascal: establece que la presión aplicada a un fluido encerrado se transmite de manera uniforme a través de todo el fluido. (p. 83)

fotovoltaico: dispositivo que transforma la energía radiante directamente en energía eléctrica. (p. 144)

energía potencial: energía almacenada en un objeto debido a su posición. (p. 128)

potencia: velocidad a la que se realiza un trabajo y que equivale al trabajo realizado dividido por el tiempo que toma realizar el trabajo; se mide en vatios (W). (p. 101)

Glossary/Glosario

Glossary/Glosario

pressure: amount of force applied per unit area on an object's surface; SI unit is the Pascal (Pa). (p. 66)

pulley: simple machine made from a grooved wheel with a rope or cable wrapped around the groove. (p. 114)

presión: cantidad de fuerza aplicada por unidad de área sobre la superficie de un objeto; la unidad internacional SI es el Pascal (Pa). (p. 66)

polea: máquina simple que consiste en una rueda acanalada con una cuerda o cable que corre alrededor del canal. (p. 114)

R

---

radiant energy: energy carried by light. (p. 129)

radiation: transfer of energy by electromagnetic waves. (p. 163)

renewable resource: energy resource that is replenished continually. (p. 142)

energía radiante: energía transportada por la luz. (p. 129)

radiación: transferencia de energía mediante ondas electromagnéticas. (p. 163)

recurso renovable: recurso energético regenerado continuamente. (p. 142)

S

---

screw: simple machine that is an inclined plane wrapped around a cylinder or post. (p. 111)

simple machine: a machine that does work with only one movement; includes the inclined plane, wedge, screw, lever, wheel and axle, and pulley. (p. 109)

specific heat: amount of heat needed to raise the temperature of 1 kg of a substance by 1ºC. (p. 166)

speed: equals the distance traveled divided by the time it takes to travel that distance. (p. 10)

temperature: a measure of the average value of the kinetic energy of the particles in a material. (p. 158)

thermal energy: energy that all objects have that increases as the object's temperature increases; the sum of the kinetic and potential energy of the particles in a material. (pp. 128, 161)

thermal pollution: increase in temperature of a natural body of water; caused by adding warmer water. (p. 167)

turbine: set of steam-powered fan blades that spins a generator at a power plant. (p. 136)

tornillo: máquina simple que consiste en un plano inclinado envuelto en espiral alrededor de un cilindro o poste. (p. 111)

máquina simple: máquina que ejecuta el trabajo con un solo movimiento; incluye el plano inclinado, la palanca, el tornillo, la rueda y el eje y la polea. (p. 109)

calor específico: cantidad de calor necesario para elevar la temperatura de 1 kilogramo de una sustancia en 1 grado centígrado. (p. 166)

rapidez: equivale a dividir la distancia recorrida por el tiempo que toma recorrer dicha distancia. (p. 10)

temperatura: medida del valor promedio de energía cinética de las partículas en un material. (p. 158)

energía térmica: energía que poseen todos los objetos y que aumenta al aumentar la temperatura de éstos; la suma de la energía cinética y potencial de las partículas en un material. (pp. 128, 161)

polución térmica: incremento de la temperatura de una masa natural de agua producido al agregarle agua a mayor temperatura. (p. 167)

turbina: conjunto de aspas de ventilador impulsadas por vapor que hacen girar a un generador en una planta de energía eléctrica. (p. 136)

U

---

unbalanced forces: two or more forces acting on an object that do not cancel, and cause the object to accelerate. (p. 37)

fuerzas no balanceadas: dos o más fuerzas que actúan sobre un objeto sin anularse y que hacen que el objeto se acelere. (p. 37)

velocity: speed and direction of a moving object. (p. 13)

velocidad: rapidez y dirección de un objeto en movimiento. (p. 13)

wedge: simple machine consisting of an inclined plane that moves; can have one or two sloping sides. (p. 110)

weight: gravitational force between an object and Earth. (p. 43)

wheel and axle: simple machine made from two circular objects of different sizes that are attached and rotate together. (p. 112)

work: is done when a force exerted on an object causes that object to move some distance; equal to force times distance; measured in joules (J). (p. 98)

cuña: máquina simple que consiste en un plano inclinado que se mueve; puede tener uno o dos lados inclinados. (p. 110)

peso: fuerza gravitacional entre un objeto y la Tierra. (p. 43)

rueda y eje: máquina simple compuesta por dos objetos circulares de diferentes tamaños que están interconectados y giran. (p. 112)

trabajo: se realiza cuando la fuerza ejercida sobre un objeto hace que el objeto se mueva determinada distancia; es igual a la fuerza multiplicada por la distancia y se mide en julios (J). (p. 98)

Glossary/Glosario

Italic numbers = illustration/photo   **Bold numbers = vocabulary term**
lab = indicates a page on which the entry is used in a lab
act = indicates a page on which the entry is used in an activity

Index

Index

Magnification Key: Magnifications listed are the magnifications at which images were originally photographed.
LM–Light Microscope
SEM–Scanning Electron Microscope
TEM–Transmission Electron Microscope

Acknowledgments: Glencoe would like to acknowledge the artists and agencies who participated in illustrating this program: Absolute Science Illustration; Andrew Evansen; Argosy; Articulate Graphics; Craig Attebery represented by Frank & Jeff Lavaty; CHK America; John Edwards and Associates; Gagliano Graphics; Pedro Julio Gonzalez represented by Melissa Turk & The Artist Network; Robert Hynes represented by Mendola Ltd.; Morgan Cain & Associates; JTH Illustration; Laurie O'Keefe; Matthew Pippin represented by Beranbaum Artist's Representative; Precision Graphics; Publisher's Art; Rolin Graphics, Inc.; Wendy Smith represented by Melissa Turk & The Artist Network; Kevin Torline represented by Berendsen and Associates, Inc.; WILDlife ART; Phil Wilson represented by Cliff Knecht Artist Representative; Zoo Botanica.

Photo Credits

Cover Gunter Marx Photography/CORBIS; **i ii** Gunter Marx Photography/CORBIS; **iv** (bkgd)John Evans, (inset)Gunter Marx Photography/CORBIS; **v** (t)PhotoDisc, (b)John Evans; **vi** (l)John Evans, (r)Geoff Butler; **vii** (l)John Evans, (r)PhotoDisc; **viii** PhotoDisc; **ix** Aaron Haupt Photography; **x** Runk/Schoenberger for Grant Heilman; **xi** Billy Hustace/Stone/Getty Images; **xii** Tom & DeeAnn McCarthy/The Stock Market/CORBIS; **1** Lori Adamski Peek/Stone/Getty Images; **2** (t)Jeremy Woodhouse/Photodisc, (b)Ted Spiegel/CORBIS; **3** (t)William James Warren/CORBIS, (b)CORBIS; **5** Dominic Oldershaw; **6–7** Brian Snyder/Reuters Newmedia Inc/Corbis; **8** Telegraph Colour Library/FPG/Getty Images; **9** Geoff Butler; **12** Richard Hutchings; **15** Runk/Schoenberger from Grant Heilman; **17** Mark Doolittle/Outside Images/Picturequest; **19** (l)Ed Bock/The Stock Market/CORBIS, (r)Will Hart/PhotoEdit, Inc.; **21** (t)Tom & DeeAnn McCarthy/The Stock Market/CORBIS, (bl)Jodi Jacobson/Peter Arnold, Inc., (br)Jules Frazier/PhotoDisc; **22** Mark Burnett; **24** Robert Brenner/PhotoEdit, Inc.; **25** Laura Sifferlin; **26 27** Icon Images; **28** Alexis Duclos/Liaison/Getty Images; **29** (l r)Rudi Von Briel/PhotoEdit, Inc., (c)PhotoDisc; **33** (l)Jodi Jacobson/Peter Arnold, Inc., (r)Runk/Schoenberger from Grant Heilman; **34–35** Wendell Metzen/Index Stock; **35** Richard Hutchings; **36** (l)Globus Brothers Studios, NYC, (r)Stock Boston; **37** Bob Daemmrich; **38** (t)Beth Wald/ImageState, (b)David Madison; **39** Rhoda Sidney/Stock Boston/PictureQuest; **41** (l)Myrleen Cate/PhotoEdit, Inc., (r)David Young-Wolff/PhotoEdit, Inc.; **42** Bob Daemmrich; **44** (t)Stone/Getty Images, (b)Myrleen Cate/PhotoEdit, Inc.; **46** David Madison; **48** Richard Megna/Fundamental Photographs; **49** Mary M. Steinbacher/PhotoEdit, Inc.; **50** (t)Betty Sederquist/Visuals Unlimited, (b)Jim Cummins/FPG/Getty Images; **51** (tl)Denis Boulanger/Allsport, (tr)Donald Miralle/Allsport, (b)Tony Freeman/PhotoEdit/PictureQuest; **52** (t)David Madison, (b)NASA; **54** NASA; **55** Richard Hutchings; **56 57** Mark Burnett; **58** (t)Tom Wright/CORBIS, (b)Didier Charre/Image Bank; **59** (tl)Philip Bailey/The Stock Market/CORBIS, (tr)Romilly Lockyer/Image Bank/Getty Images, (bl)Tony Freeman/PhotoEdit, Inc.;

63 Betty Sederquist/Visuals Unlimited; **64–65** Hughes Martin/CORBIS; **65** Matt Meadows; **66** David Young-Wolff/PhotoEdit, Inc.; **68** Runk/Schoenberger from Grant Heilman; **69** Dominic Oldershaw; **70** (t)Matt Meadows, (b)Tom Pantages; **72** (t)Bobby Model/National Geographic Image Collection, (cl)Richard Nowitz/National Geographic Image Collection, (cr)George Grall/National Geographic Image Collection, (bl)Ralph White/CORBIS, (br)CORBIS; **74** Ryan McVay/PhotoDisc; **75** CORBIS; **76** (t)Matt Meadows, (b)Vince Streano/Stone/Getty Images; **77 79** Matt Meadows; **81** John Evans; **83** KS Studios; **84** Dominic Oldershaw; **87** (t)Michael Collier/Stock Boston, (bl)George Hall/CORBIS, (br)Dean Conger/CORBIS; **88** Steve McCutcheon/Visuals Unlimited; **89** Runk/Schoenberger from Grant Heilman; **90** AP/Wide World Photos/Ray Fairall; **91** (l)D.R. & T.L. Schrichte/Stone/Getty Images, (r)CORBIS; **92** Matt Meadows; **95** Vince Streano/Stone/Getty Images; **96–97** Rich Iwasaki/Getty Images; **97** Mark Burnett; **98** Mary Kate Denny/PhotoEdit, Inc.; **106** (l)David Young-Wolff/PhotoEdit, Inc., (r)Frank Siteman/Stock Boston; **109** Duomo; **110** Robert Brenner/PhotoEdit, Inc.; **111** (t)Tom McHugh/Photo Researchers, (b)Amanita Pictures; **112** Amanita Pictures; **113** (t)Dorling Kindersley, (bl br)Bob Daemmrich; **114** (l)Wernher Krutein/Liaison Agency/Getty Images, (r)Siegfried Layda/Stone/Getty Images; **116** Tony Freeman/PhotoEdit, Inc.; **117** Aaron Haupt; **118** (t)Ed Kashi/CORBIS, (b)James Balog; **119** (l)Inc. Janeart/The Image Bank/Getty Images, (r)Ryan McVay/PhotoDisc; **123** (l)Comstock Images, (r)PhotoDisc; **124–125** Chris Knapton/Science Photo Library/Photo Researchers; **125** Matt Meadows; **126** (l c)file photo, (r)Mark Burnett; **127** (t b)Bob Daemmrich, (c)Al Tielemans/Duomo; **128** KS Studios; **129** (l r)Bob Daemmrich, (b)Andrew McClenaghan/Science Photo Library/Photo Researchers; **130** Mark Burnett/Photo Researchers; **131** Lori Adamski Peek/Stone/Getty Images; **132** Richard Hutchings; **133** Ron Kimball/Ron Kimball Photography; **134** (t)Judy Lutz, (b)Lennart Nilsson; **136 138** KS Studios; **144** (t)Jeremy Burgess/Science Photo Library/Photo Researchers, (b)John Keating/Photo Researchers; **145** Geothermal Education Office; **146** Carsand-Mosher; **147** Billy Hustace/Stone/Getty Images; **148** SuperStock; **149** Roger Ressmeyer/CORBIS; **150** (tl)Reuters NewMedia, Inc./CORBIS, (tr)PhotoDisc, (br)Dominic Oldershaw; **151** (l)Lowell Georgia/CORBIS, (r)Mark Richards/PhotoEdit, Inc.; **156–157** Peter Walton/Index Stock; **158** John Evans; **159** (t)Nancy P. Alexander/Visuals Unlimited, (b)Morton & White; **161** Tom Stack & Assoc.; **162** Doug Martin; **163** Matt Meadows; **164** Jeremy Hoare/PhotoDisc; **165** Donnie Kamin/PhotoEdit, Inc.; **166** SuperStock; **167** Colin Raw/Stone/Getty Images; **168** Aaron Haupt; **169** PhotoDisc; **170** (l)Barbara Stitzer/PhotoEdit, Inc., (c)Doug Menuez/PhotoDisc, (r)Addison Geary/Stock Boston; **172** C. Squared Studios/PhotoDisc; **174 175** Morton & White; **176** (bkgd)Chip Simons/FPG/Getty Images, (inset)Joseph Sohm/CORBIS; **177** SuperStock; **180** John Evans; **181** Michael Newman/Photo Edit, Inc.; **182** PhotoDisc; **184** Tom Pantages; **188** Michell D. Bridwell/PhotoEdit, Inc.; **189** (t)Mark Burnett, (b)Dominic Oldershaw; **190** StudiOhio; **191** Timothy Fuller; **192** Aaron Haupt; **194** KS Studios; **195** Matt Meadows; **196** Mark Burnett; **198** John Evans; **199** Amanita Pictures; **200** Bob Daemmrich; **202** Davis Barber/PhotoEdit, Inc.

PERIODIC TABLE OF THE ELEMENTS

Columns of elements are called groups. Elements in the same group have similar chemical properties.

Gas
Liquid
Solid
Synthetic

Element — Hydrogen
Atomic number — 1
Symbol — **H**
Atomic mass — 1.008
State of matter

The first three symbols tell you the state of matter of the element at room temperature. The fourth symbol identifies elements that are not present in significant amounts on Earth. Useful amounts are made synthetically.

1

1	2	3	4	5	6	7	8	9
Hydrogen 1 **H** 1.008								
Lithium 3 **Li** 6.941	Beryllium 4 **Be** 9.012							
Sodium 11 **Na** 22.990	Magnesium 12 **Mg** 24.305							
Potassium 19 **K** 39.098	Calcium 20 **Ca** 40.078	Scandium 21 **Sc** 44.956	Titanium 22 **Ti** 47.867	Vanadium 23 **V** 50.942	Chromium 24 **Cr** 51.996	Manganese 25 **Mn** 54.938	Iron 26 **Fe** 55.845	Cobalt 27 **Co** 58.933
Rubidium 37 **Rb** 85.468	Strontium 38 **Sr** 87.62	Yttrium 39 **Y** 88.906	Zirconium 40 **Zr** 91.224	Niobium 41 **Nb** 92.906	Molybdenum 42 **Mo** 95.94	Technetium 43 **Tc** (98)	Ruthenium 44 **Ru** 101.07	Rhodium 45 **Rh** 102.906
Cesium 55 **Cs** 132.905	Barium 56 **Ba** 137.327	Lanthanum 57 **La** 138.906	Hafnium 72 **Hf** 178.49	Tantalum 73 **Ta** 180.948	Tungsten 74 **W** 183.84	Rhenium 75 **Re** 186.207	Osmium 76 **Os** 190.23	Iridium 77 **Ir** 192.217
Francium 87 **Fr** (223)	Radium 88 **Ra** (226)	Actinium 89 **Ac** (227)	Rutherfordium 104 **Rf** (261)	Dubnium 105 **Db** (262)	Seaborgium 106 **Sg** (266)	Bohrium 107 **Bh** (264)	Hassium 108 **Hs** (277)	Meitnerium 109 **Mt** (268)

The number in parentheses is the mass number of the longest-lived isotope for that element.

Rows of elements are called periods. Atomic number increases across a period.

The arrow shows where these elements would fit into the periodic table. They are moved to the bottom of the table to save space.

Lanthanide series

Cerium 58 **Ce** 140.116	Praseodymium 59 **Pr** 140.908	Neodymium 60 **Nd** 144.24	Promethium 61 **Pm** (145)	Samarium 62 **Sm** 150.36

Actinide series

Thorium 90 **Th** 232.038	Protactinium 91 **Pa** 231.036	Uranium 92 **U** 238.029	Neptunium 93 **Np** (237)	Plutonium 94 **Pu** (244)